GW00775816

HONEY FARMING

by the same author

*

HONEY PRODUCTION IN THE BRITISH ISLES

BEE-KEEPING IN BRITAIN

1. Comb showing brood in all stages and two queen cells, one sealed. Also bees and honey

HONEY FARMING

by

R. O. B. MANLEY

NORTHERN BEE BOOKS
Mytholmroyd : Hebden Bridge

First published in Mcmxlvi by Faber and Faber Ltd
24 Russell Square London W.C.1
Second Impression September Mcmxlvi
Third Impression September Mcmxlviii
This edition published with acknowledgement to Faber and Faber Ltd
by Northern Bee Books, Scout Bottom Farm, Mytholmroyd,
Hebden Bridge, West Yorkshire, April 1985.
Acknowledgements are made with thanks to the following:
Cover design: Paul Taylor
Front cover photograph: Frank Vernon
Back cover photograph: Harry Wickens
(taken at Reculver, Kent, 1942)
Technical consultant: Keith Dobson
Printed by Dotesios Printers Ltd, Bradford-on-Avon, Wiltshire

British Library Cataloguing in Publication Data

Manley, R. O. B.
   Honey farming.
   1. Bee culture
   I. Title
   638'.1   SF523

ISBN 0-907908-45-4

This paperback is sold subject to the conditions that it shall not, by way
of trade or otherwise, be lent, resold, hired out, or otherwise circulated
without the publishers prior consent in any form of binding or cover
other than that in which it is published.

Since this volume was first published there have been changes in agricultural
practices and in apicultural knowledge concerning disease control.
Readers are advised that the increased acreage used for oil seed rape
production in many areas of Britain calls for earlier season
stimulation of the colony. For information concerning disease they should
consult a recent text.

PREFACE

The writing of this little book about bee-farming and honey
production was suggested by the many letters I have received
during the past ten years, since the book *Honey Production in the
British Isles* was published. I have tried to make it as useful and
interesting as I can, but I am very well aware of its imperfections.
To write an interesting account of technical operations and
methods of working is not always easy.

Honey Farming is not written for the novice, and in writing it I
have assumed some considerable experience on the part of the
reader; but I am now working on another book intended expressly
for the beginner who wishes to take up the business of beekeeping
as distinct from making a hobby of it, a rather difficult thing to do.

I have to thank those friends who have assisted me with the
photographs used in this book, especially Mr. C. P. Abbott who
did most of them. The drawings were made by Mr. R. W. Ford
of Reading.

R. O. B. MANLEY

CONTENTS

ILLUSTRATIONS

PHOTOGRAPHS

ILLUSTRATIONS

LINE DRAWINGS

CHAPTER I

RETROSPECT

It will soon be forty years ago that I first became really interested in bees. Before that, at the age of about five years, I remember being given honey for tea at my grandfather's house in Exeter and being horribly sick after it. It is still a vivid memory and since that day I have never eaten my own special product if I could avoid it, for I never did like honey much.

I also have an early recollection of seeing an old lady who lived in the lodge of Newnham Manor, Wallingford, place a skep over a swarm that had alighted on the ground in one of my father's fields, and of her placing an umbrella over it—to my surprise, the day being fine and warm with no sign of rain. Later on I saw the 'county expert' doing signs and wonders with bees in a frame hive belonging to that same old lady: he actually took bees up in his hands, and even allowed them to sit on his face, and still lived to 'tell the tale'! I don't know what that expert was supposed to be doing with the bees, but the owner told me some time afterwards that she was not 'a-going to have no more experts a-messing about with my bees'. They never seemed to do much good after these visitations, she said, and appeared to entertain a foul mistrust that the queen was removed; a most unlikely thing, I should imagine.

When I was about sixteen my father left this neighbourhood and I had to exchange our beautiful Thames Valley for the wilds of South Northants; and it was not very long after we had settled into our new home that one of our neighbours showed me his bees. How well I remember that day! A row of filbert trees, and under them a number of hives made out of Tate sugar boxes to hold standard frames. There may have been about fifteen of them, not painted, I think, and rather roughly made. Since the day of the expert I had hardly cast a thought to bees, and had never seen a hive, much less combs of honey; but I saw them then. It must have been a very good season, that year of 1906, for I can clearly remember that supers of extracting combs were fully sealed over, all white with new wax. My friend said he sometimes got as much as thirty or even forty pounds of honey from a single hive! This seemed to me almost incredible at the time; the idea that a colony of small insects could in a few weeks accumulate such a weight of honey as that seemed so marvellous; as indeed it is, though we become used to the idea after a time and cease to marvel.

This sight made a beekeeper of me. I immediately became quite fascinated by the bees and the possibilities I dimly understood, even at that early stage, must somehow or other be inherent in them. This interest has lasted to the present time, and will last, I feel sure, as long as I am able to take any interest in anything. But my beekeeper friend was not one of those who take delight in opening hives and handling bees; his beekeeping was of the more prosaic kind. He put supers on in spring, hived such swarms as there were, extracted the honey in the autumn and put the combs away ready for next year; so I did not see the brood combs at that time. I saw something else, however. Seeing my interest my friend took me to a cottage where he kept his extractor and all the other appliances, which was of course very interesting. Later on in the following winter I again saw the interior of this store where all the extracting combs were put away, and I had a lesson. On entering the room I noticed a strange rustling noise; on further investigation it was found that the stored combs were infested by the large wax moth caterpillars and that the whole had been almost completely destroyed. There was a matter of two hundred or more, I should think. So I was introduced to the sorrows as well as the joys of beekeeping at a very early stage.

My interest soon amounted to enthusiasm: I must keep bees, and at once. I borrowed an old magazine of some kind, I forget what it was, but it was not a regular bee magazine, I know. It had in it diagrams and measurements of the hive known in those days as the 'Cottager's Hive'. I made two of these and then another with a different sort of roof and also, after I had read the matter up a little, a fourth with glass panels on three sides.

But I had no bees. This was, I believe, July. I tried to get some 'late swarms' without success, and eventually was recommended to try a man named Bubb, signalman, who proved a good friend in need. He showed me how to wire frames and embed foundation —by means of a cobbler's awl with a groove filed lengthways on its convex side. Many a sheet have I embedded that way. He had a method of wiring, too, that I have never seen elsewhere; a horizontal wire top and bottom, and a crossed pair of wires between. This good man showed me his two apiaries and his honey. He had whole supers chock full of it, and this made me more excited still. I MUST have bees; but how? He said, 'Too late for swarms; why not have some "druv" bees?' Not knowing what 'druv' bees were, I could not say; but on explanation I immediately decided to have some to start with. Mr. Bubb was a fine man, not one to take advantage of ignorance or give bad advice or poor value. He loved bees as few of us do. His driven swarms were really fine, for he drove three skeps together for each swarm, and he brought them to my hives on his motor-bike, hived them himself, showed me the queens running in, and placed feeders in position, telling me just what should be done about the feeding. After that we became friendly and I used to go to see him on Sundays and in the evenings, pottering about with him when he worked among his bees and accompanying him on his rounds when he went to assist other beekeepers. It seems strange now to think of the delight I took in this; riding for miles on a push-bike beside his little motor-bicycle which he made as slow as he could to allow me to keep up, and all maybe only to see a swarm shaken or some trivial proceeding. In 1912 I left the neighbourhood to begin business in Berkshire and I never saw Bubb again. I suppose that he has long since passed on; but if he still lives he must be a very old man. I still have a bad snapshot of him with his wife and family at their cottage door, and I shall always remember him with respect and gratitude.

To return to the bees. Having got my four hives stocked with driven bees and those taking their quart of syrup down each night from four 'rapid' tinned feeders—one of which I still have in use after all these years—I looked round for more bees. All beekeepers will understand; all feverish beginners have this urge: like Twist, we all want more. And I found a skep, an old one belonging to a neighbouring farmer. The price was half a sovereign because it brought bad luck in those days not to pay for bees with gold. This I brought home and set on a stand I made, a round board set on a stake so that mice could not reach the hive.

So now I was a beekeeper at last. I don't suppose there is any greater pleasure to be found than that felt by one of us during the first weeks of beekeeping. I can never forget my first handling of the frames of new-drawn comb; the eggs and larvae seen for the first time, and the spotting of the queen as she walked among her workers. It sometimes comes back to me even now in the midst of some strenuous day's work, when stocks are being handled score by score, hour after hour, in the routine work of a honey farm.

Well, that was how I began to keep bees, and if there is a better way I have not heard of it. It starts at the beginning of the bee-keeper's yearly cycle and gives the tyro all the winter to read books and magazines, think, and listen to what others can impart. But there are other ways of making a beginning with bees, and of these the best is, I think, to buy a really good nucleus of four combs. A nucleus, being a stock in miniature, has all the requirements of a beginner who wishes to make himself familiar with the ways of bees. It has the advantage over a full colony that it is smaller, more easily handled, and above all is not complete, but must build itself up to full strength under the eyes of its owner who thereby learns much. Moreover, a really good four-comb nucleus, consisting, as it should do, of three combs almost full of brood, mostly sealed, and a fourth comb containing a good deal of food and possibly a little brood as well, if delivered before 7th June or about then, should in average districts in average seasons, build up in good time to fill a super or two before the end of the summer. Such a colony, if fed steadily from its arrival, except during honey-flows, as it ought always to be, should draw out the six sheets of foundation within a very short time; but the strain of bee must be good and the queen in good condition.

I would never recommend a beginner to buy a full stock, for it always seems to me that the advantage gained by seeing the development of the colony is very great; but when an early swarm can be had, that is quite a good method of making a beginning, though not as good as starting with driven bees. Furthermore, I do not agree with those who say a beginning should be made with a single colony; I would advise that three or four should be set up at once if it is intended to make a serious business of bees, even in a small way, for if a man hasn't sense enough to manage three or four stocks as a beginner, he had better let bees alone.

2. A near thing: After the 'ice storm' January 1940

3. Under the cherry trees. Blossom in the orchard of
Messrs. S. W. Mount & Sons, Canterbury

4. May blossom in April. Examining bees on return from fruit pollination

5. A pair of 'M.D.' hives in spring, showing our stands

My bees all wintered: a hundred per cent good come-out. I have done as well once or twice since, but never better! I often wonder if it may not be similar experiences that make small beekeepers so scornful, sometimes, of the less satisfactory results we more extensive ones obtain. They all came through, and the skep swarmed on my birthday between two tremendous thunderstorms. How well I remember that swarm! It hung in a quince tree in easy reach and was hived by me in one of some three or four more hives I had made in the winter, mostly during the night while sitting up with the lambing ewes. I believe I ended that year with seven or eight stocks, but all the honey I had in my supers was transported to Northampton in a washstand jug and sold to a man named Munn for sixpence a pound. The year 1907 was a terrible season; that I well remember. I had to buy what seemed to me at the time an enormous quantity of sugar. I remember the shop where I bought it, and that I paid 1¾d. per pound for it. And I made a great fuss about having cane sugar, for that was the current superstition in those days, and still is, I believe, in the best circles of our craft. I don't think it really matters a toss whether the sugar is derived from cane or from beet so long as it is well refined. The reason why I have long since reached this conclusion is that bees undoubtedly winter equally well on either. It is not that which causes loss, but in the matter of feeding, 'too little and too late' that kills or injures.

By this time I had saved up and bought a motor-bicycle, a brand new Triumph, three and a half horsepower. I suppose it would seem a comical sort of vehicle now, coming after our modern ones; but then it seemed to me a thing of beauty and it was certainly a joy, if not for ever, then for that time being. And I used it to pay visits to all the beekeepers I could hear of within reach. What a nuisance I must have been! Writing this down recalls their faces out of the past, or many of them. And those cottages and villages! I took to driving bees, paying the owners sixpence per hive driven. All impatience, I started driving far too early in the year. I got huge driven swarms, but they quickly dwindled, being old field bees. That is how we learn. One pound of September bees is worth five pounds in July to the driver. I remember once how I tied a piece of butter muslin over a skep containing one of these big driven swarms, two lots driven together, and hung it up in a tree while I finished driving some more. When I came to take it down honey was running through the muslin and all the bees were dead—stifled—so I learned another lesson that I never forgot.

What a host of skeps there were in those days, before acarine disease, then called 'Isle of Wight' disease, cleared them out. Every village had two or three skeppists, and most of them would let you have the bees that were to be 'taken up' rather than kill them. There was one place where they kept the bees in the large Pettigrew or bushel skeps; Paulerspury, it was. I remember it particularly because a dog always ran out at me and tried to bite my leg as I passed through. Finally I managed to run over that dog, with only minor injuries to both of us, and after that had peace. But those big skeps! What stocks they held! Why, they gave about three times as much honey as the ordinary small ones. And that was how I first learned that if you want to get large crops of honey you must use large hives. This is unorthodox; but as Mrs. Gamp remarked, 'Facts is stubborn things, not easy drove'.

Looking back, after so many years, the sequence of events is necessarily blurred in my memory, and my recollections of the less primitive beekeepers are unclear. But I vividly remember a visit to a man at Weedon, whose name I have forgotten, who electrified me by feeding back best quality sections to his bees. This seemed to me, even then, the last word in absurdity; and it does still, bearing in mind that sugar could be bought in quantities unlimited at twopence per pound, whereas a section was worth from tenpence to one shilling. Ever since I first became interested in bees my objective has been honey, and my problem how to produce it profitably, and such unbusinesslike methods have always affronted my understanding.

And even the up-to-date beekeepers, association members and the like, were not very reliable or competent, as one frequently discovered. Once I remember fetching a stock of bees on standard frames from such a one. When I reached home the honey was running out of the travelling box, and examination showed that none of the frames had ever been nailed together!

I joined the local association, and visited the secretary, a dear old man whose name I completely forget, though I remember his face well, and his house and garden. He started me as a member of the association and I was sent the official organ, a small paper with a pink cover called 'The Beekeeper's Record', a well edited little sheet, full of matter which, if somewhat trivial, was most interesting to a beginner. It was in the garden of this man that I first saw a genuine Stewarton hive. It was stocked with bees, and he showed me how honey was taken from it. I have never seen one since with bees in it, and I have often wondered what became of it when he died.

About a year after this I took the elementary examination in beekeeping proficiency known as the 'Third Class Expert Examination' and was duly awarded the certificate. My examiner was a young man named William Herrod who made me drive bees from a skep, catching the queen as she ran up. I also had to open a frame hive and take out combs, twiddling them about in the orthodox manner while looking for and pointing out the queen; and I was asked a few simple questions as well. So now I joined the ranks of the experts in beekeeping and felt quite an experienced practitioner of the art: much more so than I do now. It was the only examination I ever went in for, for I soon became convinced of the triviality of the methods employed in this country, though it was a good many years before I managed to break completely free from the hampering prejudices I absorbed during my early apprenticeship.

I took to showing honey in the local association show and took several prizes, and was particularly proud of two firsts for wood-and-glass supers of honey. These supers used to be a rather prominent feature of honey shows in the old days, and in my opinion it is a very great pity that they have been dropped, for there is no sort of advertisement that can be placed in a shop that equals one of these.

During my first few years of beekeeping I met many local men and visited their apiaries, and saw many ideas and fads in operation; but I only remember two cases in which the bees were treated as anything more than a hobby, and even those exceptions could hardly be called businesses, but were really only well-run and fairly profitable hobbies. All these people had their own pet ideas, mostly quite futile and trivial as it seems to me to-day; but if they got little profit, they at least took a great deal of pleasure from their hobby. Bubb undoubtedly did quite well out of his bees; but in a very limited degree. I remember how in 1908 he showed me what seemed to my inexperience a mountain of sections. I don't suppose there were really more than two or three gross, but they looked an awful lot to me. Also he showed me a stock of honey jars he had just got in. Nine gross! I thought there could not be enough honey in the county to fill them! I remember the price, too: eleven shillings a gross!

The thing that struck me as curious, even then, was the absence of any real quantity of honey as a result of all this fuss and activity. I never saw any quantity of honey anywhere. You read in books about bees being able to store thirty, forty, fifty pounds of surplus; but it never seemed to materialize. And there was little demand for what there was. It was years before I found the answer to that riddle.

I used to visit a beekeeper near Stony Stratford, who has only recently passed away. He had about eighty or one hundred stocks, I think, all or most of them in 'W.B.C.' hives. He was the only man I have ever known to distemper the interior of hives. The first thing I ever saw him doing was this. It certainly gave the hives a very clean appearance inside, and at all events can have done no harm.

The year 1908 was a very remarkable one, and so far as I can judge from this distance of time, must have been a very good season for honey. My bees came through the winter well with, I think, one casualty. On 26th April a very curious thing occurred. It suddenly began to snow, and in a couple of hours there lay on the ground the deepest snow I have ever seen except in drifts. Where it did drift at all sheep were practically buried. I have several photographs of that snow, taken on the 27th April. Hives were piled high with snow. That was the first time I saw bees perish in any numbers through flying in warm sun over snow.

I bought an extractor that year, a Meadows's 'guinea' machine, and was able to extract for myself. I don't think there can have been much honey. Somehow in those early years there never was. Something always happened: bees swarmed or something. They were never left in peace long enough to do much good, I expect. And the whole system they were worked upon was wrong, even if properly carried out. Probably one of the chief reasons why the enthusiastic beginner rarely gets honey is that he cannot let the bees alone. He is always disturbing them and looking to see how they are getting on. It is much as if one dug up a plant every day to see how its roots were progressing.

About this time the secretary of the local association offered me four stocks of bees in rather old wooden hives. They had been placed with him for sale by some member. I came, saw, purchased, and brought home those bees. Alas! In those days I knew nothing of brood diseases except perhaps from hearsay. To do him justice, I don't think the old gentleman who sold them to me knew either; I am sure he was innocent of anything but lack of knowledge. But those four stocks all had American foul brood, although I knew nothing of this until they had been bought and paid for several weeks.

This set-back cost me a lot of worry at the time and a great deal of disappointment; still I don't regret that I had this early lesson. I sent a sample of diseased brood to the *British Bee Journal* who diagnosed 'Black Brood'. I am not, even to this day, quite clear what black brood was supposed to be, and I am a little doubtful if the authorities at Bedford Street (or was it Henrietta Street then?) were either. Much less was known of brood disease then than now. However, I tried the numerous remedies recommended at the time. Naphthol beta fed to the bees in syrup—if you could persuade them to take it. Formaldehyde administered by tacking bits of flannel on to a dummy and soaking the flannel with it, 'Apicure', consisting of small tablets which I fancy were made of naphthaline and formaldehyde, a proprietary preparation. Phenol (Cheshire's remedy), but the bees would have none of that at any price. Also there was the salicylic acid treatment commended in France and Germany. Then I was lent a copy of Simmins's book, *A Modern Bee Farm*, and was carried away by his notions, one of which was that 'foul brood' could be cured by a dilute solution of 'Izal' by feeding it to the bees in syrup and spraying the combs and soaking the quilts with it. I tried all these except the salicylic acid, faithfully and with care, only to find that in my hands, so far as American foul brood was concerned, every one of them was totally valueless and utterly futile. Finally I got rid of the disease by destroying the bees' combs, hives and every bit of equipment except metal work. This was, I know now, quite unnecessary, but it was at any rate effectual; and I had learned a good deal that was useful afterwards.

The next two years, 1909 and 1910, were not, as far as I can remember, good honey seasons, but during them my apiary was re-established and built up to about twenty stocks, and following my Simmins enthusiasm, I bought one of his 'Conqueror' hives and then a 'Double Conqueror'. They were well named in this case for they conquered me. Of all the many absurdities that have been produced in this country for the delectation of bee hobbyists, these hives were surely the most remarkable. Just expensive, complicated toys, a plague and a nuisance from first to last. Well, I suppose we should be willing to try almost anything once, and once was enough for me in this case, and too much.

During all this period and long after it, British beekeeping was largely dominated by two men, the late T. W. Cowan and W. B. Carr. Both were amateur enthusiasts without any serious stake in the business of honey production. Indeed, in those days hardly anyone thought of beekeeping as anything much more than the merest hobby, and the idea of anyone attempting to get a living from beekeeping on modern lines would have seemed to most people the wildest of fantasies. Mr. Cowan was, I believe, a fairly wealthy man of considerable intellectual attainments. He invented the extractor with hinged baskets and the hive that was named after him. He was for many years chairman of the British Beekeepers' Association and editor and owner of the *British Bee Journal*. He wrote three books concerning beekeeping, *The British Beekeepers' Guide Book*, a small text-book on the hobby of beekeeping on a system that has become orthodox in this country and which, first published in 1881, has run through a great many editions and sold a great many thousand copies. Also *The Honey Bee, Its Anatomy and Physiology*, two editions at least of which have been sold. Thirdly, there is his *Wax Craft*, a very interesting little work, and so far as I know, the only book of the sort ever written. Mr. Carr was a somewhat lesser light who at one time edited or jointly edited the *Beekeepers' Record*. As I have said, in my early days hardly anyone dreamed that bees could be made to provide a decent income as a whole-time business, and the activities of these and other stars in our firmament rather confirmed this belief. Messrs. Cowan and Carr were greatly admired by the rank and file of small beekeepers of their day, indeed the lengths to which this adulation was carried was somewhat absurd at times. I remember once at a meeting of the British Beekeepers' Association in London while we were listening to a speech by one of the men on the platform, Mr. Cowan walked in late. To my surprise the entire congregation rose to their feet and reverently remained standing until the great man had taken his seat—like the King opening Parliament!

Another personality in beekeeping and the author of another guide to the beekeeping hobby was J. R. G. Digges who started *The Irish Bee Journal* in, I believe, 1901, and followed this up by writing and publishing *The Irish Bee Guide* in 1904. This was a somewhat larger book than the Cowan guide and was written in a more poetical style. Unfortunately it led to trouble. Digges and Cowan would seem to have been friendly enough at first, for I have a copy of Cowan's *Honey Bee* which he presented to Digges and autographed to that effect; also a sixth edition of Cowan's *Guide Book* interleaved, and annotated in Digges's hand. However, on publication of the Irish book Cowan claimed that Digges had infringed his copyright. A number of blocks that Digges borrowed from various appliance dealers and others were claimed as his property by Cowan, and Digges was faced with the alternative of signing a stringent apology or losing his book; so he swallowed his pride and the apology was framed and triumphantly displayed on the walls of the headquarters of the British Beekeepers' Association for many years. To the day of his death Digges believed that Cowan had cribbed a good deal of his matter in *The Honey Bee* from Cheshire's *Bees and Beekeeping*, for whole paragraphs in the former are almost verbatim the same as corresponding passages in the latter, and the plan or framework follows closely in the same way. But, although Cowan undoubtedly used Cheshire as a sort of scaffolding, I believe that in actual fact he did not use Cheshire in any other way; but that both of them copied from foreign authors, Cowan acknowledging the fact and Cheshire doing nothing of the kind. Digges frankly took his material for the anatomy section of his book from Cheshire by arrangement and his matter was therefore necessarily much like Cowan's. Incidentally, I will mention that three blocks that had to be replaced by others in the second edition of Digges's book on account of this bother were the illustrations of a queen, drone and worker which appear to have been taken from the fine steel engraving on the title page of the second edition of *The Honey Bee* of Bevan, 1838. Since that time, Digges's book under the new title *Practical Bee Guide* has sold some 65,000 copies.

One queer personality I met once and heard a good deal about at that time was the late John Hewitt who hated Cowan and Carr with a deep and abiding hatred. Hewitt had a grievance because they would not give him credit for getting the Government to allow queen bees to travel by letter post which it appears was largely due to his agitation. Probably the big men thought such agitation should come only through them. Hewitt was just a little cracked, I believe, partly through worrying over his wrongs (?). At all events he managed to get from North Africa some Tunisian bees which he christened 'Punics'. This was about 1892, I think, and Frank Benton had brought some to the U.S.A. about the same time. However, Hewitt started to push these bees. He described them as being absolutely faultless in every respect, and advertised virgins by hundreds. He went too far in describing them as 'proof against foul brood'. *The British Bee Journal*, then the only advertising medium, very properly refused to print these advertisements, and the fat was in the fire. Hewitt started a magazine, *The Bee Master*, apparently as a vehicle for his advertisements and to allow scope for abuse of his enemies of the *British Bee Journal*. He literally could not write a page without a whole string of accusations of swindling, lying, and general wickedness, directed against Messrs. Cowan and Carr. It was libel of the grossest kind; but the abused were too wary to issue any writ for damages, knowing that blood cannot be got from a stone. The little magazine published seven numbers at irregular intervals during 1897–8 and then stopped. Hardly anyone dared advertise in it, of course, for fear of losing advertising facilities in the *B.B.J.* There was room for a second paper then, and if Hewitt could have put his personal grievances aside, he might have established it with a little financial help from outside, but he could no more keep Cowan and Carr out of a page of it than Mr. Dick could keep King Charles's head out of his memorial.

Hewitt was, I am pretty sure, the first man to make the overlapping pyramid-shaped lifts such as are now so commonly seen in modern W.B.C. hives. He also was probably the first to introduce the glass sections such as Simmins later put forward. He was a clever man in his way, and seems to have been especially good at raising queens. He claimed that he could with his Punics have a number of virgin queens running loose in a hive together. This seems very improbable; but Bartlett once told me that he had actually seen it. In any case Punic bees do not appear to have been much good; they were a small black variety, spiteful, and with the curious habit of biting as well as stinging. But all this was in days gone by.

To return once more to the bees: the year 1911 was the greatest honey season in this country within the memory of beekeepers, and it is probable that it may never have had and will never have its equal. I remember it clearly. Bees were strong in spring and never looked back. In June and July, for weeks on end the weather was ideal; there would be dense fog and very heavy dew in the morning, so that hay-making could hardly be started before mid-day. Then, about eleven o'clock, the sun would gradually come through the mist and the face of the land would become steaming hot. Honey poured into hives in just such streams as we have frequently known in recent years, but instead of this lasting only a few days, it went on for weeks. I left my home for a short stay with friends during this flow and thought I had left ample storage room on my few hives. When I returned I found that two stocks had built combs under their floors and filled them with honey. They had become congested, had hung out and clustered under the hives, and the flow being heavy, they had started combs in the outside cluster. What a season! It was rumoured that Mr. Bartlett, an extensive Oxfordshire beekeeper, had produced forty tons of honey, chiefly in sections. In later years he confirmed this to me orally, adding that it took him two years to sell it.

But Nemesis lay in wait.

Fate steals along with silent tread,
Found oftenest in what least we dread;
Frowns in the storm with angry brow,
But in the sunshine strikes the blow.

There had come most alarming tales from the South of a new and devastating plague. Whole apiaries had been wiped out in the Isle of Wight; the trouble had spread to the mainland, was rapidly travelling north and spreading far and wide. Towards the end of this most glorious of English summers for beekeeping, I noticed a large number of bees running about in front of their hives unable to fly, and these towards evening tended to bunch on grass and lumps of earth. Even then, being inexperienced, I did not quite realize what was coming, and like all amateurs, I looked about for someone to tell me what to do about it.

All who remember those days will also recollect the host of remedies that were peddled around. Ayles's cure; Flavine; Izal; Yadil; decoctions of onions; and the indefatigable Simmins was soon to the fore with bottles of stuff he called 'Bee-well'. None of these was of any real use.

In the autumn of 1912 I moved what few bees I had left to my new home near Abingdon and by the following June every stock but one had died out and for the time being I could hardly call myself a beekeeper any longer. But the next year I started off again. I found a swarm on my farm and hived it. Every bee was dead in a few weeks of Isle of Wight disease. I had one stock that had for some reason survived the holocaust, and from it I managed to stock several of my hives, and in 1915 I had quite a little honey to sell. The plague seemed to have been to some extent stayed: in fact it never returned with the same devastating virulence so far as my bees were concerned. It was, however, still present, and seemed likely to remain so.

Being offered a much better farm at Wallingford, I moved there in the autumn of 1915 and having decided to make a completely new start with bees, destroyed most of my equipment. Then, in the spring of 1916, having meanwhile prepared a few hives, I bought a full stock of black bees from Mr. Robertson of Wormit. All the hives I then made were of the kind called 'W.B.C.' and were large enough to take inner chambers for either standard or Simmins's frames. I stocked them with Dutch bees, then being imported in large numbers in the erroneous belief that they were immune to Isle of Wight disease, now known as Acarine Disease. But the Dutch I had were quite hopeless; they would do nothing but swarm and I soon got rid of them and tried some nuclei from Simmins. These were much better, though rather too much inclined to swarm. They were wonderfully prolific and the nuclei sent out by Simmins were magnificent. These bees would gather large crops of honey in good seasons, when honey-flows were prolonged; but in poor seasons, when fine weather came only in short spells, they were not of very much use, I think. The fact of the matter is that in this country it is very difficult to build up a queen business unless the bees sent out are rather light-coloured Italians, very prolific and good tempered. Those who go in for this trade will usually, therefore, tend to breed for these selling characteristics. Now a long experience has taught me that good honey producing strains are rarely *very* placid in temperament. That is not to say that quite easily handled and managed bees may not be excellent honey storers, but I do maintain that ultra amiable bees are, like ultra amiable humans, apt to be rather easy-going and without the acquisitive spirit so necessary if one is to accumulate wealth in this world.

There is probably no bee equal to the Italian for all-round honey production *if of the right strain.* This last point should be stressed. It can hardly be over emphasized. Most of the Italian bees in use in England are not nearly as good as they might be. Breeders cannot be blamed, for their customers demand three attributes in the bees they buy; gentleness, yellow colour, and prolificness. Honey seems to be quite a secondary matter with the average hobbyist beekeeper, and in this country it is the hobbyist who spends his money on fancy bees and fancy equipment, and who, therefore, sets the fashion.

Mention has been made of the late Samuel Simmins and his various ideas. I have never really been able to decide whether this man was in any sense a practical honey producer, or simply one who, having become interested in the subject of beekeeping, devoted his active mind to devising all sorts of theories with their accompanying gadgets and crotchets. He advertised and sold bees and also queens as being something very remarkable in their honey producing proclivities. He invented the 'Conqueror' hives, and a patent device for uncapping both sides of a comb at once, and put forward all sorts of ideas that seemed very plausible to me until I tried them out. He wrote a book in which he ventilated all his theories, and in which he warns us on no account to rely on beekeeping by itself for a living. From this, in conjunction with the fact that he was obliged to pass through the bankruptcy court, I think we are entitled to assume that he never got very much out of the business himself.

It was about the fourth year of my beekeeping experiences that I got into touch with Simmins after reading his book. He wrote me many letters that were of great interest at the time, and would still be interesting if I had them by me. Through this correspondence I became interested in the idea of using frames of a larger size than the British standard, and purchased a couple of nuclei from Simmins on the frames he advocated, called by him the 'Commercial' frames. These measured 16" x 10" and the top bar was 17½" long. I found that these frames were certainly an improvement in many ways on the smaller standard frame, and in my enthusiasm I even tried to make others see that this was so.

The 'Commercial' frames were larger than the standard, and this seemed to me to be a great improvement, though I later came to prefer the still larger 'Modified Dadant' frames; but their short top bars constituted their greatest asset in comparison with the British frames, for whereas the latter require double walls to their hives in order to accommodate them, the Simmins, like all modern frames except the British standard, has short top bars which project only ¾" at each end, and so can be hung on a rabbet cut in the thickness of a ⅞" board, which allows one to use plain, single-walled hives.

At this time I first became interested in American and Australasian beekeeping literature. I purchased several books dealing with this subject and subscribed to the two principal American bee magazines. At first the methods therein given seemed to me rather extraordinary. The flat-roofed, plinthless hives, and the strange floors repelled me. But I soon realized that if such things were used almost exclusively throughout the American continent, Australia, New Zealand, and many other countries, they could not well be other than efficient, at all events in those parts, seeing that by far the greater part of the world's honey was produced therein.

But would they answer here? There was only one way to find out, and that was to try them. I tried them. They answered well. I have used them ever since, and I am now running, jointly with another, what for England is a very large honey farm. I have depended entirely upon the business for many years, and have not done so very badly in spite of many failures caused by mistakes and by diseases of various kinds.

My complete acceptance of the American system of beekeeping and the appropriate equipment did not come without a good deal of hesitation. Habit and prejudice are not readily overcome; but I did finally come to see quite clearly that if I intended to make honey production my business in life, I must abandon the orthodox methods as practised in our country and adopt the more practical and economical system in use in almost all the countries where beekeeping is a serious commercial proposition, and from that time I began to have some success.

Having decided that I would abandon agricultural farming and attempt to get my living by producing honey, I left my farm and spent one year with the late Julian Lockwood with the view of building up a large bee farm in North Norfolk; but things turned out unfortunately. Lockwood had been very severely wounded in the Near East, one lung being virtually destroyed, and he really was not up to the rough and strenuous labour of building up such a business: on top of that he sustained a bad compound fracture of the leg early in the year which effectually laid him by for many weeks and greatly handicapped him for months. I saw that there was no hope of carrying out our intentions, so we decided to abandon the idea and parted with mutual regret. That year of 1921 was one of the pleasantest in my life and a very good honey season.

I returned to Oxfordshire, having gained a good deal of insight into the business; and after having devoted a few more years to building up a considerable stock of bees with the necessary equipment, I finally gave up all other business activities and, having secured a cottage and some land, devoted my whole time to beekeeping. Since then I have depended solely upon my bees for my bread and butter. I have had hard times to come through; but I have never for one moment regretted my decision; such regrets as I have had have been rather that I did not screw up my courage to the sticking place long before.

CHAPTER II

ESSENTIALS

I don't know if it is the same with other men who are in the bee-keeping business in a fairly big way, but in my case hardly a season passes without my being asked by some wistful young enthusiast whether it is really possible to make a comfortable living from honey production in this country. And it is a very awkward question, because, although it is certain that the reply must be in the affirmative, most of these young people have not the faintest idea of what is really implied; they do not grasp the basis on which the business must rest or understand the essential things that assure success.

Usually it is possible, after a short talk with these would-be bee farmers, to judge fairly well whether they are definitely unlikely to succeed, or the reverse. I have myself had nothing to live on outside my bees for many years, so I suppose I may claim to have succeeded; but I only just managed it; only just worked out the right technique in time. If I had taken another two or three years to learn the game, I should have failed, I think. And that is what happens to so many who start in this bee business so full of enthusiasm: they spend all their money in finding out how to run the business, and by the time they have the experience someone else has the capital. I have seen it happen again and again.

For the establishment on a firm basis of a honey producing business it is necessary that there shall be two essentials; *knowledge* and *capital*. And the two must be concurrent; the bee farmer must have capital and experience at the same time; and it so often happens that by the time knowledge is accumulated, capital is dissipated. The prospective bee farmer must be willing to work hard and to learn; and he must also have a natural aptitude for the work; and he must bear in mind always that the business of beekeeping for honey production is a very different thing from keeping bees as a hobby.

Probably the great majority of British beekeepers are not making any profit from their bees: certainly very few make a living from honey production. This is not so much because there is any inherent reason why it should not be done, as because the methods of management, and corresponding equipment so generally in use here, are quite inefficient for business beekeeping, except for the parasitic branches, as perhaps one may term them, such as queen-rearing for the trade, and the sale of bees. These methods and equipment appear to have become more or less established some sixty years ago, at about the time the late T. W. Cowan published the first edition of his well-known book, *The British Beekeepers' Guide Book*.

And to all those who wish to keep some bees as a hobby, I commend this little work. Therein will be found all the fads and unnecessary trimmings that so delight the hearts of enthusiasts who want to 'keep bees'. The idea of such people is, so far as possible, to find some excuse for doing something to the bees. It is called 'manipulating' them. The poor little creatures are to be commenced upon in March and ceaselessly tormented until winter brings them respite. Even then they are not to be left altogether in peace, for 'candy' is to be administered from time to time. The whole thing is capitally done, and if you want to keep some bees as a pleasant pastime which may probably supply your table with honey and at the same time afford you much pleasure and interest, without being obliged to worry much about costs and profits, I can think of no better work to follow. If you have time and cash to spare for your hobby, I know of no more pleasant outlet for your enthusiasm than beekeeping on strictly orthodox British principles. How well I remember the enthusiasm I felt about it all in the days of my youth! My admiration of those pictures of smiling old gentlemen fiddling about with beautiful and complicated hives, piled high with supers which it never occurred to me might be empty, like dummy whisky bottles in a grocer's window! But there is a lot of difference between keeping bees and being kept by bees, and orthodox British methods cater strictly for the former. I don't say that profit cannot be made that way; but I do think that to make a living from honey production while working on orthodox British lines is virtually impossible, and I do not think it has ever been done. In any case profit gained in that way is made under every possible handicap, and anyone who should attempt it would have to work, figuratively speaking, with his hands tied.

For success as a honey farmer a man must know how to run the business; in other words, knowledge is the first essential. All knowledge, as distinguished from instinct, is gathered from experience; but not necessarily from our own. What one generation has learned has, all down through the ages, passed on to the next, and the sum of this accumulated wisdom is to-day at the disposal of anyone who can use it. There is not the least doubt that if you want to make a living by producing honey, you must learn the right way to set about it, so far as is known at the time. What is learned by personal experience is generally learned well, but that is often rather an expensive way of gathering knowledge. Better, as far as may be, profit by the experience of successful contemporaries, and from those who have made good in days gone by and who have left written records of their work; but beware of writers who have never had to rely on their bees for any part of their livelihood. These are often very good and well-meaning people, and their writings are frequently both interesting and glib; but they don't really know what the business of honey production entails, for their point of view is that of the hobbyist.

So I advise prospective honey farmers to visit as many of the more successful bee farms as they can in order to see for themselves how the work is done; but don't be surprised if you are not received with excessive enthusiasm in the busy season. Remember that you will be a nuisance, and that the least you can do is to realize this and try to be as accommodating as you can. I have had young men write to me saying that they were coming along to see my work and giving the date and hour of arrival. Such people are annoyed and offended when they find that we are all maybe twenty miles away in the wilds; but it is their own fault. Most bee farmers are glad to help serious beginners, but they cannot possibly have their time-table upset on that account. Such visits, if properly arranged, should be very useful to the would-be bee farmer, and not only to the tyro, for in a longish experience I cannot remember ever having paid a visit to another bee farmer without learning something worth while.

Magazines

It will pay to take several beekeeping magazines. These are all monthly except one. In England *The Bee World* deals largely with the scientific side of the matter. It keeps readers up to date regarding the latest findings of investigators in connection with the diseases of bees and various important subjects of a similar nature, and it prints translated extracts from the principal bee journals which circulate in foreign countries. It is owned by the Apis Club. *The British Bee Journal* is a privately owned weekly which deals almost entirely with the hobby side of beekeeping. It is, I think, the only weekly bee journal in existence. Established in 1873, it is one of the oldest bee papers, and being a weekly makes it an excellent advertising medium. It is, however, not a magazine likely to be of much assistance to anyone who thinks of setting up a bee farm on business lines in order to make a living thereby. *The Beekeepers' Record* is a small monthly publication in the same ownership as the *B.B.J.*, and chiefly devoted to the same interests. Several of the Beekeepers' Associations use it as their official organ. *Bee Craft* is a monthly paper which was first issued in 1919 as the official journal of the Kent Beekeepers' Association. Its circulation has reached the very considerable number of about 10,000. It has a less conservative outlook than the *B.B.J.* and will probably, when not as at the time of writing hampered by shortage of paper supplies, become an extensive and important publication. Scotland has its own magazine for beekeepers, *The Scottish Beekeeper*, an excellent monthly, which is very general in its interest and is very far from confined to its native land for its circulation.

The two principal American bee papers are *The American Bee Journal*, the oldest bee magazine in the English language, which has for many years been owned and published by Dadant and Sons, honey producers and foundation manufacturers of note; and *Gleanings in Bee Culture* which was first issued in 1873, the same year as saw the advent of the *British Bee Journal*, by the late Amos I. Root at Medina, Ohio. It has remained ever since a publication of the Root Company, first as a quarterly, which was almost at once changed to monthly; then after a time it became fortnightly, reverting to monthly in 1917. Like the *American Bee Journal* it is of the very widest interest to all classes of beekeepers, and both papers contain a very large amount of reading matter.

Both these American papers, and others, if you are enthusiastic to find out all you can, should be taken and studied, together with the British publications above listed. Up to the time of writing the American papers have been incomparably more useful from the point of view of the honey farmer and should certainly be read regularly. They should be read and filed for reference. They don't cost much and useful information will certainly be found in all.

Some years ago, in the course of an article in a beekeeping periodical, I strongly advised any young man who seriously contemplated taking up bee farming for a livelihood to work for a year or two with some successful honey producer, even should it be necessary for him to work for nothing or to pay for the privilege. This brought a retort from the late John Anderson suggesting that I was fishing for a pupil myself so as to get my work done for me gratis. Such are the amenities of the bee world! So, while repeating this advice with emphasis, I may as well say, to avoid misunderstanding, that I am not looking for pupils, paying or otherwise.

I have been asked, time and again, what books are best for a man to read to help him with bee farming. Now most of the useful works in the English language on this subject are of American origin. This is because in Canada and the U.S.A. honey production is quite an extensive and important business. There are hundreds of these enterprises established there, whereas in Britain there are only very few. Nearly all potential buyers of bee books here are interested in bees solely as a hobby, and have no aspirations or interest in beekeeping as a serious whole-time business, and that is why so few books published in this country deal with bee farming. Just as the American bee magazines deal with beekeeping very largely from the business point of view and the British from the standpoint of the hobbyist, so it is with the more modern books. To publish a book that is likely to interest only a few is to court trouble; but of late years the production of honey as a business proposition has attracted more attention than formerly, partly through the introduction and increasing popularity of the American type of hives and system of management, which has made the enterprise more practicable on a scale large enough to provide a livelihood, and partly, perhaps, because a number of honey farms are known to be in being in Britain, and to be solvent.

Although extensive bee farming is tacitly supposed by the majority of beekeepers to be virtually non-existent in this country, there is, in fact, a number of successful undertakings of this kind well established here. Not many are of very large size, but there are certainly two and possibly three honey farms in England of over 1,000 stocks each, and a few of over 500. There are several of from 200 to 500; but the great majority of these businesses are part-time undertakings of from 40 to 200 stocks.

Books

With books published before about 1850 the prospective honey farmer need not trouble himself. They are interesting in their way, but cannot be said to be of practical value to the modern bee-keeper. Hyll, Gedde, Butler, Rusden, Warder, Thorley, after their kind are little more than curiosities to-day, but towards the end of the nineteenth century a few writers produced works showing that the possibilities of bee farming as a business were beginning to be understood. In this country Pettigrew and in America the brothers Harbison, Quinby, and Miner were successful men who wrote accounts of their ideas and methods. They wrote before, or just after the introduction of the movable-comb, hanging-frame hive by Langstroth, but a later book by Quinby, edited and published posthumously, shows that this great bee-man was fully alive to the possibilities of a very important invention. Langstroth published his first edition of *The Hive and the Honey-Bee* in 1853, and a copy of this very scarce edition is one of my treasures. It is one of the most important books on beekeeping ever written and reprints are not difficult to get. W. C. and J. S. Harbison wrote in 1860 and 1861, Quinby in 1853, Miner in 1849. The Harbison books are very scarce, but those of Quinby and Miner are not difficult to obtain in reprints or later editions. All these books are well worth study and show what a great stride had been made since the end of the eighteenth century when the best that could be produced was such nonsense as was written by Bonner.

In 1880 was published *British Bee Farming* by James Robinson. This writer seems really to have had some practical idea of the profits obtainable. He draws largely from Miner and Quinby, but has no use for supers at all. He gives no profit and loss accounts and no balance sheets as examples, but says that on a very low computation the yield per hive would be eighty pounds, but does not explain what this means. However, judging from the context and remembering that he advocates a hive only large enough to accommodate the stock or swarm for one season without the use of supers, I think he must mean that from every stock successfully wintered together with its increase, eighty pounds should be obtainable, the whole being 'taken up' at the end of the season. The whole thing is confused, but we should not forget that in those days there were usually no supers, the hives being simply made about the size that might be expected to be required by the bees for the summer, everything being 'taken up' at the end. Robinson thought that hives should be rather small, because if large the bees would not fill them in one season; a remark which shows that we have moved a bit since his time at any rate. Here I will give a quotation from his book which goes to explain matters as seen from the viewpoint of 1880. 'Quinby uses a bar-frame hive in his own apiary 12″ deep by 19½″ long and 12″ in width. We have with care tested this hive, of which we had three made, but they never sent out a single swarm, and yielded a very small amount of honey; however we would not blame Quinby for this for he does not farm his stocks for the sake of swarms, or even hive honey; he endeavours to get as much super honey as possible, which he sends to the market in the comb.' The moral of all this is that when you use large hives you must use supers, and plenty of them. My modified Dadant hives, similar to what Quinby used, but much larger, are usually fully occupied as to their supers quite as soon and generally sooner than British standard hives under the same conditions.

But that is a book of long ago: what of the moderns? I have them all on my shelves here and have read as much of them as I have found possible. Almost all the British ones are written by more or less inexperienced amateur enthusiasts who treat the matter quite simply as a hobby. Most of them call it a profitable hobby. I have nothing to say against hobbies or their riders: I have had hobbies myself, but never a profitable one, and we may do well to remember Mr. Deane's dictum in George Eliot's great novel, 'The worst of all hobbies are those that people think they can get money at. They shoot their money down like corn out of a sack then'—(*The Mill on the Floss*). And if that is true at all it is certainly true of bee-keeping. We cannot run a business on which our livelihood depends, either wholly or in part, on principles and by practices which are suitable for hobbies.

The hobby of beekeeping is always said to be profitable, and does no doubt in some cases show an actual monetary profit, but the cold fact is that, by and large, it is pretty certain that the amount of money spent on it, as is the case with most other similar pastimes, greatly exceeds what is realized from it, so we must of necessity pass by all those books which deal with beekeeping primarily as a hobby and examine what remain.

Simmins's *A Modern Bee Farm* contains some useful matter, but the greater part is in my opinion unreliable, for it is the product of a mind far too much under the influence of amateurish enthusiasm. Simmins's idea of a bee farm was, to judge from his book, a smallholding stocked with milking cows, poultry, pigs, etc., with bees thrown in as a make-weight. I do not think he ever had under his management anything that could be legitimately called a bee farm. It is doubtful if he ever produced any great quantity of honey. He was a queen-breeder, but not an extensive one. He never could keep even tolerably up with orders, and in some cases buyers waited two years before delivery, as was the case with me. He kept almost as many bees in his bonnet as in his hives, I think, and harboured some curious ideas, particularly as to the origin of foul brood. It seems to me that he spent a good part of his time thinking up all sorts of theories, and got so enthusiastic about them that he mistook them for facts, without sufficient tests. For my part I never could make any of his theories work, though I was for a long time one of his disciples; like his 'Conqueror' hives, they all worked capitally until you brought them into practical issue with the bees. But Simmins may be read with circumspection once the reader has grasped the basic facts of the business.

Sturges, in 1924, published a volume of 300 pages, *Practical Beekeeping*. He seems to have understood bees, but had not the faintest notion of the economics of honey production when he wrote his book. He made the mistake of formulating his theories first, then writing the book to elucidate them, and afterwards setting up a bee-farm; but the book has good points and may be read with profit if the reader will but bear in mind that had Sturges lived to write again, he would probably have very greatly modified many of his ideas as set forth in this book. He had an idea, probably gleaned from American writings, that, to winter well, bees need to be packed up in extravagantly thick wrappings, and the hive he suggested was such as no honey farm could use by any possible chance. His breeding section is good, but the work as a whole is spoiled by being written too soon, and the author was rather over-enthusiastic about American methods, a fault that cannot at any rate be ascribed to the next writer on the list.

Herrod-Hempsall produced in 1930 and 1937 a spectacular work, *Beekeeping New and Old*. It consists of two large volumes with 1,800 pages and over 3,000 illustrations. While the book can hardly be said to deal with beekeeping as a whole-time business it contains a lot of interesting information. The illustrations, a large portion of which are photographs by the author, are in the majority of cases very good, many of those illustrating the natural history of the bee being really magnificent, and proving him an accomplished photographer, having much patience and great skill. This nature photography, a good deal of which is microscopic work, will in itself probably make the book a classic. Beekeeping is treated throughout in the traditional British manner as a hobby or an amateur's side-line, and the author holds resolutely to the orthodox system and equipment of this country with a fervour of patriotism that is quite affecting. He touches on the possible profits which he considers may be derived from bees, and gives a few balance sheets concerning small side-line or part-time enterprises, for the most part relating to isolated particularly good seasons. The most impressive account of this kind given is that of a man in the excellent locality of Newmarket who made a profit of £700 or so from fifty stocks of bees; but as we are not told how many years it took to do this the conclusion to be drawn is not particularly obvious. However, this gentleman's considered opinion is that 'beekeeping on a large scale is an impossible proposition for making a living; in fact, there is not a single person who can, or does, make a living from beekeeping alone'. And again, 'Beekeeping is an occupation that, owing to climatic conditions, cannot be made a full-time job in the British Isles . . . it is an occupation that can be followed by a large number of people on a small scale, but to attempt it on a gigantic scale will lead surely and certainly to disaster.' I quote from his two books. But his opinion would seem to have changed with the years, for in 1909 he was writing in *Gleanings* in criticism of an article by Tinsley, '. . . with regard to the statement that there is not a single beekeeper who depends entirely on his bees for a livelihood. The number certainly is limited, and could be counted on the fingers of one hand; but I could give the names of several who depend upon their bees as a means of livelihood; and though certainly our climate and seasons are fickle, they do very well. It is more the limitation of forage in any particular district that prevents a living being made out of the industry than the above reasons.'

These pronouncements are by one who has for many years used his influence, which has been considerable, to recommend to the beekeepers of this country the system of management and the hives and appliances described at great length in his writings. He admits the failure of beekeeping here as anything more than a pastime or an adjunct to some more serious occupation. He attributes this to our climate now: in 1909 he put the blame upon lack of forage; but in my opinion the difficulty arises from neither the one nor the other, but is rather to be ascribed to the system of management and to the equipment which is in such general use here.

This large book is, in fact, a sort of glorified guide to the hobby of keeping bees on orthodox British lines, with which is incorporated an immense collection of miscellaneous facts and theories connected with bees and beekeeping, and is a work which represents enormous labour and patience on the part of its author. It is marred by an atmosphere of what might almost be mistaken for intolerant egotism, and there is an unpleasantly acrimonious anti-American bias. The section on brood diseases expresses views that are incompatible with the latest findings of investigators as I understand them, and should be read with caution, the writer's opinions, apparently, having remained substantially unchanged since Cheshire's time. But it is a great book, and every beekeeper should have a copy if he can get one.

One of the most useful books issued of late years is Wedmore's *Manual of Beekeeping*. This is a compendium of beekeeping information in which each subject is allotted a separate numbered paragraph. In all, there are 1,776 paragraphs, but as many of these are allotted to two or three lines, the whole are contained in four hundred pages. In these four hundred pages are collected facts connected with virtually every aspect of bee work, and every theory besides, with the usual exception of economics. This work should be on every beekeeper's shelves, for it gives all sorts of information not easily found in the absence of such a reference book. It is not a book that one reads right off for pleasure, neither is it a beginner's guide; it is a reference work, pure and simple.

The little book by Wadey, *The Bee Craftsman*, is something rather new and unusual in beekeeping literature. It is a guide; but not to orthodox beekeeping as a hobby, after the usual style of British guides. It deals seriously with beekeeping for profit. Its worst fault is that it is far too short to allow the author to do more than touch upon the fringe of his subject. It is a realistic little book and it is clear that the author has based his teaching on experience, and that unlike Herrod-Hempsall, he thinks a living can be made from beekeeping, though he is not himself a whole-time man like many I could name. But this book more nearly approaches what we may understand as a guide to honey production for the purpose of gaining a livelihood in the British Isles than any other I know.

These are the largest and most advanced books on bees published in Britain to-day. Simmins and Herrod-Hempsall say that beekeeping is profitable, but you can't live by it; Wedmore and Wadey make no mention of costs and profits. Sturgess, while somewhat vague, and rightly, since he had no personal experience of bee farming when he wrote, makes the most extravagant statements as to the crops that might be expected as average annual surplus, placing it at 100 pounds weight, but gives no estimate of costs and profits.

Popular guide books to the hobby of keeping bees in these Islands are legion. There are such books as Cowan's guide, Digges's *Practical Bee Guide*, Herrod-Hempsall's *Beekeepers' Guide*, a beautifully illustrated work, Mace's *Modern Beekeeping*, and the books of Tickner Edwardes, Flower, Jackson, Lawson, and other writers; but none deals with honey production as a business that a man could live on.

On the scientific side we are rich here. Cheshire's book, *Bees and Beekeeping* was at one time the leading work on bee anatomy; there are also Cowan's *Anatomy and Physiology of the Honey-bee* and Herrod-Hempsall's very fine book with a similar title, and finally, Miss Betts's *Practical Bee Anatomy*.

If practical books dealing with the business of farming bees for honey, written in this country, are scarce, such is not the case with those of America. Several writers of that country have really lived by their bees and have taken great pains to set down their accounts of their experiences and methods of management. The more useful American works are Root's *A.B.C. & X.Y.Z. of Bee-keeping*, a very large volume which has had a sale of almost a quarter of a million copies. It is really an encyclopaedia of bee-keeping, and every bee farmer should have a copy. Then there are such works on general beekeeping as Phillips's *Beekeeping*, Dadant's *The Honey-bee*, Pellett's *Productive Beekeeping*, and Miller's *Fifty Years Among the Bees*, in which he gives a racy, though rather discursive account of his own methods. Other books which describe their authors' various systems and ideas are *The Dadant System*, *The Townsend Bee Book* by E. D. Townsend and *Wilder's System* by J. J. Wilder, who I believe at one time ran 15,000 stocks in Georgia. *Advanced Beekeeping*, by Hutchinson, is also a valuable work by a successful man.

Books dealing with special branches are also plentiful. There are the queen-rearing books of Smith, Doolittle and Pellett, and also *The Management of Out-Apiaries*, by Doolittle, *Out-Apiaries*, by Pellett, and others. Anatomy is represented by that famous work, *The Anatomy of the Honeybee* by Snodgrass. These and many others are worth reading and studying well.

The books listed here are probably the best for the prospective bee farmer; but there are literally hundreds, old and new, which can be read with interest and profit. I have about 300, or maybe more, but I have never managed to read them all in their entirety. Over and above these books there is a very useful fund of know-ledge to be gathered from reading bound copies of all sorts of bee magazines, if you can get hold of them; there is nothing I enjoy more than browsing over past volumes of *Gleanings* or *The American Bee Journal* or *The Beekeepers' Review* or *Bee Craft*. I think one really gets almost more helpful hints from doing this and making notes of items found than from reading regular books.

Capital

Knowledge, then, is the first essential, and with it we may bracket skill, aptitude and determination. Both brains and brawn are quite necessary, too; but the latter may in some circumstances be hired. The other vital necessary is *Capital*, which I print in

italics and with a capital letter. Here I have reached that difficult
subject of beekeeping economics which has been treated in British
beekeeping literature with such shyness and diffidence by almost
all writers on bees and beekeeping. To give him his due, Simmins
did go into figures; but his economics were quite preposterous
considered as an exposition of the possibilities of honey production
as a business.

The question of the capital required for a bee farm conducted
mainly for honey production is not really a very difficult one to
answer in terms of capital goods, by anyone who has had to find
the necessary capital for the purpose, and who has thus learned by
actual experience what is necessary; but to reduce these items to
pounds, shillings and pence at a time like the present is very difficult. This is being written during a great world war, when cur-
rency values are unstable, and prices expressed in terms of cash
must be unstable also. In 1936, I estimated[1] the necessary minimum
capital with which it would then have been safe to start a bee farm
of 200—300 colonies at about £5 to £6 per unit of production.
All values have quite doubled since then, and may rise still higher
or fall again; it depends entirely on circumstances over which
beekeepers, at any rate, have no control. One thing is certain:
granted good management, the larger the business the lower the
capital required per unit and the more economically the whole
thing can be run. I do not think anyone should attempt to gain
a livelihood from a bee farm of less than 200 colonies, and that
being in all probability about the very smallest to be relied upon,
it follows that it is also the least profitable. Granted the necessary
capital, a man with 500 or 1,000 stocks is in an incomparably
stronger position than a small man.

There is this further serious fact to be considered. It is very
doubtful indeed whether it is at all safe for any man to attempt to
live by a one-man bee farm. We are all liable to be placed *hors de
combat* at times, and in the case of a small one-man bee business,
should that time be the busy season consequences might be disastrous. My considered opinion is that bee-farming is a job for
two or three persons which means that it is safe only when large
enough to justify the employment of assistance. In a later chapter
I hope to go into the questions which arise in connection with the

[1] *Honey Production in the British Isles.*

starting of a bee farm going on sound lines as distinct from commencing to keep bees.

The principal items of capital outlay required on a bee farm run
for honey production are land and buildings; hives and their
appurtenances; livestock; and enough money to maintain the
owner for two or three years while he is setting the thing
going.

CHAPTER III

CLIMATE, PASTURAGE, AND APIARIES

Three things are necessary for the production of a crop of honey: bees, nectar, and weather. In Chapter V, I will give my ideas about how to improve the first of this trinity, and of the last it may be said that in our country the weather in summer-time is as a general rule about as bad as it can well be, considered from the point of view of the beekeeper. All honey producers complain of it, but none of them do anything else about it. The climate, then, is a liability here and if you are going to succeed in making honey production pay, why, it must be done in spite of a climate that gives really good seasons only occasionally. This means that with us the average season is poor as regards weather. You have only to read American books and literature on beekeeping to understand the great difference there is between their climate over there, and ours. The cold, dark weather that is so familiar a feature of British summers is almost unknown in continental countries, where summer is more apt to be sunny and warm. Our honey-flows are often extremely heavy when they come, but the time of their advent is entirely problematical. Usually we have about three weeks of good weather between 1st May and 31st August. Good weather for bees, I mean. The rest of the time weather is chilly, cloudy, windy, wet, foggy, or even downright cold, but interspersed with short intervals of sunny days. Our country is in summer usually suffering from a prolonged drought or from constant deluges; but from the beekeeping angle the worst trouble is low temperature. From May to August, in my experience, hot, really hot weather will always bring a honey-flow. Early flows are not very desirable, as they are almost always followed by long spells of dearth in which what has been stored is eaten up by the bees. July is in my part of the country the most important month, so far as flowers that yield nectar are concerned, but hot weather good for bees is quite uncommon in that month. I write in 1944 and the last good July honey-flow was in 1935.

In order to give the beginner some idea of the difficulties that our climate has in store for him, I will just give a short sketch of what we have had to put up with during the past twenty-five years. It will not be absolutely accurate, for memory is not always exact, but it will be near enough for the purpose. 1920 was a rather poor season as well as I recollect, but not too bad. I had quite a good crop. 1921 was a very good season indeed—one of the best in my time. 1922 was an extremely bad one. An early flow which ended with May. There was no honey-flow worth the name from 20th May 1922 to 1st July 1923, an interval of thirteen months, and the longest I have ever known. 1923 was an excellent season, there being a tremendous flow for about four weeks from 1st July. 1924, 1925 and 1926 were all good seasons, especially 1925. 1924 was poor in the North, and in Scotland it was a really disastrous time. But I did well. Those three years 1923–5 were the only three seasons I ever averaged over 100 lbs. on the number of colonies, reckoning by autumn count.

1927 was the most completely ruinous season I ever had. The summer consisted of one fine day, 16th June. The rest was deluge and swamp. That was the only year I have ever seen the heads of white clover grow into green leaves. Thousands of these flowering heads were to be found in which the white florets were represented by tiny green trefoils. 1928 was a splendid season. The average yield must have been nearer 150 lbs. than 100, but so many stocks had died out from acarine disease that the crop on autumn count was quite small. 1929 was a year of medium yield. 1930 and 1931 were both terrible seasons when no worthwhile crop could be produced by any means. There then followed four really good seasons 1932–5. Honey became a glut through beekeepers dumping it on a full market. Many got the wind up badly; a Honey Producers' Association was started to deal with the matter. But there was no need to worry about too much English honey: there never was and never will be. In the spring of 1936 I was offered almost unlimited quantities of good English honey at seventy shillings per 112 lbs. carriage paid home. I did buy a little and soon wished I could have bought a lot. 1936 turned out to be one of those miserable cold sunless summers that we know so well. There was almost no honey; the glut was liquidated in a day, and I hope a lesson learned.

1937 was a sort of average season, not very good, but looking all the better for coming after 1936. 1938 was as bad as 1936. 1939 was much like 1937—rather better if anything, but nothing to write home about. 1940 was one of the strangest seasons I have known. The winter had been extremely severe and exposed apiaries suffered badly. Following this, bees had a poor time all the spring and summer and very little honey was stored until August. There then followed one of the heaviest flows of honey I have experienced, especially in some apiaries. Whole 50-lbs. supers of foundation were filled and sealed in a week, and in one apiary right on the top of the hills, 700 feet up, where stocks had come through the terrible winter as mere handfuls of bees and had built up all through the summer, I put supers on hives on 30th August and had them almost filled! This sort of thing happens in Ireland, and I believe in parts of Scotland, but in Southern England it was unprecedented. Strangely enough, the same thing occurred again in a lesser degree in 1941, when almost all our honey in my district was stored in August. 1942 was a very poor time for beekeepers, a failure in fact, and, curiously enough, 1943 again had an August flow which gave us half a crop and so saved our bacon by turning a disastrous season into a fair one.

The present season of 1944 has been another curious experience. Bees came out exceptionally well after a very mild winter. They had plenty of stores of honey and built up rapidly in March and April. Honey was heavily stored in May and for three or four days of June. The warm weather then ended, and without rain. No honey at all was stored all through June and July. Stocks that were very heavy in May were almost starving by mid-July, but early in August a short, sharp flow, chiefly from red clover, saved the situation to a certain extent; but it was a very poor season, and was made worse by the total failure of the heather. This last is a rare thing to happen. It is seldom that both heather and summer flowers fail to give honey, but it was so in 1944. An especially annoying thing about it was that while the stocks taken to the heather stored nothing, those left behind stored a good deal; so we actually took our bees away from the honey-flow that time.

These vagaries of our climate make honey production difficult. It must be so. Beginners who read our bee press will often see a lot of nonsense about how there should be no such thing as a bad season, and would be none if only bees were managed properly—

that is to say managed as advised by the writers. But when you hear anyone say that there is no such thing as a bad season, take no notice. It is bunk. If you go in for honey production on any such supposition you will pretty soon find out your mistake. Our chief troubles in this land of ours, so far as beekeeping goes, are too much cold, dark weather, and too little sunshine in the summer. Sometimes, for whole weeks at a time our weather is cool, windy and overcast, with light at times so bad that we seem to be fumbling in a sort of twilight: but the work must be done, for our object is to keep our apiaries in good condition for the always-expected honey-flow that really does materialize some time or other in nine seasons out of ten. That is all we can do about the climate.

But if we can't help ourselves as regards the weather, we can do something about nectar. Honey is a manufactured commodity and the bees provide the necessary labour. The raw material is nectar, a by-product of the sexual organs (flowers) of plants, and certain plants are particularly valuable for their copious secretion of this sweet fluid, and it is by placing our apiaries in situations where these plants are to be found in large quantities and where they yield nectar well, that we can greatly assist the bees to give as good an account of themselves as the seasons allow.

The chief nectar plants do not give of their best everywhere, even if they grow well, but only in certain districts, under the influence of suitable soils, and in favourable climates. Our small country has a great variety of soils and even of climates, and if you want to get a living from honey you must choose the right place for the enterprise. The hobbyist and the sideline man are usually compelled by circumstances to place their bees without reference to the suitability of the district, and it is largely a matter of chance with them; but one who proposes to depend wholly or largely on bees for a living must exercise great care and judgment in deciding where to make a start. Now first-class sites for honey farms are not as easily found as might be supposed. In the first place, a locality must be found where the necessary plants exist in large quantities, and where such plants flower over as long a period as possible. That is to say, there should be a *succession* of these plants to follow on after one another. It is essential, also, that the soil of the district should be favourable to the secretion of nectar, for it would be a serious mistake to think that wherever there are large areas of some notable honey-plant, there will necessarily be a heavy secretion of nectar over the average run of seasons. Then, too, it would be a mistake to start a bee farm in a locality where the average rainfall is very heavy, no matter what the soil and flora.

Before going into this matter further, it may be a good thing to examine the more valuable sources of nectar in this country, of which there are two or three fairly distinct types. There are the heavy soil districts, which are usually well wooded, giving a good early honey-flow from flowering trees such as Willow, Sycamore, Box, Blackthorn and many others, combined with the cultivated fruits. Of such districts I have no direct experience. These localities are generally well provided with large areas of White Clover, which, when conditions are favourable (which is not always by any means), will yield heavily. This kind of country is usually pasture land, for the most part, and the chief industry, dairy farming. Crops also grown on heavy land, that yield nectar, are Field Beans and Crimson Clover (which is not always crimson, but sometimes white). Probably the best all-round districts for honey production are the chalk and limestone lands bordering the hills of the southern and South Midland counties and the flat lands of Cambridgeshire, Norfolk and Suffolk. In Scotland the Eastern dry belt contains some of the finest honey country in these Islands, and Ireland contains by far the best white clover districts in the British Isles.

Hundreds of species of plants are visited by honey bees for the sake of their nectar or pollen or both; but those that really matter are quite few in number. In chalk and limestone districts, the class of locality that I have had to do with most, no apiary of any size can be expected to gather enough honey to maintain itself, no matter how propitious the weather, before May, and rarely before June, though we generally have light early flows of short duration from various plants and trees, especially from the Wild Cherries. Dandelions help a good deal, too, at this time; but the first real flow of nectar is almost always from the Sainfoin which begins to yield very punctually about 5th June. From this time right through until August, if weather is suitable, there will be a fairly good honey-flow. But weather is hardly ever propitious for more than a couple of weeks at a time.

Most of our principal honey-plants in these Islands belong to the *Leguminosae* and *Cruciferae*. The former include the Clovers, Sainfoin, Melilots, Peas, Beans, Vetches, Lucerne, Birdsfoot, etc. Among the latter are Charlock, Mustard, all the Turnip and Cabbage tribe, and the Wild Radish, or White Charlock, as it is sometimes called. Besides these we have two major honey-plants in the Rosebay Willowherb and the Ling. The labiate plants are very numerous and widely distributed and almost all give nectar and are worked by honey-bees. They are most of them wild flowers.

The plants that matter most to the honey-farmer are so few in number that they may be counted on the fingers. White Clover, Sainfoin, Red Clover, Alsike, Field Beans, Charlock, Willowherb, and Heather are the chief; while secondary, but important plants are Lime or Linden, White Charlock, Trifolium or Crimson Clover and all the Turnip and Cabbage family. These are the foundation of our crops of honey; but we should not undervalue other plants that help us greatly, such as Thyme and Marjoram, Wood Sage, Wild Clematis, Holly, Bramble and Hawthorn. Many of the Composite flowers are useful, too, Thistles of various kinds, Knapweed or Blackhead, Scabious, after their kind are all worked by bees; but it is from the great honey-plants that we must expect to have our supers filled.

Apart from trees of various kinds which give a major honey-flow in some districts, Sainfoin, then, is our earliest important source, but this plant is cultivated only on soils based on limestone or chalk. Where Sainfoin is, there will Charlock be also, and the two will be in flower at the same time. There are two kinds of Sainfoin which we call in my district 'Giant' and 'Common'. The latter flowers but once a year, the former, two or three times, if cut as often. The Common is less valuable to beekeepers, of course, but to the farmer it is the more useful crop, because, when once established by good husbandry, it will carry on as a paying crop for several years, giving each season one crop of hay and after it a most wholesome grazing for sheep, though it flowers but once. Giant Sainfoin is little grown in my locality, but in Norfolk, Suffolk, Cambridge and other places it is the kind usually sown.

About mid-June the White Clover will begin to yield nectar when the weather is suitable, but this plant, though about the most important of all honey yielders when the weather suits it, is not as reliable a source as one could wish. In really hot weather when there is some moisture in the soil, I have known honey to come pouring in from the White Clover in almost unbelievable quantities. I have known a good colony store over 100 lbs. in a week—and I have seen thousands of acres of pasture literally white with it and never a bee so much as looking at it.

Willowherb, also called Fireweed and Rosebay, grows in certain favourable places such as woods that have been cleared and burnt off. It will sometimes give very heavy yields, while in other seasons little is got from it. It begins to attract the bees directly the first flowers open, about the third week in June, and in favourable summers the yield continues for three or four weeks.

In my young days we always considered that Red Clover was useless to honey-bees on account of the length of the corolla tubes. This was the orthodox teaching and I never doubted it for years. In 1921, however, while in North Norfolk, a very heavy flow of honey came on in early August. Much of the hay crop there consisted of a mixture of Red Clover and Giant Sainfoin, both of which spring up after being cut for the first hay crop and flower a second time in August. At first I thought this great flow was from the Sainfoin, but the cappings of the honey were not of the pale yellow colour so typical of the wax produced from the honey of that plant, but nearly pure white. The honey was very pale in colour, almost what they call 'water white' in America. Its flavour, too, was not that of sainfoin honey, but rather insipid. On investigation I found that the bees were working almost exclusively on the red clover.

Since that time I have found out that Red Clover yields good crops of honey in August pretty regularly, whenever the weather is suitable for bees to work; but it is only in certain localities that this is so. However, it certainly yields well occasionally in my district, for the late flows of 1940, 1941 and 1943 were all almost exclusively from this plant. These flows, when they do come, are extremely heavy; but the quality of the honey is not too good. It is very light in colour and its flavour is extremely faint; but blended with darker honeys of somewhat stronger flavour it goes down well with the consuming public.

It is only the second growth of the common Red Clover (*T. pratense*) that provides much nectar for honey-bees; but I have known the perennial Red Clover (*T. medium*) to yield quite well. A neighbour here used to save a good deal for seed each year and bees worked it well, storing quite a bit of honey from it. The heads of this plant are not noticeably different from the other, but possibly the corolla tubes are shorter when grown in certain places.

Where there are Lime trees in any number, these often provide a heavy flow of nectar for a few days; but this source is not as a rule to be found in the best districts, and where it is present the weather makes it somewhat unreliable as it requires warm and rather humid conditions. Limes have the troublesome habit of becoming covered with honeydew of an almost black kind. It is horrible stuff. In 1925 two or three of my colonies stored large quantities of this stuff which completely spoiled the honey from them. I presented several friends with twenty-eight pound tins of this. It was accepted with enthusiasm, but returned with thanks after a decent interval!

Charlock gives a very fine-flavoured honey and is one of the most important sources on chalk and limestone soils. It is almost continually in flower somewhere or other all through the summer, for it comes up first in corn and after that there is a continual relay of it coming up on fallows and in root fields.

Mustard looks like a large charlock plant, but is in reality very different. Its honey is white and has a grain, when it sets, so fine as to resemble soap to the touch. I am no judge of honey, but to me its flavour is positively nauseous. Its seed is yellow, while that of charlock is almost black.

I suppose the absolute queen of all bee-forage plants must be the Melilot, commonly called Sweet Clover. Bees get great quantities of honey from it where it is grown to any extent; but there is little hope of seeing it adopted by our farmers as a hay or grazing plant in its present form. It is altogether too coarse in its habit. Its stems are hard and woody; but if, as is possible, breeders could by selection produce a smaller, finer form it might well catch on for growing on poor lands, for it is an extremely valuable plant in some ways. Stock must at first be almost starved into eating it; but once they have taken to it they are greedy for it and thrive upon it. There are already some sports of it that may be valuable. I tried a few seeds of what has been called 'Melana' which seems to be just a very fine variety of white melilot. My plants reached about eighteen inches in height last summer and though the stems were rather woody, they were far less so than the ordinary melilot which grows several feet in height and has stalks like peasticks. I wish some farmer would plant fifty acres close by each of my apiaries. The quality of the honey is excellent and the flowering goes on for months.

After all other sources have ceased to yield nectar there remains the heather crop to be gathered on the moors to which bees have to be transported. The production of heather honey is quite a separate branch of beekeeping and must be dealt with separately.

For honey farming, the places to be particularly avoided are those where the soil is acid sand or gravel, and those where rainfall is excessive. Generally speaking, if you see plenty of sheep living in folds on the arable land, you may be fairly sure that bees will do well. Standing on some low hill in early June, if, looking around you you can see fields of charlock and sainfoin lying like yellow and pink carpets in the sunshine and can hear the soft tinkling of sheep-bells coming from folded flocks, and scattered here and there you can see chalkpits scarring the hillsides, then you may be sure that you are in a honey country.

It is, however, very far from easy to judge accurately the probable quality of many localities, and there is only one real test that is quite reliable. If you place forty stocks of bees in any situation and keep them there for three years you will know with a high degree of certainty whether that place is a good one for your purpose or not. That is the acid test. No single season will tell you much. A district may give a large yield one year and not again for several years, and it is the *average annual surplus* that we have to live on. I well remember how several years ago when paying a visit to my friend Gale, he took me to see his most productive apiary. I was astonished. I said, 'But what in the world do they find to work on?' Gale said he didn't know, but that he put the bees there because when he drove bees in the neighbourhood there was always more honey in the skeps there than anywhere else. It was mostly open down country and I couldn't see much at all for bees; but it seems that on this down-land there are many good honey-plants, including much scattered white clover, birdsfoot, thyme and many other small plants, and as all the land is much the same for many square miles, the actual quantity of bee forage may be more than equal to that provided by fields of cultivated plants such as sain-foin and clover, which are only a small portion of the total area covered by the flight of the bees.

There is another thing to be considered when choosing a bee farm site. No one with any sense would start a bee farm or set up a large apiary in any locality that already carries a large number of bees, whether they belong to one man or to many; but when it is intended to set up a series of apiaries to be run as a honey farm it is necessary to make certain that these apiaries can be established within reasonable distance of the headquarters of the business, without encroaching on territory that is already covered by the flight of bees belonging to others; for to heavily overstock in that way would simply spoil the chances of all concerned. There are not very many places where more than fifty stocks of bees will do well. I have had ninety in one place, but it was an isolated one where few other bees were situated within some two or three miles, and the flora was good and abundant. Probably about forty stocks to the apiary is enough, and when it is expected that several apiaries will be required, although all will not be set up to begin with, it would be wise to start in some district where there is room for them without encroaching upon land already covered by established apiaries. And one must not forget that in counting the bee population of any neighbourhood all the bees therein must be included; it is not only the bees belonging to the more extensive beekeepers that matter, but those of the small men count as well, and in good localities there are generally a good many bees in the hands of such men.

I have said that there are not many localities that will profitably carry more than about fifty stocks of bees in one apiary; but what is the area that such an apiary will cover? In other words, how far does a hive-bee fly in search of nectar? It has been repeatedly stated that a bee's range is two miles. This seems to have been accepted quite generally as the distance it is necessary to provide for in locating our stocks; that is to say that apiaries should be four miles apart. That bees will fly much more than two miles in still, warm weather when some good nectar plant lies at that distance, is no doubt true, but my experience is that the effective range of bees in the average summers of this country does not much exceed one mile, and is probably less. Two miles, certainly, bees can readily fly, but I believe very few of them do it unless their apiary is so situated that there is little forage nearer home. I believe that bees should be so placed that they can collect all the nectar that they can carry in their working hours within a radius of about three-quarters of a mile. If the flora within that area is not enough to provide fifty stocks with a full-time job, it is far better to reduce the number of colonies rather than expect the bees to fly farther afield. It is far better in all but the very best districts to have 150 stocks arranged in five apiaries of thirty stocks each one mile apart, than in three apiaries of fifty covering the same area.

It is not until one learns, by the experience of working a number of apiaries, how greatly the crop of honey stored will often vary between two sites not a mile apart that one realizes how short the effective flight of bees in this country really is. This fact is much better understood, I believe, by the more extensive bee farmers than by the average keeper of bees. I have seen on one of the largest bee farms in England, two apiaries that could not have been more than three-quarters of a mile apart, and the owner was satisfied with the result in honey. Each of these apiaries carried about fifty stocks. Not only do apiaries that are quite near together do well, but the honey stored in one of them is often found to be of a different quality from that taken from the other, showing that the bees of each must have worked over different areas.

The actual site of an apiary should be chosen with care. Ideal sites are not at all easy to find, and it is generally necessary to make do with something that falls far short of what we would like. But there are certain requirements that must be satisfied. First, there must be shelter from the north and east winds; second, the place must be accessible to vehicles; third, the site must not be where the bees are liable to sting people on public roads; and fourth, the apiary must not be under dense shade; the sun must shine into it. A desirable feature is to have the hives situated so that it is to some extent under the observation of some friendly house, or where mischievous people are not likely to play the fool with them. It is surprising how ready boys and men are to destroy a stock of bees when they would never dream of setting out to kill a farmer's sheep or cattle. I have many times had my hives deliberately thrown over in the dead of winter, apparently just for the fun of the thing. Here I may as well point out that it is foolish to paint hives white on a bee farm for they can be seen from far away when this is done. It is far better to paint them some dull colour that blends with the background, or to dress with some wood preservative other than paint.

Ideally, the site would be backed to a corner at the north-east, with a thick hedge or copse breaking the wind, and with some low bushes around the rest of it. It should not be on a high hill to which the bees must fly when carrying heavy loads; it is far better to have the hives in a hollow if possible, but with the land sloping to the south a little. Completely sheltered sites, where the air is always still, such as the interior of close copses or in places enclosed by walls or by thick yew or other evergreen hedges which come close up to the hives, are very undesirable, for as there is no free draught of air through them, the hives usually get very damp in winter, and in summer, when the sun shines down almost vertically, they become too hot. Never place an apiary where the bees must take flights over high trees; they seldom thrive in such spots. There is an old saying that 'Bees in a wood never do any good', and I think it is nothing but the truth; but an apiary may with advantage be set in an open clearing just inside a small copse from which the bees can fly without passing over large trees. Damp is the greatest winter enemy that bees have in Britain, I believe, and I may point out here that the period when damp does the mischief is a fairly long one which very often lasts almost four months. I reckon that the year is roughly divided into two parts; eight months when the air dries up moisture faster than it is deposited, and four months during which moisture accumulates. This last four months usually begins about the middle of October. Clear, dry, frosty weather is good for bees so that the temperature does not fall abnormally low for this country; but damp, cold, especially when accompanied by fog, is very bad, and a good circulation of air through every apiary should be our aim. But exposure to direct wind is to be avoided as a plague.

As for the direction which hives should face in the apiaries, that has been a matter of some controversy, but like most of our controversial topics in Britain, it really matters very little. Usually we stand hives facing to the south or south-east or south-west, but this is because our apiaries should be, and generally are, backed to a shelter against the north, and one does not face hives to a dark hedge as a rule.

When you want an apiary site in your selected district, look for it yourself, and try to find more than one. When you have found what you require, go to the occupier of the land and ask him to let you have that place, offering either cash or honey. Don't go and ask some farmer if he has a place where you can keep some bees, for if you do, the reply is almost sure to be in the negative. Don't forget that most people hate the sight of bees, and the thought of what bees usually suggest—stings. Most people like honey; few like stings; so emphasize the honey side of the matter. Once you are established you will seldom have trouble, if the place is suitable and you are careful. With one or two exceptions, my 'landlords' have always been disappointed when I have, for various reasons, had to withdraw my bees from their land.

Here I will give a word of advice. When anyone is stung by your bees, remember that it is a painful experience for the victim, and don't make light of it, but rather see what you can do in the shape of consolation which may, perhaps, take the form of a jar of honey. Put yourself in the place of the injured and act accordingly. These things will happen sometimes in the best regulated apiaries, and are more likely to occur in those which form part of a large bee farm where the bees must be handled to some extent regardless of weather, and I need not point out that handling bees in unsuitable weather makes them spiteful and inclined to sting any innocent person who may come along at the critical time or soon after.

In addition to nectar, bees gather from flowers very large quantities of pollen, which is used by them to provide nitrogenous food. It is of vital importance to bees, for without it they are unable to rear their young. The weight of pollen consumed by a powerful stock of bees in a year is believed to be very large, estimates vary from forty to a hundred pounds, and anyone who has noticed how rapidly pollen accumulates in the combs of a strong colony that has become queenless will, I think, readily believe that the larger figure is probably not much too high an estimate. I have never experienced a shortage of pollen myself, nor have I ever met anyone who has, but it is necessary to remember that bees must always have a good supply in their combs if they are to thrive in spring before flowers begin to provide forage. I think it is necessary to emphasize this point, because we often see in the bee press mention of 'pollen-clogged combs'. We never hear much about honey-clogged combs, and since pollen is just as valuable a food as honey, we ought not to hear of it clogging combs either. We see methods of getting combs free of pollen; but, except of course for mouldy pollen, the right way of getting rid of this food is to have the bees eat it; and if there is a lot of pollen in our combs in the autumn, the way to do is to preserve it by feeding the bees so that they cover it with syrup and seal over the whole.

I believe that almost all nectar-bearing plants provide pollen, and that some plants that have no nectar are visited by bees for the sake of it. Early in spring, the first sign of a prosperous colony is the carrying in of loads of pollen by the workers, and it is of some interest to know from the colour of the pellets on their legs, what the plants are that are being worked. While there are books devoted to the appearance of various kinds of pollen grains as seen under the microscope, and illustrating them in order to help us to infer from the pollen found floating in it, the source of any honey; these are no guide to help us to judge by the colours of their burdens what the bees are working on. The two principal works of this kind that have been published in England are *Nectar Producing Plants and Their Pollen* by George Hayes, and *European Bee Plants and their Pollen* by Yate Allen.

I know of no reliable account of the colours as seen by the naked eye as the bees carry the pollen into their hives; but the fact is that, with the exception of a few pollens of somewhat unusual shades, it is very difficult indeed to be sure what the source is from the colour. Most pollens are of some shade of yellow or orange. The poet Gay has indicated this by, 'With golden treasures load his little thighs', and this description fits many of the more common and conspicuous pollens. All I can do here is to give a short and very rough list of the more easily identified kinds, so far as I have been able to make them out myself.

Elm is about the earliest of the pollen yielders, but I have never been able to see bees actually taking the pollen up, for flowering elm trees are rather difficult to get at. However, when to the best of my belief my bees are working on elm, the pollen they bring in is of a dull greyish shade. Hazel is also a very early source of pollen which the bees take from the male flowers, or catkins. Its colour is a dull yellowish green, and very inconspicuous. All the pollen-yielding willows are early sources of a pale yellow pollen, with a very slight tendency to green. Dandelions give great quantities of a deep yellow pollen. Lesser celandines in this locality give a good deal of early yellow pollen. Another very important source is the field bean which produces large quantities of a pollen of a very distinctive grey shade, hard to describe, but once seen, quite unmistakable. This pollen, as carried by the bees, is never seen in a smooth, compact mass on the bee's leg, but has a loose, ragged look as if carelessly packed. It was a long time before I identified a bright pink pollen, gathered in my district early in the spring, as that of the red dead-nettle, a plant that grows very abundantly on the black river gravel soil here.

The pollen from horse-chestnut is of a deep pink colour, and very distinctive. Charlock pollen is light yellow, as, I think, is mustard pollen, and both of these pollens very often stick to the bees' heads and thoraces so as to make them look as if they had been smeared with a yellow paste. The white clover yields very large quantities of brown pollen, while that of sainfoin is of a peculiar bright tan colour. Willow-herb pollen is of a unique shade of saxe-blue. Poppy pollen is very nearly black, and is often very heavily stored when the plant is plentiful. I think that all the root crops, such as turnips, swedes, kale, etc., give yellow pollen. Ivy gives the last pollen of the year, which is, I believe, greenish-yellow in colour. A great many garden flowers yield pollen too, and there are pollens of almost every imaginable shade except, so far as I know, bright green; at least I have never seen bees carrying pollen of that colour; but every shade of red, yellow, orange and brown is represented. Mauve, green, purple, crimson, orange-red, all are seen, to say nothing of white, a dull white being the colour of the pollen of ling.

CHAPTER IV

APIARY EQUIPMENT

The most important unit of beekeeping equipment is the hive. There can be no doubt about that; but essential as it certainly is to have good hives, there has been, ever since the first wooden hive was made, an altogether disproportionate fuss among beekeepers about hives and their designs. We have all of us, I suppose, fallen for this nonsense about how this hive is better than that, generally without bothering much as to any particular evidence with which to back our opinions. Very few enthusiasts who are beginners in beekeeping escape this phase, and with some it lasts through all their time, but very few indeed who wax eloquent about some alleged advantage that is claimed for some particular pattern ask themselves whether they have any real proof that the bees produce more honey when housed in their special kind of hive.

I found out long ago that if one wants to make a living by producing honey, it is necessary to shelve all these fads and to choose a hive for its actual merits as a tool for use in the business, and for nothing else. What we must have in a beehive for business purposes, that is for use on a honey farm, are moderate cost, compactness, simplicity, and general efficiency. Our hive must be strongly made of sound timber and must keep out the rain. It must be so made that it can be easily and quickly fastened together for transport, and be without legs or projections of any kind. The roof must be quite flat, so that hives can be stacked upon one another, and entrances must be easily and quickly closable. Such hives are in use the world over where beekeeping is treated as a serious business. Their cost is quite moderate, considering how strongly they are made, and this is due to the simplicity of their design.

If you are interested in the many and various hives that have been introduced during the last century, and especially since the invention of the movable frame, all you have to do is to read the scores of books devoted to the hobby of beekeeping. It is an interesting study to note how, since Langstroth first brought out his hive, what I may call the fancy type has grown 'curiouser and curiouser', while the business type has become more severely simple as time passed.

I won't waste space here on a long account of the alleged merits of the numerous patterns of hives that have been advocated from time to time. In Britain and Ireland beekeeping has until quite recent times been considered almost entirely as a hobby, and the result is seen in the hives and appliances most generally in use here. The hive now considered to be the most popular in England is the 'W.B.C.', a popularity which, I think, may largely be attributed to continual advertisement from platform and in the press. Its attractive appearance probably accounts for a good deal of the favour with which it is accepted so generally, and it has the additional charm for the hobbyist in its numerous parts; for I think that when I was a beginner it was those two items that captivated me. But, although the hive has merits, no doubt, it is quite useless to the honey-farmer, and may in that connection stand as an illustration of what to avoid if you wish to rely upon the production of honey for your bread-and-butter. Apart from anything else, it would be a physical impossibility to carry on the business while using hives of this type. If anyone should set out to make a living from honey-production while using W.B.C. hives, I believe that he must inevitably fail, even should the hives themselves cost him nothing.

I am rather confirmed than refuted in this conviction by the assertion of some of those who are wont to publicly advocate the use of this type of hive, that it is impossible for a livelihood to be made at all from honey-production in this country, for I can only attribute the failure implied by these leaders of British beekeeping to the equipment they advocate and to the system they pursue. It would, of course, be possible to manage one apiary, or perhaps two or three while using these hives; but to make a living much more is required, and this entails a great deal of moving about of bees in their hives, for which purpose the W.B.C. is probably about the most unsuitable of any modern hive invented. This is what I think myself; and what I do is based on my opinion, which in turn is founded on experience; but I have no wish to persuade anyone to use any particular kind of hive.

I propose, therefore, to deal here only with hives and other appliances that are suitable for use on a bee farm, or for honey-production generally when carried on for profit as a business. I would like to point out, however, that although such hives as the W.B.C. and similar patterns are satisfactory enough in a small apiary and have the advantage of looking pretty when nicely painted, yet there is no doubt at all that any hives and appliances that are satisfactory for business beekeeping will be found equally so for the small garden apiaries of amateur hobbyists, though they are not so pleasing to the eye. I think if I were wishing to keep a few colonies of bees for pleasure I should have nice-looking white-painted hives of some kind; but they would be useless to me as I am situated to-day. Those who wish to use the British orthodox equipment and hives of various kinds, can find plenty of books telling how these are constructed and how they are used.

The hives now to be described are known as single-walled American type hives, and with them must be included the appurtenances that are used with them. These hives are of very simple design, and embody every feature *necessary* for success. Those who read this book will probably be familiar with them, and there is no need for me to describe their details. There are, however, two parts of these hives which may be modified to advantage without in any way interfering with the standardization that is so important.

The roof as made in America, the standard American factory-made cover, is a poor one. It is only three inches deep, or even less, and its sides are boards of $\frac{7}{8}$-inch thickness. The sheet of galvanized iron with which it is covered is so small as to allow of an overlap to turn down over the sides of only about half an inch. These roofs are something of a nuisance, for they are so shallow that they are very easily blown off in rough weather, and in winter must be tied on with string or have stones laid on them. A roof should always be deep enough so that if it is lifted by the fingers on one side only, as wind will lift it, it will jam against the top of the hive-body before it is high enough to be blown off.

No roof should on any account be less than $4\frac{1}{2}$ inches deep inside; 6 inches is quite a useful depth, and deep roofs of 9 inches are good in many respects; but are sometimes troublesome through the warping inwards of the boards which makes the lifting of the hives into and out of them difficult (see Chapter IX). In any case it is very important, when bees are to be kept in out-apiaries, that all roofs shall be deep enough to cover the hand-holds cut in the hive walls, for out-apiaries are liable to be attacked by wood-peckers, and it is at the hand-holds where the wood is thin that the birds like to make a start.

There is no possible doubt, too, that the metal covering sheet should lap down over the roof sides for at least 2 inches, the corners being folded and not cut. In this way rain is conducted well down over the joint between the top boards and the sides, which latter should be painted or dressed with some sort of waterproof coating *before* the metal is fastened on, so that wet shall not creep up the sides by soaking the wood. It is also a very good plan to paint or similarly dress the insides of the roof sides. I usually cover the roof under the metal with $\frac{3}{8}$-inch 'celotex', and in this case it is particularly necessary to take these steps, for if wet does creep up as far as this material it will be absorbed by it almost as a sponge would absorb it.

Instead of using thick boards as they do in America, I much prefer to have $\frac{5}{8}$-inch wood for roof sides. This is thick enough for every purpose, and the thinner boards lighten the roof. The slight reduction in the overall width of the roof is also an advantage when hives have to be loaded on lorries, for these often are only just wide enough to take three hives. A roof made of six-inch deal sides with a celotex top is light and handy. I know of nothing better, taking it all round.

Floors also may be usefully changed without altering the essential measurements. As usually made, floors project 2 inches beyond the front of the hives, and when this is so I have found that the life of the hive is shortened through decay caused by the accumulation of damp on the projection which catches the rain-drip from the roof. This keeps the parts of the hive-body that are in contact with the projecting floor more or less continually damp during the winter. So I now have all floors cut the same length as the hive-body, so that they are flush with it in front as well as behind. It is sometimes argued that, since the floor projections act as alighting platforms, their removal will result in the loss of bees through their having nothing to settle on when returning to their hives. However, after some years of using short floors with hundreds of hives I have not been able to detect any loss from this cause. Bees that are healthy can get back into their hives all right, I think, without any special platform to settle on.

But from my point of view the most important advantage of the short floor is that it so greatly assists in the preparation of hives of bees for travelling. For transport, bees must be securely confined, and the closure of the entrance is quite a troublesome business when floors project, as anyone will very soon find out who tries to pack up a number of stocks in hives with such floors. With the short floor the job is simple, rapid, and easy. It was David James who first pointed this out to me; which shows how old hands can learn from young ones. However, I shall describe this process when dealing with the subject of moving bees (Chapter IX). The short floor has also the advantage of allowing hives to stand inside their roofs for moving.

A particularly good feature of the American style hive is its inner cover or crown board. This is usually made of thin tongue and groove material, and cleated around all four sides. In the usual American hives where the hive sides are $\frac{5}{16}$-inch higher than the frame top-bars, this board is automatically raised a bee-space and so allows a free passage over the combs all the time. When, as in the 'National' hive, the hive sides and frames are flush, it is necessary to nail a thin rim around the under side of the inner cover. These boards are a great improvement on the messy pieces of calico or canvas often so strongly recommended in this country, and almost universally used here, for when boards are used the top-bars of the frames remain clean and bees are not crushed as is almost inevitably the case when textile materials are used as coverings. The latter, too, being in contact with the frames, are soon covered with propolis and wax and become a regular trap for bees when replaced after being lifted. The textile coverings also provide a very fine harbour for wax-moth larvae; besides which, the bees soon gnaw these 'quilts' all to rags. It has been said that if the material used is unbleached, bees will not destroy it; but this is not so. About the only materials that are not very quickly ruined by the bees are good green tarpaulin, dressed sailcloth, and American oil-cloth. Strong, hard carpet will last a long time also, but it is rather too stiff to go next the bees. You can use textile covering on American hives, of course, but it is a very poor plan to do it. There is nothing to equal a good crown-board or inner cover.

It may be of interest to beginners to mention that the American hives were, until about twenty-five or thirty years ago, made with simple flat board covers. This wide board was cleated at each end to keep it from warping and was just laid on the top of the hive, the bees being left to propolize it down. Of course the overhead bee-space prevented propolization except at the contact with the hive walls. These covers were, and are, probably a great nuisance through warping; so most modern beekeepers now use a telescopic metal-covered roof as shown in the photographs in this book. This necessitated an inner cover because the telescopic roof prevents the hive-tool from getting at the joint to pry it off. We now lift off the roof and then pry loose the inner cover.

Factory-made hives are usually made with lock-corners or some kind of dovetailing so that they can be sold in the flat for assembly by the purchaser, but it is not at all certain that this is altogether a good thing. If hives are painted, and kept painted, it may be all right, but I don't see how any bee-farm could contemplate such huge expenditure of time and labour as would be implied in keeping all the hives painted. No doubt the hives would look very smart, and the apiaries picturesque, but the banking account of the owner would, I think, tend to look very much the reverse after a course of regular hive painting. There is no doubt at all that lock-corners absorb the wet unless kept constantly painted, and I believe that a much better joint is the rabbet. This can be nailed both ways and made very rigid.

Hives made with plain butt joints are in some ways better than either rabbet or lock-corner ones. I have found this out under stress of circumstances attributable to the war. Soon after the war broke out, timber became very hard to obtain, labour also was scarce, and hives of American design could not be bought from the regular makers of hives and appliances, for these people immediately ceased to make anything but British standard stuff. So, there being nothing for it but to make our own, we got hold of a good stock of suitable timber before it was rationed, bought a saw bench, and made our own. We have now learned how to do it, and are independent of manufacturers for hives and supers, though we have to buy our frames. We may be making them some day in the not too distant future. In any case, every large bee farm should have a good circular saw with a sliding table for cross-cutting; without this it is nearly impossible to make hives accurately without the expenditure of altogether too much time on the job.

Having accepted the American type as essential for practical honey-production on any considerable scale, the beekeeper must decide which size to use, and I must now, I suppose, try to describe the principal kinds of this hive that are in general use. The movable frame is made in several styles and sizes, but only three of these need concern us here. There are one or two others that are used by a few bee-men who prefer to plough a lone furrow, the chief of these being the 16″ x 10″ of Simmins, and the so-called deep standard, measuring 14″ x 12″. However, it would, I consider, be a grave mistake, for many and obvious reasons, for anyone intending to start up a honey-producing business to adopt any other than one of the three regular standardized frames; the British standard, the Langstroth, and the Modified Dadant.

The British standard frame requires that its hives shall have rabbets wide enough to take its very long lugs, and this means that the hives for it shall either have double walls on two sides, or else that there shall be some other arrangement to accommodate those lugs which project beyond the frames, quite unnecessarily, for $1\frac{1}{2}$ inches. There are several different hives that combine the American principle, so essential for business purposes, with the distinctly unbusinesslike long top-bars of the British standard frames. The 'National' hive is one. This is a square hive taking eleven frames and having double walls on two sides. It is hardly large enough for use as a single-chamber hive, and is rather flimsy in construction, being made of too thin material; but it is cheap and apparently satisfies a good many beekeepers. Personally, I would not have it as a gift if I had to use it, for its designers embodied in it the abominable fault of not allowing a bee-space over the frames. This, combined with the metal-end spacers, completely ruins the whole affair from my point of view; but as I say, others seem to like it, and it apparently answers its purpose moderately well.

This hive, however, represents a step forward from the W.B.C., and similar unbusinesslike patterns so commonly used up to recent years, and if it is made at home or bought in the flat it can be nailed together in such a way that the bee-space is allowed above instead of below the frames. This makes an altogether better job of it, but of course hives so changed are not standard, and will not combine with the regular pattern, but must be kept to them-

63

selves. You can't use standard 'national' bodies or supers in conjunction with the altered ones. There is no doubt, however, about the immense advantage of having the bee-space over the frames.

Mr. Gale, of Marlborough, who is, I believe, our most extensive bee farmer, uses a hive that takes thirteen British standard frames, has two double walls, and is, of course, larger than the M.D. hive in superficial area. His entrances are on the long side of the hive which is therefore longer from side to side than from front to back.

There is another quite useful type of hive for use by those who wish to run a bee farm with British frames alone, but especially so for those who, while using the M.D. hives as their main unit, wish to keep some hives with standard British frames as well. This hive, which is the one we use here, is in every respect the same as the M.D. with the exception of the brood-chamber which, instead of holding eleven of the large frames running from front to back, takes twelve British frames running the other way, the hive-body being of the correct depth for the small frames, and having inner walls to take the long top-bars. This hive can take all fittings exactly as for M.D. hives, supers, excluders, inner covers, bee-escape boards, and roofs. Its entrance is, of course, on the narrow side to match the M.D. entrance and so is parallel with the combs.

I have already mentioned the Modified Dadant hive several times. This is the hive I have used now for about twenty-five years. It is strictly a single brood-chamber hive. There are eleven frames measuring $17\frac{5}{8}''$ x $11\frac{1}{4}''$, with short lugs or projections. This hive measures 20" x $18\frac{1}{2}''$ outside by $11\frac{1}{2}''$ deep. Its supers are fitted with frames $6\frac{1}{4}''$ deep. I have got on pretty well with it, and have never wished to change.

Finally, we have the Langstroth hive which is more extensively used than any other in the world. It is virtually the standard in the North American Continent, Australia, New Zealand, and the West Indies. I understand that the U.S.S.R. has largely adopted it also. This hive takes ten frames which measure $17\frac{5}{8}''$ x $9\frac{1}{8}''$ which are more closely spaced than others. It is very commonly used as a double brood-chamber hive. It is the same length from back to front as the Dadant, but a good deal narrower and shallower. My personal experiences of it, which have been considerable, have not led me to a very favourable judgment of its merits. I dislike the shape of the combs, which I consider too shallow, and the close spacing of the frames is a feature I dislike very much also; but these are only my own personal opinions, and there are several beekeepers in this country who think the Langstroth an excellent hive.

Any one of these hives is suitable for a honey farm; but I would strongly advise the prospective honey farmer to adopt one of those which have short-lugged, self-spacing frames. These are known as

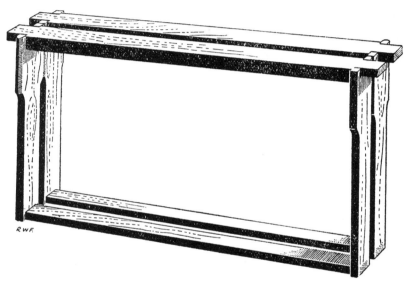

Figure 1

HOFFMANN FRAMES, MODIFIED DADANT SIZE

'Hoffmann' frames, after their inventor, and the spacing is given by widening the upper third of the end-pieces, and this enables the manipulator to pry the frames apart, or push them over in a body without fear of either crushing bees or breaking any spacer. Until one has had to handle a large number of colonies, as fast as it can possibly be done, in the work of a bee farm, it is difficult to realize what a very great boon these Hoffmann frames are.

The British standard frames are spaced, as most people know, by means of the 'metal end', a device which embodies every possible fault a spacer of frames can well have, and the worst of the business is that it is almost impossible to devise any practicable substitute, for the simple reason that any efficient frame spacing device must space the end bars of the frames, but no such spacers can be made to interact with metal ends, and this is necessary if a transition is to be made. I would, therefore, advise all who intend to make honey production their vocation to choose one of the two standardized American hives and stick to it.

If, however, it is proposed to go in largely, or even to a considerable extent, for selling bees on combs and to enter upon the business of selling appliances, it may be well to keep to the British standard frame which is ideal for this purpose. However, here I am treating of the business of producing honey, and since I have found that single-walled American style hives and the appropriate appliances are much the more efficient for that purpose, I naturally recommend them. At the same time, it will, I think, always be wise to have some bees on British frames if it is proposed to rear our own queens, for the small frames are very convenient indeed for making up nuclei.

The metal end method of spacing frames is in my opinion one of the most objectionable features of the British equipment. Combs so spaced, since these spacers contact only at the level of the top-bars, can swing when travelling, unless held down tightly on the rabbets which support them. This, in turn, makes it usual for the bee-space between the frames of the different stories to be allowed below the frames, so that the top-bars shall be flush with the hive walls. Then the bottoms of the super walls rest on the ends of the frames and hold them securely in place, but when we wish to lift a super, the lower edges of the super walls are stuck to the top-bars of the brood frames, and the latter are liable to be raised with the super.

When metal ends are used in hives with the bee-space over the top-bars, frames in travelled hives will often move, the metal ends slipping and passing one another, and allowing the combs to come adrift, which makes a horrible mess of things. These spacers have other faults; they are flimsy and one cannot use any considerable pressure on the frames to push them across the hive *en bloc*: they will collapse if that is done; and they are a great nuisance at extracting time as they must be removed and replaced. They also become gummed up with propolis very soon and are a great bother to get clean. The best way I have discovered to clean them is to boil them in a solution of caustic soda, an ounce or so of this in a gallon of water will do it. Metal ends will often drop off when you want them to stay put, and will be difficult to pull off when you want to remove them. They have sharp edges and cut the fingers, too; and altogether they are best avoided as much as possible on a bee farm. Gale now uses them only in the brood-chambers, I believe. At any rate he has substituted notched metal plates for them in his supers; but as frames cannot be moved without being separately lifted out of the notches, I cannot think that such plates are practically workable in brood-chambers.

In extracting supers metal ends are an unmitigated nuisance. Nobody who has had to handle honey by the ton, as the successful bee farmer must, can for one moment dispute this, but the American type of super frame, considered as a practical appliance to be used in the production of honey, is really an extraordinarily inept idea. It seems strange that these abominations should have apparently satisfied our colleagues across the water for so many years, for although the thing would appear to be sufficiently obvious, it seems never to have occurred to American bee-men that since a super frame is used for an entirely different purpose, it should be designed for that purpose, and not be just another brood-frame. I shall be told that these frames are intended to be used for both purposes. They are, over there; which is one reason why they have found it so difficult to control foul brood; but they make their shallow extracting frames, apart from depth, exactly the same as the deep ones. These Hoffmann frames, so good for the brood-chamber, are abominations in supers, for an extracting frame should be spaced wide enough for the comb to be easily uncapped. I have used these frames for extracting by setting nine instead of ten in each super; but they are troublesome to arrange, and this wastes more time than bee farmers can spare, and when so arranged you cannot move the super without having the frames move too. So some of us are now using wide, close-ended frames; that is having their end bars just wide enough so that ten of them fill the super of a Dadant hive allowing a little play. This is practically the same as having nine frames in a British ten-frame super.

All our super frames, also, have their top and bottom bars of the same width, $1\frac{1}{8}''$, which is a great assistance in rapid uncapping, the knife passing under the cappings in contact with both top and bottom bars. Why extracting frames are ever made with narrow bottoms, I cannot even guess. Years ago, I widened all mine by nailing strips on each side, since when all new frames have been properly made with wide bottoms, and I certainly never will use narrow-bottomed frames for extracting any more, for the mess caused by brace-comb is generally a great nuisance when the frames in supers have narrow bottoms. Supers fitted with frames such as I have described can be handled rapidly without the slightest fear of any movement of the frames, and there are no loose parts or metal fittings of any kind.

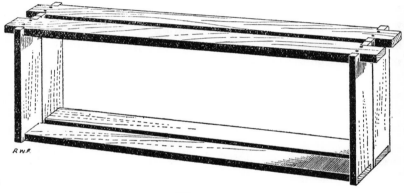

Figure 2

THE SPECIAL EXTRACTING FRAMES WE USE IN OUR SUPERS

When apiaries have to be set up all about the countryside, a lot of them will be in places where grass and weeds grow high. The ideal place, of course, from this point of view, is where a host of rabbits keep down the growth; but as a rule grass and nettles are a nuisance unavoidable. This means that fairly high stands must be used if the hive entrances are not to be too much obstructed. I don't know that a good deal of grass does much harm to the bees, for they will alight on the front of the hive and run down to the entrance; in fact some stocks have that habit whether entrances are clear or not; but high nettles and long grass are bad, not only in blocking the entrances and obstructing the bees, but in tending to keep hives damp, and also making things unpleasant for the bee-man. It is usually advised by amateur writers on beekeeping that grass must be cut short, Mr. Mace going so far as to consider a lawn mower an essential implement in bee farming! As a matter of fact, any such thing as keeping grass short in his apiaries when a large bee farm is concerned, is altogether out of the question, for the bee farmer finds that he has more than enough work on his hands all the summer long, without this constant grass cutting.

Probably the best way of keeping hives fairly clear of herbage without involving ourselves in such labour is to provide stands. These can be of many kinds, according to the fancy of the individual. The sort most commonly used is probably that made of four boards, three of them standing vertically and the fourth, which forms the front, sloping to make an alighting board. This is the kind generally listed in American appliance catalogues. It is used by Gale in this country. If it is well steeped in hot or boiling creosote when dry, it can be stood on the ground without any bricks under it, and will last some years. As very cheap, rough wood will do quite well, its cost is very small. It is not easy to set these stands level, especially on sloping land, and although I suppose this is not a very important matter, I must say I like hives to stand level from side to side with a forward slope from back to front. The sloping board in front enables bees to get back into the hive when they would not be able to do so without it; but this is a point that has a bad aspect as well as a good one.

We use stands made from six oak or creosote-soaked pegs, driven into the ground and supporting two rails of 2″ x 2″ wood, 4½′ long. This accommodates two hives. If the rails are well soaked in creosote and the pegs either boiled in it or soaked for a few days, when thoroughly dry, these stands will last for many years. They have the advantage of being readily levelled on uneven ground, and they raise the hives well off the damp earth, and well away from the grass. Of course, long grass or nettles must be cut once or twice to keep the entrance clear enough, for nettles, especially, will quite block the hive from sight if let grow unchecked. Madoc prevents this obstruction by means of a very wide alighting board (see illustration). Generally speaking, I have found that to stand hives on bricks leads to endless bother through the bricks sinking into the ground, assisted by moles and worms, and this, in turn, leads to distortion of the hives; besides which it is quite a troublesome job to level hives on bricks unless the ground is fairly flat.

Queen excluders are, in my opinion, an absolute necessity for practical bee farming, and one should be provided for every stock worked for honey. This has been disputed by some beekeepers; but I could not work without these appliances myself, and I cannot imagine how it could be done with any satisfactory method of management. Excluders are made either of wire or sheet zinc. The former are in some ways preferable; but I have not found that their use really improves net results in the slightest. They take more room to store, being mounted on thicker wood than is necessary with the zinc kind, and they are more trouble to clean. They are rather expensive, too. I think, however, I would use them in preference to zinc ones if they could be obtained at a cost not much in excess of the cost of mounted zinc sheets.

In all hives with bee-spacing over the top-bars, zinc excluders must be mounted. We use quarter-inch strips for this, the wood being about an inch wide, and the zinc being simply nailed to this material with a lot of small, wide-headed gimp-pins, and the corners bound with metal. We make all ours ourselves. These excluders answer the purpose quite efficiently, are not expensive, and as stated, can be made up at home.

There are two kinds of perforated zinc excluders, the short-slot and long-slot varieties. The latter is supposed by some to be an improvement on the other; but I have not found it so; in fact I would not use the long-slot variety. It is not so strong as the other, and the length of the slots allows bending of the strips of zinc between them, which may, and often does allow the passage of queens. It is thought, I suppose, that the longer slots allow for freer passage by the bees, but I don't think the difference is appreciable, and certainly any slight advantage that might possibly be gained in that direction is more than offset by the obvious faults I have mentioned. All zinc excluders are liable to be made from too thin metal, and it is always worth while to have them made of zinc of fairly heavy gauge.

Comb-foundation is another very important item in equipment, as everyone knows, and it is one of the most costly if it must be bought every year; but on a well-managed bee farm, there should be an annual production of wax that will about cover this item.

The foundation used should be of good quality and heavy if we are to have first-rate combs built on it, and it is of great consequence to have our combs as perfect as possible. It is false economy to try to save expense by using foundation that is too thin, whether in brood frames or in those used only for extracting. If foundation be used of such thickness that one pound of it will give seven or eight sheets of the size for British standard frames, good combs should result if the foundation is of good quality and the frames are properly wired. For use in larger frames, such as the Dadant, four and a half sheets to the pound will answer well. For the smaller frames, like the British and Langstroth, four horizontal wires are plenty, three being quite satisfactory for the shorter British frame. In Dadant frames, five wires should always be used.

A lot of trouble has been caused by using too thin foundation that will not stand up to the strain, and while it is always well to avoid extravagance, the use of heavy enough foundation is a good investment. There is no doubt at all that a great deal of the trouble experienced in getting good straight combs is due to the use of thin foundation, and to foundation made from inferior wax, containing an excess of propolis and similar resinous matter, which when cold is brittle, but at the temperature of the hive becomes a soft and tacky material.

There is one point that I have never seen mentioned in any book I have read (though of course I may have missed some such reference). To build comb on a sheet of wax is an unnatural proceeding for bees. In nature, except when they repair comb after digging out mouldy pollen and clearing the cells to the septum in the process, bees form the septum as they build the cells. I think bees prefer that way of working, because I have very often known them to build new comb behind a dummy or in some other space, while foundation has been provided in a convenient position in the hive.

Frames are usually wired by threading fine wire through small holes bored in their end-bars. I suppose every reader is familiar with the process. All sorts of other ways have been advocated, such as putting hooks through instead of boring holes, but they all come to much the same thing except that the hooks are a nuisance when you want to cut the comb out of the frame in order to fit new foundation. Wiring is usually considered a troublesome job, and this has led to the emergence of several methods of reinforcing foundation other than by the simple process of wiring the frames and embedding the wires into the wax. This plan is still, I think, the most generally in use, and is probably still the most satisfactory.

Other methods of strengthening foundation consist of various forms of ready-wired foundation, invented for the avoidance of the manual labour of wiring frames. The reader, if not already familiar with these, must look the matter up elsewhere; they all answer their purpose more or less satisfactorily; but I have not, so far, met a honey farmer in an extensive way of business who does not prefer to wire his own frames. The principal English makes are the plain vertically wired of Messrs. Taylor, Ltd., and the two forms of zig-zag wiring by Messrs. Lee & Sons. In America the most important form of wired foundation is probably the crimp-wired of Messrs. Dadant & Sons; but there are several others.

The only other way of reinforcing foundation that is, so far as I know, in general use to-day is the 'three-ply' of the A. I. Root Co. of Ohio. This firm, after several essays in others directions, brought out about the year 1923, a new and very satisfactory foundation in which they utilized a central layer, or ply, of wax which consisted, not of pure beeswax, but of beeswax slightly alloyed with carnauba wax. This is believed to have an effect similar to that whereby the addition of small quantities of certain metals to steel increases the hardness, toughness, or tensile strength of that alloy, just as the addition of a small percentage of tin to copper gives bronze a far harder substance.

That this foundation is excellent material for the purpose for which it is recommended is a fact; but it is difficult to avoid a certain repugnance to its use on account of the inevitable adulteration of the wax which must result when the combs are rendered in due course. At the same time, this adulteration must be exceedingly slight, for beeswax rendered from old brood-combs is a very small fraction of all the wax produced in any apiary; cappings being responsible for the great bulk of it: they probably account for 90 per cent. Whatever the difference of opinion on this subject may be, the fact remains that this foundation is one of the most satisfactory ever manufactured, and it seems to me that if men are prepared to condone so-called beeswax that contains a considerable admixture of propolis, which is certainly a substance very detrimental in foundation, it is rather unreasonable to cavil too much at an adulteration by a slight admixture of a toughening wax for the purpose of strengthening the product. If we are to make a living from honey production, we must consider all these matters strictly from the point of view of business, and should not allow our judgment to be swayed by the abstract arguments of people who may be actuated by personal animosities. This matter of three-ply foundation is a case in point, for much has been said against it at one time or another, which cannot be considered relevant so far as concerns the view-point of beekeeping that this book is written to express.

As an example, I will cite an amusing incident which occurred in 1929. A Mr. Price produced, after the annual meeting of the British Beekeepers' Association, a brood-comb in which the mid-rib, i.e. the foundation, had melted through being left in an empty hive in the stroke of the sun, and had run out on to the face of the comb. The comb was alleged to have been built on three-ply foundation, as no doubt it was. This is, of course, an everyday phenomenon, whether the foundation be pure beeswax or not, and may be seen during any hot spell whenever dark-coloured combs are left standing in the sun, or are left in empty, unshaded hives where the sun's rays strike down, especially if the hive be dark in colour. But Mr. Price, apparently without bothering about any evidence to substantiate his statement, plainly asserted that the exudation was caused by the wax of the three-ply foundation having a lower melting point than pure beeswax. As a matter of fact, so far is this from being the case, it is asserted by the makers that the strengthening wax used has a melting point considerably higher than that of beeswax, a fact confirmed by the late T. W. Cowan in his wax book.

What struck me at the time as the most interesting circumstance brought to light by this somewhat childish controversy was the statement by Mr. Price in the *British Bee Journal* at a later date, that his sole object was to present to the assembly, the annual meeting of the British Beekeepers' Association, an abnormal occurrence that *he had never seen before, and which everyone present admitted to be unique.* The Root Co., not to be behind Mr. Price in making remarkable assertions, has stated, point blank, that the wax melted from combs built on their foundation (which they admit contains carnauba wax) conforms in all respects to the wax rendered from cappings; which seems to me to be, on the face of it, absurd; for if the addition of carnauba wax makes no difference, why add it?

What all this fuss amounts to is this: honey-comb built on foundation is unnatural: there is a much larger amount of wax in the septum of such comb than in that of one naturally built. When a dark-coloured comb is exposed to the sun in hot weather, or if, while it is in an empty hive which stands in the sun, its temperature rises above the melting point of the wax in its mid-rib, that wax will melt and run out on the surface of the comb, where it will solidify. If a newly-built comb were exposed to the same temperature it would just melt away, but in the case of a brood-comb the cell linings, that is the discarded cocoons, preserve the shape of the comb after much of its wax has melted. So let us beware of such silly controversies. The only consideration we need bother about is whether or not the good points of any foundation or of any hive or appliance, do or do not exceed its defects for the purpose for which we wish to use it.

I used some three-ply foundation many years ago, and found it excellent except that I thought it rather more liable to become hard and brittle in cool weather than ordinary foundation, but I am not sure about this; it may have been my fault for using it when not warm enough. I have used English foundation for a good many years since and have found it satisfactory enough; but I sometimes wish that three-ply foundation had been first invented here, for then we may be sure that it would have been given a far more cordial reception in this country than has been the case.

The question of the use of substitutes for natural beeswax in the manufacture of comb-foundation is a controversial one. In my own opinion, if any method of using such substitutes is found to give a really superior article for use in our hives, we should welcome its advent; but that is not to say that the wax resulting from the rendering of combs built upon such comb-foundation should be regarded as beeswax. It is not beeswax, and cannot be beeswax, and while it may be equal or even superior to beeswax for the purpose of comb-foundation manufacture (I am not saying that it is, of course) its sale as pure beeswax should be considered an indictable offence. It is not difficult to ascertain by proper chemical tests whether wax is pure beeswax or not, and no manufacturer should use any kind of alloy for his foundation unless he declare the fact. This question is of some importance for a patent has lately been taken out in U.S.A. by the A. I. Root Co., covering the manufacture of foundation from material 'comprising a mixture of beeswax and a substantial percentage such as thirty to fifty per cent of hydrogenated vegetable oil which will blend homogeneously with beeswax'. This, even if used only in the central sheet of three-ply foundation constitutes a very serious adulteration of the wax that will result from the rendering of the combs built upon it, and such wax would not be beeswax. It might be an excellent material for the manufacture of foundation all the same; while it might in any case be entirely unsuitable for other uses to which pure beeswax is usually put; but there can be no doubt that all wax melted from combs built upon this material must give an impure, adulterated product, and could honestly be sold only as such.

Few appliances are more necessary on a bee farm than really effective smokers that will produce plenty of smoke when required to do so, but will burn for a long time, and wear well. For my part, I know of no better pattern than that made by Roots, and called the 'Jumbo'; but there are plenty of other excellent makes just as good. That pattern, however, is really excellent. The rubbish usually recommended and used in this country should not for one moment be considered as a practical tool for use on any bee farm or large apiary. These little upright smokers may do pretty well for people with a few hives, though I think them little else but toys; but they are quite useless for business. A large smoker of the Root or similar pattern will burn for a long time, and the most convenient fuel is half-rotten sacking, I consider. We use some hundreds of old bags each season here, and can often pick them up from rubbish dumps; or farmers sometimes have a lot of ragged old bags and sacks lying around that they are quite willing to exchange for a pot of honey.

To light up a smoker quickly, take a little wood-wool or shavings and put it into the smoker after firing it. As soon as it flames up well, put in a roll of the bagging and blow until this is well alight. A good big smoker thus fuelled will burn all day if more bag is added as required; but the ashes and dirt should be turned out from time to time to avoid the choking of the grating. All smokers

75

should have a hook on their bellows so that they can be hung on the hive, so that one's hands shall be free, and it is better for the nozzle to be of the American rather than the English type, for the long vertical nozzle is nothing but a nuisance, as anyone can soon find out for himself if he compare the two. The bellows of a smoker should never be leather on any account; but should be made of rubber. There is nothing so nice as a motor-cycle tyre tube for this. Thinnish car tyre tubes are good, but rather thick and heavy. Some of the American firms use a sort of strong American oil-cloth, but it does not last long.

One of the most important things to have for work among bees is a thoroughly good hive-tool. This is quite essential for use with the single-walled hives used on bee farms. Some beekeepers will prefer one style, while to others something quite different may seem best; but for me there has never for a moment been any doubt that the best pattern of all is that made by the Root Co. With some difficulty I have managed to get some of these exactly copied in this country at last. They look so simple and easy to make, and yet are quite hard to come by in England. Roots make two sizes, eight inch and ten inch. There are, of course, other patterns made in America which can, no doubt, be copied here; but whatever the pattern, hive-tools *must* be made of high quality steel so that they shall be light and at the same time fit to stand very hard usage. They must be strong enough to lever up very heavy weights without either bending permanently, or breaking. The tools we use will stand the full strength of a man weighing on them while levering up supers of honey, and yet they are no more than about three-sixteenths of an inch thick.

I had nearly forgotten one important appliance, the feeder. There are a great many different kinds of feeders, but for honey-farming only those known as rapid feeders are used. The various slow feeders, so popular with amateurs, are quite out of order where the object is, not so much to have some excuse for fiddling about with the bees, as to supply stocks with food to carry them through the winter and well into the spring, and to do this with a minimum of labour and as fast as possible, while doing it properly. On a bee farm, spring feeding is done in very much the same way as autumn feeding, and is resorted to only when a late spring causes stores to run short, or as an addition to stores of granulated honey, and the same kind of feeders are used for all purposes; that is to say, rapid feeders of some sort.

There are three classes of feeders to be considered: lever-lid tins with holes punched in their covers; dummy feeders with floats, and top feeders of many patterns. I think it would be a good plan on any bee farm to have a number of ten-pound feeders made exactly in the same way as honey-tins, but low and wide. They would look like halved honey-tins, that is to say, of the same diameter, but only half as tall, or less. They could be made of galvanized iron, or good tinplate, lacquered inside and out, or perhaps painted outside. They should have a wire handle for easy carrying. A number of these could be filled with syrup and taken out with us when we go out to make the first examination of the bees in the spring, and then, in case a stock should be found to need it, it would be the work of a moment to set a full feeder over the hole in the inner cover. A deep roof will easily cover such low tins as those suggested, and it is a good plan to have at least a few of these in every apiary. These lever-lid tins used as feeders in this way have the great advantage of bringing the food into direct contact with the bees, for in spring these will generally be close up against the inner cover, and a tin set over the feed-hole attracts them immediately, whereas when ordinary rapid tin feeders are used, bees are often very reluctant to leave the cluster to go up into them.

These round tin feeders, generally called 'rapid' feeders in English appliance catalogues can, of course, be made in any size, and there is no need to visualize the absurd little things that are commonly sold in this country, and which hold a pint or two; but even when made of large size they are something of a nuisance to a bee farmer who uses single-walled hives, because it is generally necessary to use empty supers to cover them. It is true that when deep roofs are used it is possible to let the roof rest on the feeder, but this is not a satisfactory plan. Bees do not readily pass up into ordinary feeders when the weather is at all cold, unless the stocks are very strong; therefore such feeders really need to be wrapped up warmly. This is possible with such hives as are commonly used in Britain, but not in the case of single-walled ones. This applies equally to what are called 'Canadian' rapid feeders and all others that do not completely cover the hive as a super covers it.

Dummy feeders are useful appliances, but like most other things, they have serious drawbacks. If wide enough to hold a good feed of syrup they take up too much room in the hive. They cannot be filled without opening the hive to some extent, either. I would not advise anyone to go in for this type of feeder extensively, but a few are always handy. In a queen-breeding apiary, there is probably nothing equal to small dummy feeders, which, being made narrow, require no floats.

I remember how interested I was in the feeder the late Dr. Miller described in his book when first I read that work. I made some on the same principle. Miller made his feeder just the right size to fit inside a super, so it was not a very large feeder, for he used eight-frame Langstroth hives. But why, why didn't Miller think of making the feeder of thick wood, and of having it the same size as a super, so that it could stand on the hive just as a super is put on? He just did not think of it, I suppose, and neither did I. I have often wondered how Miller failed to see the advantages of such a feeder; and how I came not to think of it, I can't imagine.

The fact that the Miller feeder required always to be used in connection with a super, placed it under the disadvantage common to all feeders that are smaller than the hive, in that an empty super is needed for each feeder in use. This is a great nuisance, because, on a bee farm, all supers are wanted at all times to hold the extracting combs, and unless extra supers are stocked for the purpose of covering feeders, combs must be removed from a great many of them and piled up in some storeroom while the empty supers are in use for covering feeders in the apiaries, and no bee farmer could contemplate that with any satisfaction. By making Miller feeders exactly the same size as the hives they are to be used on, or very slightly smaller to avoid jamming, the need for any covering except the roof is done away with. We are now using in our apiaries two patterns of these all-over feeders, as I will call them, and we have made hundreds of them.

It was not until Brother Adam of Buckfast Abbey brought out his patent feeder that I thought of this plan of having the feeder cover the whole hive. I believe the patent of Brother Adam is concerned with the method of giving access, by means of which the thing can be used as a slow as well as a rapid feeder; but that part did not interest me. It was the fact that it entirely covered the hive that caught my imagination. The Adam feeder is very shallow

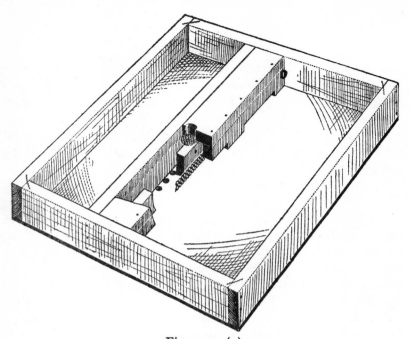

Figure 3 (a)

SINGLE-COMPARTMENT FEEDER as made and used by myself.
Drawing shows the division the wrong way; it should run from
side to side the short way

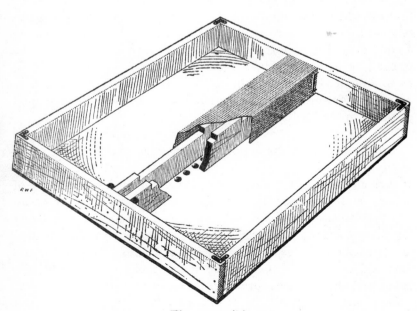

Figure 3 (b)

TWO-COMPARTMENT 'MILLER' FEEDER

and has a hole in its centre through which the bees gain access to the syrup, neither of which points seems to me desirable. All hives should slope forward, I think, and as in practice hives rarely stand perfectly level, even when we try to keep them so, it is much better that they should definitely slope slightly forward. A central place of access, therefore, prevents the bees from reaching all the syrup, as this, of course, runs to the lowest point of the feeder floor.

So I made feeders on the Miller principle of admittance, but with only the rear two-thirds of the container used for holding syrup, the forward part remaining empty. This enables the bees to take down the syrup to the last drop. These feeders of mine are made three and a half inches deep. They answer quite well, but do not hold more than about twenty pounds of syrup. I have also made a number of true Miller feeders, but of the size of the hive-top, like the others. These have two food compartments, one on each side of the central part which is open to the bees. They are of the same depth as the others, but hold about thirty-five pounds of syrup. The illustration should make this clear.

Our feeders are of wood, the bottoms being plywood, and for this purpose it is almost essential to use the kind made with waterproof cement and not with glue. The joints are pitched and the whole interior and under side painted with two coats of bitumen paint of good quality. These feeders are rather heavy, and they take up a good deal of storage room; but they are very strong, and can be stacked up to any height. All feeders for use on a bee farm must be so designed that syrup can be poured into them from a honey-tin or similar vessel, and the feeders here described are very good in that respect (see illustration).

It is necessary to have a considerable number of bee-escape boards for taking off the honey. Some people simply use the inner covers of the hives, putting a porter bee-trap into the feed hole of each cover; but I would strongly recommend that a number of boards should be kept specially for the purpose. They are easily and very cheaply made out of tea chests. They should have fairly thick cleats around their edges, so that the super combs shall have plenty of room in case of there being any comb built below the frames. I use rims of about three-quarters of an inch round the upper side and of about three-eighths of an inch round the under.

These are almost all the appliances that are needed for the

6. One of Mr. Madoc's apiaries in winter, showing the kind of stand used by him

7. A useful wind-break

8. Wood-and-wire and home-made zinc queen excluders

9. Home-made Miller feeder

apiaries, except that fencing tools will be needed, such as an iron bar for making post holes, a beetle for driving posts, and tools for erecting barbed wire.

As for clothes, there is nothing to equal a white or light-coloured boiler suit, having a zip fastener down the front, and, if possible, zip-fastened ends to the trousers of it. Bees don't run up your legs so much when you wear these, especially if you have them made a little on the long side. Sometimes people ask me why we use white when working among bees. It soon gets dirty, but there is no doubt of its value. If you want to get properly stung by bees, wear a dark blue overall or boiler suit. The late S. H. Smith made a sort of slogan of the phrase, 'Let the bees tell you'. They will tell you all right, without any letting, if you wear blue overalls. Besides, white is cool in hot weather, and if one wears just a shirt and shorts under it, one can be quite comfortable in a white or light-coloured boiler suit in the very hottest weather.

The veil is one of those things that are absolutely requisite and necessary. There are several kinds of veils, but most of them are made too small I think. Black net is what I like best; and a panama hat. Some prefer wire veils, and these are nice in some ways. I think they are cooler, perhaps; but on the whole I consider them rather a nuisance. I like something that I can roll up and put into my pocket. I think veils should have elastic bands around their bottoms, so that they can be fastened round the waist. But different people like different veils, and it is quite a matter for choice so long as the thing is efficient. The purpose of a veil is to keep bees away from the face. Soft net veils are apt to blow against the face in windy weather, whereas wire ones do not, but for all that I prefer a net veil every time.

Apart from vehicles, I think that practically everything needful has now been mentioned; but before ending this chapter I want to write a few words of caution for those who may be thinking of setting up beekeeping on a scale more extensive than that of a hobby.

You will find that advice given by many 'experts' about hives and appliances is liable to be coloured by prejudice. Some men, you know, are obstinately conservative; others have, presumably, had such a struggle to get any idea at all into their heads, that they altogether decline to face the strain of trying to assimilate a new one. There is no pain to some people like the pain of taking in a new idea. Such people cannot bear the thought that what they have accustomed themselves to believe is best can possibly be improved upon. This state of mind gives rise to a sort of bigoted intolerance that amounts to utter stagnation, and a successful business, certainly a bee-farming business in this country at this time, requires the exercise of an active, progressive, and open mind. Try to cultivate the habit of looking for good ideas, and of then bringing them to the acid test of experiment, like Galileo.

CHAPTER V

BREEDING BEES

It is clear that if a man is going to depend for a living on the produce of livestock of any kind, he must pay a great deal of attention to the quality of the animals concerned. Just as dairying or poultry farming must stand or fall by the production of milk or eggs, so a honey farm must depend for its success upon the ability of its bees to store honey in profitable quantities.

Honey-bees differ widely; some strains are excellent, others are worthless; and it is obvious that if we are to make a success of a thousand-colony bee farm or of half a dozen stocks, it is necessary to have bees that will get honey. The more honey they get, the better the business will pay; therefore the first thing to be done is to secure a good reliable strain of bees, and then to maintain and improve it.

In order to raise first-class stock it is of vital importance to procure breeding animals of high quality, both male and female. In most farm stock stress is laid particularly on the male because he may sire a large number of offspring, whereas the direct progeny of the female are very limited in number. Now we breeders of hive-bees have the great advantage over those who have to do with most domestic animals in that from one desirable breeding queen we can readily produce a virtually unlimited number of young queens. Though in a state of nature a honey-bee queen would only produce half a dozen or so daughter queens, and maybe a couple of thousand drones, in the hands of a competent breeder she can be made to give an almost unlimited number of both.

It is usually considered that too much in-breeding may lead to deterioration in the stamina and fecundity of animals, though about this there is some disagreement. When there is no trace of any bad or degenerate strain in the stock, in-breeding does no harm, I think; but unless one is quite sure that this is the case, it is probably better to arrange, as far as possible, in our breeding apiaries, that the drones flying there shall be produced by queens of the very highest character, while the young queens with which they are expected to mate shall be derived from breeder queens of a different strain, but equally outstanding qualities. In this way, although it is impossible to be certain that all matings will be as desired, yet it can be managed that a very large proportion of our young queens will be the product of the male and female parents from which we wish them to be derived.

The Breeding Stock

I think it very important that the breeding mothers used for the production of virgin queens shall be pure-bred and that they shall have mated with pure-bred drones, thus ensuring that their virgins shall be of pure blood also, for if such breeding stock are used to produce queens, our apiaries can never become progressively mongrelized, as is so commonly the case when this precaution is not taken. In the out-apiaries, of which a honey farm must consist, there will, of course, inevitably be a certain amount of 'slipping back'. There will always be a good many swarm-raised and super-sedure queens that will be likely to mate with inferior drones, or at any rate with drones that we should not choose; but steady work at the breeding apiary will enable us to replace undesirables to a large extent, and as time goes on less and less of our out-apiary queens should meet with objectionable drones because these will become less numerous.

The *ideal* way to choose a mother for producing virgins is to note a few of our very best honey-producing colonies whose queens show the characteristics mentioned in the last paragraph, and the workers of which are reasonably easy to handle, not being vicious and stinging unduly, and not being nervous and easily frightened when the hive is opened, but remaining quietly on the combs while being handled. This last is of importance, for nervous bees are very troublesome and hindering to manage, because when the hive is opened they rush around, balling up on the combs and falling off in bunches, making the finding of the queen almost impossible at times. From the selected queens a few virgins should be bred for introduction to stocks which require to be re-queened, in order that they may be tested during the following summer. If these young queens prove to have inherited their mother's good qualities, and if their mother shows that she has sufficient stamina to give a good account of herself through her second season, then we have a breeder worth taking care of. She should be introduced to one of our mating nuclei where she can remain for the rest of her life, producing enough eggs to keep her small colony in being, and to provide larvae for grafting. Such a queen, if taken care of, will often last four years; some breeders say more, but I have never had a queen that lived more than two years in a honey-producing colony and two in a nucleus. Occasionally a queen will last in full production in a honey-producing colony for three summers and may be used for breeding if her other characteristics are desirable; she will, however, rarely survive the winter following her third summer.

Of course, one may always use a first-rate queen that has done well for two seasons as a honey producer without first trying out her virgins; but I think the test outlined above is a very useful one, for it is not uncommon to find that some remarkably good queen will produce quite inferior daughters because, presumably, she has mated with a drone carrying bad qualities which are perpetuated in her offspring. Perhaps an experienced man can to a great extent judge of what is probable, but we are all liable to find ourselves mistaken. The best queen I ever owned mothered a colony that stored, together with a nucleus taken from it, just about 380 pounds of surplus honey in 1928. The next year I bred quite a lot of queens from her, thinking how good they would be sure to turn out, but not one of them was even a poor average mother. Again in 1939-40 I had an outstanding queen. Her workers were true to type and her drones seemed to be the same. No attempt at swarming was made in the two summers I had her heading a honey-producing stock, and she was brought home and placed in a nucleus. During 1941 a large number of very fine queens were bred from her which turned out to be good in every way but one; they had the fatal fault of excessive swarming. This queen cost us a lot: she reduced our crop and caused much trouble and expense before her daughters were finally weeded out.

The first of these two cases occurred before I quite realized that mis-mated or crossbred queens are altogether unreliable as breeding stock, though they may be excellent as honey producers. The queen, though a really marvellous one, was quite incapable of transmitting her valuable qualities to her daughters, though it is likely that her drones were extra good. The later incident was an unusual one, unique in my experience, for in the great majority of cases the good qualities of a queen whose drones and workers are both correctly marked will be reproduced in her daughters.

These occurrences, together with many others of a similar nature, serve to emphasize the extremely complicated nature of the mechanism of heredity. We are, almost all of us, much too apt to think of the transmission of hereditary characteristics as quite a simple and straightforward process, but that is very far from being the case. Hereditary qualities are transmitted from parents to off-spring through the chromosomes of the germ-cells. In the honey-bee these number thirty-two, sixteen being derived from each parent in the case of workers and queens, while the drone is haploid, having sixteen chromosomes only, all derived from his mother. These chromosome threads may be combined with one another in an enormous number of ways, as anyone may assure himself by taking a pencil and a piece of paper and working the matter out, or by a short study of some elementary work on gene-tics. This is why, although parents with good or bad qualities will, more often than not, transmit those qualities to their offspring, this does not always happen. We can see for ourselves, any day in our lives, how greatly children often differ from their parents, and how different the children of the same parents can be from one another, both physically and mentally, and who can wonder at this when it is remembered that the human species has the very large number of forty-eight chromosomes.

In breeding bees, however, we have a great advantage in the shortness of the time required to try out the qualities of the daughters of any given breeding mother. If a large batch of the daughters of some selected breeder prove to be better than the average during their first season as mother queens in our honey-producing apiaries, their mother queen should be used to the utmost extent to produce more such queens, until a better one is found, or she goes the way of all queens. It does not follow, how-ever, that those daughter queens are particularly likely to prove reliable breeding mothers themselves. A few may; but the majority will probably be found inferior for that purpose. It depends upon the hereditary qualities of the drone with which they have mated. No matter how good a queen may prove herself to be, if her daughters are not on the whole a good deal better than the average queens in the apiaries, they must not be used as breeders.

I may here point out that I am dealing with this matter of breeding from the point of view of one who uses Italian bees, and my remarks about colouring refer to that variety. The rules for breeding are, of course, the same for all other pure races, but I am quite unable to see how it is possible in this country to breed any pure strain of black or brown bees, because these are so much alike in colour and markings that I cannot understand how one could tell for certain whether a queen had mated correctly or not. 'Blacks' are usually crossbred or mongrels, or at any rate I don't see how one could know whether they are or not, and Caucasians, Carniolans, Dutch, and the rest are somewhat difficult to distinguish from one another, for they vary a good deal in appearance even when of pure imported strains. Italians, on the other hand, have the definite distinction of three tan or yellow bands.

The queens to be used as breeders of drones require to be chosen for the virtues exhibited by their mothers' colonies rather than for those of their own, for the simple reason that the male honey-bee is a haploid insect produced from an unfertilized egg and therefore carrying no genetic characters other than those derived from his female (and only) parent. I think we ought to be particularly careful to use as drone-breeding queens, only those whose mothers have headed colonies in which the workers have shown themselves to be good-tempered and to have the very desirable trait of remaining quietly on the combs while being handled. Experience has led me to form the opinion that these characteristics in bees are probably linked genetically with the male sex. I have many a time known an excessively vicious colony, such as were so many of those black French bees we used to import as combless packages in the interval between the two world wars, to become quite docile and easily handled after one of their young queens had mated with an Italian drone of peaceable temperament, and I think nearly every beekeeper must have noticed how very vicious a stock of quiet bees will often become after their young queen has mated with a drone of some vicious strain. I incline, also, to the opinion that the factor which induces undue swarming may also be carried by the male and, although this may be mere guesswork, there can be no harm in being especially careful when making the choice of mothers for our drones for the breeding apiary, to select those that are daughters of queens whose colonies have shown no inclination to swarm, and have at all times been good-tempered and easily handled. Given these qualities, combined of course with a good honey record, I do not think it matters whether the drone breeders have mated with a pure-bred male, since their drones will in any case be pure.

One of the difficulties in breeding bees is the fact that no direct control over mating is possible, but in well-managed breeding apiaries, where care is taken to have a large force of vigorous drones of the desired strain always present and at all times on the look-out for flying virgins, comparatively few wrong matings will take place, and this will be more so as time goes on, for where there are such masses of drones flying, neighbouring apiaries, if any, are likely to become, through matings with our drones, almost of the same strain. In this way queens bred in large breeding apiaries are likely to mate correctly in the great majority of cases.

I am well aware that this statement may be disputed, for it has long been an accepted theory that virgin queens mate with drones high up in the air and at considerable distances from their hives. I do not now think this is really the case, at all events in breeding apiaries where there are large numbers of drones ready to give chase to every virgin when she flies. I think that in such situations the young queens are normally mated within quite a short distance of the hives and usually at no great height. All the cases I have heard of in which the coming together of drone and virgin have been seen have been quite near to the hives as has been the case with me in the very few instances of it that I have seen. Of course this only shows that mating can and often does take place near the hives and low down, for no distant or high mating could be seen at all. Still, it does seem very probable that the greater part of the very considerable time that is usually taken by a virgin in effecting a successful mating may be passed on the ground while the two insects are in sexual connection with one another rather than in a long flight which would have no purpose whatever that I can see. I have known a queen to be thirty-five minutes away from her hive while mating, and it seems to me very unlikely that so much time would be occupied in flying about.

Two instances that bear on this question may be cited. First there is the incident given by Herrod-Hempsall in his two-volume book. In this case he not only saw the drone and virgin come together in flight, but spotted where they fell and succeeded in killing them with cyanide and taking a photograph of them while in actual sexual connection. This must be almost unique, though I dare say if large commercial breeders could spare the time to watch long enough, many similar instances would transpire. The other case in point was related to me in a letter two or three years ago in the following words: 'Some years ago, watching the bees one Sunday, we saw a virgin emerge for her mating flight, and noted the time. The situation of the apiary, flanked on two sides by very tall fir trees, enabled the flight of the bees in the sun to be followed clearly against the dark background. We saw the virgin pursued by a considerable number of drones, and the race continued swiftly in long zig-zags, a number of drones being "tailed off" at each sharp turn at a height of about forty feet. These zig-zags continued for a considerable time, the height being evenly maintained and the distance from us not appreciably increasing. Suddenly something fell, fairly slowly, from the crowd, and, my father keeping watch on the hive, I ran to the spot to search. Unfortunately I misjudged the distance and went too far, for after a vain search I saw a queen rising apparently from the path in front of me. I at once looked for the drone, and sure enough found one on the grass verge, just as my father announced the return of the queen to her hive. The genital organs of the drone were missing, and my father was able to report that the queen had returned with the drone appendage clearly visible, having been absent from the hive twenty-five and a half minutes. We did not, unfortunately, time the period when the bees were on the ground, but we estimated it at about twenty minutes. We formed the opinion that the drone remains alive until all the seminal fluid has been injected into the queen (it may be that this takes a considerable time) and that the death of the drone occurs when the queen wrenches herself free.'

I myself have never seen anything of this kind, but then I never have time to watch bees. Maybe when I get old and retire from the more strenuous labour of a bee farm I may be able to spend some part of the evening of my days in watching the behaviour of my bees and of other interesting animals. I believe, however, that in the ordinary way queens do not fly far to mate, and as further evidence of this probability, I may point out that when they are seen to leave their hives as if to mate, and to return unmated, their flight will rarely, if ever, have lasted for more than five minutes or so.

On the other hand, drones undoubtedly do take long flights; at least I certainly think this is so, and it is probably this fact that accounts for the very common occurrence of cross-mating in breeding apiaries in which very large numbers of pure-bred drones are maintained. It is probable that, in our present state of knowledge at all events, there is no remedy for this mis-mating, and that breeders will just have to allow for a certain percentage of it, and be thankful it is no worse.

There is no doubt that virgin queens do sometimes mate more than once. I have seen this myself; but whether it is a comparatively rare event or quite a common one, I do not know. Recent observations in the U.S.A. seem to indicate that it is quite a common thing for a virgin to mate twice. Double mating may possibly explain the rather curious variations in the markings of the bees of certain colonies that have caused discussions in various bee magazines in the past; but it seems to me that we can find an ample explanation of all such variations in the genetic mix-up brought about by the mating of queens and drones in the ordinary way, for it should be remembered that, although we speak of 'pure' strains of Italian or other varieties, yet it is probably a fact that there is no such thing as a genetically pure strain at all. Most likely all our modern breeds harbour recessive genes which are liable to show when certain individuals mate.

There is another point that we should not forget when considering double mating. Drones are not sexually mature until they are a fortnight old, and the mating of virgin queens with immature drones will result in their becoming drone-breeders or in their producing a very large proportion of drone brood from the eggs they lay in worker comb. This was completely proved by the late F. W. Sladen in his elaborate experiments on Duck Island while working for the Canadian Government, but it is unlikely that immature drones will have much chance of securing a mate while plenty of vigorous, fully developed ones are about. Sladen had quite a difficult job in fixing up the island experiment, to make certain that only drones under the fully potent age could be present.

Of course we cannot be sure; but it seems probable to me that when a second mating occurs it is extremely likely that the first has not been effective. Should a virgin copulate with a fully potent drone, we may, I think, presume that the result, since it fills the spermatheca with living sperms, is the satisfaction of the sexual urge of the queen from that time on, and that consequently no further mating will take place. On the other hand, if the mating does not result in satisfying the queen's sexual demand by filling the spermatheca with sperms, then the urge to mate remains and the queen will fly out again to meet a drone.

Virgins commonly fly out two or three days after leaving their cells, and may mate then or at any time after, up to a month. The earlier they mate the better, in my opinion, though any time up to fifteen days seems to be satisfactory. I have known young queens to lay fertile eggs on the fifth day, but there is little doubt that when laying commences as soon as this the virgins have been confined to their cells for some time after they were mature. The workers often prevent the egress of mature virgins for some days when the weather is unsuitable for the issue of swarms, and in these cases, on the beekeeper opening the hive and disturbing the bees that are holding the virgin confined, she will immediately emerge, and will quite frequently take to flight immediately. Such virgins, if introduced to mating nuclei, will quite often be laying fertile eggs within sixty hours. It is, incidentally, this fact that makes an incubator useful in a breeding apiary.

Generally speaking, when the weather is favourable, our young queens will be laying about the tenth to twelfth day after leaving their cells. After virgins are fifteen days old their matings become more and more dubious and less satisfactory in their results, even when they take place, and after twenty days may be considered so unreliable that it will usually be good business to destroy all such virgins as are still unmated by that time. The reason for this is now known to be a tendency of the fluid in the spermatheca to gradually solidify, a process which we must suppose to commence about fifteen days or so after the emergence of the queen and to be completed about ten or twelve days later.

Before describing the methods now employed for rearing queen bees in large numbers and of good quality, I would point out that it is probable that no artificial system of raising queen-cells will ever quite equal Nature's plan of having this done spontaneously by the bees under the influence of the swarming urge, or of natural supersedure when carried out sufficiently early in the season. But the honey farmer could not have all his queens reared in these natural ways if he wanted to. Excessive swarming is a thing to be avoided as much as possible, and queens reared under the swarming impulse, while generally excellent in other ways, are liable to carry those factors that produce too much swarming. It is necessary, therefore, to undertake the raising of a sufficient number of queens each year to meet the requirements of the business.

Rearing Queens

Having provided for the breeding stock, it remains to raise from it the young queens we need, and to do it as efficiently as possible, so that we may, through them, carry the good qualities of their parents into our honey-producing apiaries in order to ensure that the utmost advantage shall be taken of such honey-flows as the season may bring. Since mating cannot be entirely controlled, and as drones will be plentiful in a properly arranged breeding apiary where selected drone-breeding mothers are encouraged to produce them in large numbers, we need concern ourselves solely with the raising of young queens from our chosen breeders in such a way as to ensure as far as possible they shall be well grown and with vigour and stamina sufficient to carry them through at least two seasons as mothers in honey-producing colonies; for, quite apart from the hereditary qualities they derive from their parents, much depends upon the way these young queens are reared from the hatching of the eggs.

The period of incubation is three days; at the end of that time the larva leaves the egg and at once commences to feed upon the special food provided for it by the nurse bees. This food is a secretion of the bees themselves, just as milk is a glandular secretion in mammals, and it has very remarkable properties. When the newly emerged larva is destined to become a worker bee, it is fed on this material for the first two days only, after which, it is generally believed, a digested preparation of honey and pollen is added to or substituted for it. Growth is very rapid: so prodigious, indeed, is this development that when fully grown and ready for pupation at the end of about five and a half days, weight is said to have increased some fifteen hundred times.

The larvae destined to develop into queens are fed quite differ-ently and are supplied immediately on hatching from the eggs with relatively enormous quantities of this brood-food, the supply being maintained throughout the time of growth, and at five and half days the queen larvae are somewhere about double the size of worker grubs at the same stage. At Rothamsted Experimental Laboratory and elsewhere, investigation of this matter has given every reason to believe that both queen and worker larvae do in fact receive the same food, so far as the food's composition is con-cerned, during the first forty-eight hours of larval life; but that a larva from an egg laid in a queen-cell, where plenty of nurse bees are present, receives a superfluity of food during that period, whereas a worker larva never receives such lavish feeding, and under unfavourable conditions, may receive only a bare minimum of food.

There is no doubt that some additional substance is contained in the royal jelly fed to queen larvae after the first two days of larval life, and Dr. C. G. Butler tells me that for experimental purposes, they have hand-reared larvae, and that it has been found that if these are merely given royal jelly taken from an advanced queen-cell throughout their time of growth, the result is just a very large worker bee. Similarly, if the food that is naturally fed to larval bees for the first forty-eight hours of life, is fed to larvae throughout the five and a half days from hatching until feeding ceases, again the result is only an extra large worker. This shows that something must be added to the brood-food fed to queens after the second day of larval life onwards, and in order to produce queens experimentally, it is necessary to feed the royal jelly appropriate to the age of the larva concerned.

When the larva is fully grown the cell is sealed over by the workers and thereafter occurs one of the most wonderful processes in nature. In the course of only seven and a half to eight days the white, soft, limbless grub is transformed into a perfect queen bee which will, in favourable circumstances, fly to mate with a drone within a week, and may herself be laying fertile eggs forty-eight hours later. Such is the material with which we are working when we rear queens, and it must be apparent to any intelligent beekeeper that a good deal of care is necessary when interfering with such an extremely delicate process.

The rearing of queen bees may be divided into two distinct parts; the raising of the queen-cells and the mating of the virgins that emerge from those cells. In order that large, vigorous queens may be obtained it is absolutely necessary that the larvae shall have recieved an ample supply of the larval food called 'royal jelly' from hatching to the end of larval life. In a state of nature queens are raised in three different ways; under the swarming impulse; the supersedure impulse; or under the stress of emergency caused by the sudden loss of a queen. Under the first, bees build queen-cells in preparation for swarming; the queen lays an egg in each, and the young queens so bred are usually of the very best, if of good parentage, for they will have received from birth every possible advantage in the way of nourishment and care.

Queens reared by bees when superseding an old worn-out mother are generally good, though perhaps less so than those reared when swarming is taking place. They are good because, while royal jelly is not particularly plentiful at the season when supersedure usually takes place, as it is at swarming time, yet what there is is usually concentrated into a few queen-cells—for when superseding, bees seldom build more than three or four; in fact they often limit themselves to a single cell which receives a large quantity of royal jelly.

In both these cases the new queens are raised from the egg; but in the case of emergency, caused by the sudden loss of a queen by accident or otherwise, the case is quite different, for the bees, finding themselves without their queen, will often begin to supply with royal jelly larvae in worker cells that are too far advanced in growth for the full effect of such feeding to take place, and as the queens that will be produced in this way will be quite inferior, the first of these emergency cells to be sealed over should be destroyed, and only those started from very young larvae allowed to mature. It is better, in any case, not to rely upon this method of rearing mothers for our colonies, though excellent queens can be produced in strong stocks if care is taken that only the best cells shall produce queens.

There are several plans for rearing queens on a considerable scale and known by the names of those who first described them. The Alley plan is not now much used, I believe, though excellent queens can be produced by it. A strip of new comb containing eggs is cut and the cells on one side having been shaved down to the septum, the strip is fastened to the bottom of a shallow dummy or cut-down brood-comb in such a way that the remaining cells with eggs hang mouth down. About two cells out of three are then deprived of their eggs in order to leave space between the queen-cells that will be built. The whole is then placed in the cell-building colony where as soon as the eggs hatch they are at once fed with royal jelly and fine cells result, which may be cut out when sealed over.

Isaac Hopkins of New Zealand took a frame of new comb full of eggs, and having destroyed three rows of cells out of every four, and having also removed the eggs from alternate cells in the remaining rows, placed the whole flat on the top-bars of a queenless colony, raising it clear of the top-bars by means of an empty frame laid under it.

Dr. Miller recommended that a frame fitted with four vee-shaped starters of worker foundation, about two inches wide at the top and tapering to a point near the bottom bar, be placed in the colony of the queen from which it is desired to breed. In due course the starters will be built out and filled with eggs, when they are to be given to the cell-building colony. Queen-cells will be built along the edges of the triangular combs and these may be readily cut out for use where needed.

Another plan is to have a new comb built out and filled with eggs in the colony of the breeder and then to cut an inch or two off the bottom of it. The larvae close to the point of cutting off will be accepted by a cell-building colony and fed for queen-raising as soon as they hatch. It is recommended that eggs should be left only at intervals of about half to three-quarters of an inch, the intermediate ones being destroyed and the cells slightly enlarged where eggs are left.

Good queens can be raised in all these ways, but the objection to them is that the cells must be cut out from the comb on which they are built, and may be damaged in the process which is in any case messy and inconvenient, and practically all modern queen-rearing that is conducted on any scale is carried out by some variation of what is known as the Doolittle system.

G. M. Doolittle of New York, U.S.A. was the pioneer in the art of rearing queens by the use of artificial cell-cups to which the desired larvae are transferred by hand, and practically all modern large-scale queen rearing is carried out by some variation of this system. Artificial cell-cups are made by dipping suitably shaped pieces into hot beeswax; they can be purchased ready made in the form of pressed cell-cups. These cups are fastened by hot wax to a wooden dummy board about half to two-thirds the depth of a frame, which is my favourite plan, or to bars made to fit into an empty or partly filled brood frame. They may also be fixed to small wooden cell-cups which in turn are fastened to the bar or dummy. Before these cell-cups have larvae grafted into them it is a very good plan to place them in the cell-building colony over night, for when this is done the bees will work on them, cleaning them out and bringing them more nearly to the natural shape, which causes them to be more readily accepted when finally grafted. It is really an excellent plan to keep a bar of these cell-cups in the cell-building colony at the same time as the bees are actually building cells on another which has been grafted and given to them, for then we always have a set of cell-cups ready for immediate grafting at any time.

Grafting the Larvae

The grafting of larvae is a very simple process, only requiring good sight, a steady hand, and a knowledge of the correct size of the grubs to be transferred. First of all it is usual, though not absolutely necessary, to collect some royal jelly for the purpose of supplying a small quantity of it to the bottom of each cell-cup. This royal jelly should be taken from queen-cells in the early stage while the larvae in them are quite small, and certainly not from sealed cells; at least that is what I think, though, as we shall see, it is improbable that the grafted larvae feed much upon the royal jelly we graft them on. Royal jelly is said to keep quite well if stored in a perfectly clean and air-tight porcelain jar. Jay Smith recommends those small white jars that cosmetics are sold in; but it is quite a job to rid them of the scent with which they are usually permeated when bought full of face cream, or whatever the stuff is, and repeated washing in hot water is generally necessary to rid them of the smell. For my part, I have never managed to keep royal jelly good for any length of time, however stored, and breeders will, I believe, be well advised to use freshly made jelly on all occasions.

10. Pouring syrup into a Miller feeder

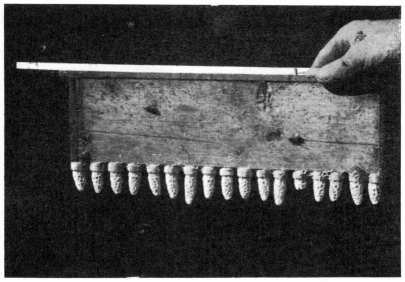

11. A graft dummy with sealed queen-cells

12. A four-section mating hive with the cover of one division turned back

13. Bees hanging out at the entrance of a mating hive in hot weather

To graft larvae take a small quantity of this royal jelly and thin it with water in the ratio of about 50 per cent, and with a small camel hair brush or the spoon end of a small instrument made for the purpose, called a grafting needle, place on the bottom of each cell-cup a particle of the mixture of about the size of the letter 'o' of this type. Do not use a larger quantity, for the utility of this royal jelly in grafting is really more to facilitate the transfer of the larvae than anything else, it being much easier to place the tiny grub on a speck of this creamy fluid to which it readily adheres, than to transfer it from the grafting needle to a dry cell-bottom. Some beekeepers say they find that the bees accept grafted larvae just as readily if simply placed on a speck of saliva, which would seem to show that the given jelly is not of very much use to the larvae that are grafted on it.

Grafting should be done in a warm room in order to avoid risk of chilling, and a small building should be erected for the purpose even when no very large number of queens are to be raised, such a convenience being quite necessary where extensive work is carried out and when batches of larvae must be grafted every few days. A small electric radiator is the best way of heating such a place, but where no current is available, some other means of warming must be provided. This matter is, I believe, important, because it allows the work to be done in an unhurried manner.

Having prepared the cell-cups with a speck of royal jelly in each, a comb containing a number of very young grubs, preferably a newly built comb, is taken from the colony of the queen we intend to breed from. If this queen is kept in a nucleus which is well supplied with honey, there will usually be suitable larvae present in sufficient numbers. Combs can be occasionally removed from this nucleus as they are filled with sealed brood, and may be replaced with foundation so that the hive shall not become over-crowded. All the bees having been shaken or brushed from this comb, we look for a row of cells containing larvae of the right age, that is to say about fifteen to twenty hours old, or rather smaller than a pin's head as they lie curled up. It is almost certainly better not to use larvae younger than twelve hours, and on no account should they be more than thirty hours old when grafted, for reasons made obvious a few pages back.

For grafting always select grubs that are found to be floating on an abundance of brood-food, because these will certainly never have been on short commons from birth, as might otherwise be the case, for worker larvae are very often found supplied with only a very small amount of food. However, if our breeder's colony is well supplied with young bees and richly stored with honey and pollen it will be found that the young larvae are amply supplied; but it is important not to graft from colonies in which there is the least danger of shortage of brood-food, for the grubs therein may have had their diet restricted, and it is *necessary* that queens shall not have suffered from shortage of food at any period of their lives. So on no account graft larvae that are lying almost high and dry on the cell-bottoms, but, I repeat, only those that have a lavish supply. These latter have the advantage, also, that they are very much more easily removed on the grafting tool.

What is known as 'double grafting' is advocated by some; but since ordinary grafting as above described is perfectly satisfactory if properly carried out, double grafting would appear to be a mere fad which wastes a lot of valuable time. However, this system is simply to graft in the normal way, and after a couple of days remove the larvae from the cells that have been accepted and replace them by another set of grubs. I do not advise it. For one thing, while it makes it certain that the second set of larvae shall receive ample food from their transference, it does not ensure that that food shall be of exactly the correct consistency to correspond with the age of the grubs placed upon it. This is, apparently, of some importance according to the findings of Rothamsted.

To graft larvae, the cell-walls are pressed aside with the blade of a small knife in order to widen the opening and allow easy access, and the grubs are lifted one by one on a small tool, the grafting needle aforesaid, or on a quill prepared with a pointed and bent end, and are gently laid on the royal jelly. The whole, when ready, is at once placed in the cell-building colony. An hour later, if we examine the grafted cells, we shall usually find that the whole of the royal jelly has been removed by the bees, which always replace it with a fresh supply of their own elaboration. One reason for using only a very small quantity of royal jelly in grafting is that when large masses are placed in the cups the bees are very liable to clear out the grubs and all, an excess of zeal equivalent to throwing the baby out with the bath-water.

When taking the comb of larvae from the nucleus, care should be taken that the queen is not shaken off when freeing the comb of bees. If she is on the comb taken out, she should be gently picked off and placed on another comb before shaking off the workers, for these old breeders are heavy and rather easily injured, just like old ladies, so treat them nicely.

Cell Building

This process is, next to the selection of the breeding stock, the most important of all queen-rearing operations. In order that the young queens shall be well grown, strong, and prolific, they must receive from birth to maturity an unstinted supply of royal jelly. This can only be assured by giving the grafted larvae to colonies that have large numbers of worker bees of the correct age to supply the royal food.

This food, which was at one time thought to be chyle from the stomach, and which is even to-day called 'chyle food' by some, is now known to be a secretion of the pharyngeal glands of worker bees. It is a white material of a creamy consistency and has a bitter taste. It does not appear to be definitely known at what age bees are first able to produce this secretion, but in normal colonies my own observations have led me to believe that young bees from about ten days on are probably at their best for providing larval food and royal jelly.

That quite old bees will raise queen-cells and worker brood in certain circumstances is well known, but it is almost certain, I think, that the period of nursing ability is in all cases limited; bees that have already secreted brood-food in the normal way being incapable of rearing brood or queens satisfactorily. In a normal colony, where a constant succession of workers are emerging and taking up the work of the community, these first of all do little or no work of any kind for a few days, after which they for a time take up the feeding and care of the larvae of both workers and drones, and of producing royal jelly if required, until in due course they begin field work, after which I don't much think they ever revert to brood-food secretion, and most likely they are unable to do so. When, however, brood-rearing is interrupted, as in the case of a swarm headed by a virgin queen whose mating is delayed, or in any similar case, or when the approach of winter brings about the cessation of breeding, we find that the bees, not having acted as brood-food producers early in life, are just as capable of brood-rearing as are younger bees in normal circumstances.

From the viewpoint of the breeder, however, it is certain that in order to have the grafted larvae fed with an ample supply of royal jelly, it is necessary to use for cell-building purposes only colonies containing large numbers of young bees. This is the considered opinion of all competent breeders. Jay Smith says, 'For the best results in cell-building we must have plenty of young bees that are being lavishly fed either from a honey-flow or from receiving sugar syrup.' By 'young' bees I don't mean bees only a day or two old, for these are useless; but after eight or ten days they are probably at their best as brood-food producers and for supplying queen-cells with royal jelly, for royal jelly is brood-food with subtle additions that are not yet understood. If the brood-food glands of these young bees are used as they mature to feed larvae in a normal colony in spring and summer, those organs probably become exhausted in the course of a few days, the bees then taking up foraging and other duties and retiring from the nursing profession for good. I do not know at exactly what age bees become brood-food producers, nor how long they can continue to provide that secretion, but I am pretty sure that the effective period is a short one, and may only be a matter of a day or two.

If for the purpose of cell-building we make an artificial swarm by shaking bees of all ages from a number of combs, we find that the first batch of grafted larvae is eagerly accepted and is lavishly supplied with royal jelly. These being sealed and removed on the fifth or sixth day and a second batch given, it will be found that this is also accepted in a satisfactory manner. A third is sometimes as successful as the other two; but after that, such cells as are built are poor and meagrely supplied with food, and the virgins from them are small and ill-nourished. I think that the reason for this is that for about twelve or fifteen days the young bees become brood-food producers as they reach the critical age, after which time all, or almost all, have exhausted their power of secretion, showing that this power is quickly lost as bees age, if it is exercised.

Nurse bees then, are those which have reached the age at which their pharyngeal glands mature, and continue to be potential nurses until those glands are exhausted. As brood-rearing ends in the late autumn, brood-food secretion ceases also, and those bees which have not exercised the function can and do, every spring, take up the work of brood-rearing in a perfectly satisfactory manner. Most probably it is a misunderstanding of this fact that has caused argument at times which might have been avoided by the employment of a little thought.

There are several methods of arranging satisfactory cell-building colonies, according to circumstances and the time of year; but at all times the colony must be a powerful one, well found in honey and pollen and having a large force of nurse bees to supply the necessary royal jelly. In the early part of the season, when honey is being brought into the hives and bees are rather inclined to build queen-cells, it is a fairly simple matter to have cells started and finished in queen-right colonies. Take a strong stock with a good queen, which should be one from which it is desirable to breed drones, and having a large amount of brood in two brood-chambers. If necessary, brood from other hives can be added to fill the two bodies. See that the queen is in the lower chamber and place upon it a queen excluder. Over this set a shallow extracting super of worker combs, or if the colony is a very strong one, a full depth chamber, and over this again place the second brood-chamber full of brood in all stages. The bees in the upper body will usually accept grafted cells twenty-four hours later and will proceed to fill them lavishly with royal jelly. Unless a honey-flow is going on the colony should be fed daily. If the first batch of grafted cells is rejected, try another the next day, when it will be almost certainly successful. If from time to time sealed brood from the lower chamber be exchanged for broodless combs from the upper one as the brood emerges there, a colony so managed will go on building a moderate number of queen-cells of excellent quality throughout May, June, and half July. If combs can be spared either from other hives or from over-strong mating nuclei and are placed in the upper story of the cell-building colony occasionally as well as moving brood up from below the excluder, it stands to reason that the strength of that colony will be even more increased and its efficiency made greater. The two chambers may also have their places changed every three weeks, the queen being left in the lower one.

A cell-building colony cannot be too strong, and it need never incline to swarm if brood is taken every now and then from the lower chamber where the queen is, so that there is always plenty of room for her to lay eggs down there. It is believed by some breeders that it is necessary to have unsealed brood in the top story of a queen-right cell-building colony: but I have not found it so, so long as there are plenty of young bees constantly emerging there, whereas I have found that the presence of young brood often leads to trouble through the bees building 'wild' cells on it which necessitates examinations for the purpose of destroying any such cells, for should only one of these escape detection and mature, the resulting virgin will immediately destroy all our grafted cells and will very often lead us a fine dance before she can be caught.

A colony arranged as I have described should not be given very many grated larvae at one time; but the number should be limited to about twelve or fifteen for each batch. I have myself found twelve prepared cells set on one graft dummy a satisfactory number, and that if the larvae are grafted at about twelve hours old, the cells will be completed or nearly so four to five days later. Thus, if the grafted larvae are given in the evening, it should be in order to remove the finished cells on the morning of the fifth day following, and for another batch to be given the same evening. It is a good plan, as soon as the cells have been removed, to well sprinkle the top-bars of the cell-building colony with thick syrup and to place a small rapid feeder on it as well, for in this way the nurse bees will be brought to a condition wherein they will eagerly accept the new set of grafted cells in the evening. Such a colony can, and will, if well looked after, continue to supply from ten to fifteen finished queen-cells every five days right through the summer.

This method of raising queen-cells is very suitable for honey producers and others who are not rearing queens for sale, but only to provide young queens for their own use. When it is intended to embark upon large-scale queen breeding some other system must be adopted. I have no experience of large-scale queen rearing, having never had more than about 150 mating nuclei from which to rear five or six hundred queens for use in our own apiaries, and I would refer those interested to the works of such men as Pritchard and Smith for further information.

There is one point I would like to make while dealing with using queen-right colonies in this way. It will often be found that the cells built appear rather small beside those constructed by swarming colonies or by artificial swarms as described below. I think this is caused by the established queen-right cell-building colonies not being in the state that favours heavy secretion of wax, whereas swarms or bees about to swarm, are. The cells look small because they are less massively constructed, and may appear quite diminutive when compared with those built by swarming bees or by artificial swarms made queenless, but the virgins from them are usually as good as can be desired. It is not the size of the cell or its external appearance that matters, but the amount of royal jelly consumed by its occupant. There are few things more misleading than cell size as a means of judging what sort of queen may be expected to emerge. I have seen very small, weedy-looking virgins come from large and well-built cells, and as often have seen very fine ones issue from cells that would be discarded if judged only by appearance.

I think, myself, that a good deal more care should be taken in handling completed queen-cells than is generally supposed. I think that it is a mistake, for instance, to hold them upside down. After pupation a queen pupa lies quite loosely in its cell. If you hold a newly sealed queen-cell up against a bright light and turn it point upwards you will see the shadow of the pupa fall sharply downwards. Now the white, newly formed pupa is a very soft and delicate thing, and I cannot think it can be good for it to suddenly slip down to rest on its tail and reverse the move as the cell is returned to its normal position. Yet it seems to be a common practice to invert these cells, comb and all; in fact several illustrations will be found in Herrod-Hempsall's book in which combs with queen-cells are actually set bottom up while the cells are cut from them. I believe this is very bad practice indeed. You can't handle queen-cells too carefully. They are quite different from other cells in which pupae are in contact with the cell walls all round. You can even shake worker and drone brood without injuring it; but not queen brood, at any rate after pupation. It has always puzzled me to understand what the reason can be for the cells used to raise queens being made so much too large, or perhaps I should say, so much larger than would appear to be necessary.

For carrying queen cells I use a block of wood with a number of holes in it about five-eighths of an inch deep. I usually bore them a good deal deeper and bring them to the required depth by partly filling them with some soft material like cotton wool or a bit of butter muslin. When taking cells, I gently remove them from the comb or graft dummy after either hanging it up or else laying it gently on its side, and then set the cells in the holes in their natural position. Queen-cells containing pupae should not be left lying on their sides for very long, though to lie so for a few minutes seems to do them no harm. Never shake combs with queen-cells, and take extreme care not to chill them at any stage. Chilled pupae will usually emerge with useless wings.

As a matter of fact, young larvae will stand quite a lot of chilling and general ill-treatment without being killed or, in fact, showing any signs of ill-effects; but we should not rely upon the mere appearance of the queens into which they develop, and for my part, I think we can hardly be too careful to avoid any chilling of larvae in grafting, for we can surely not be wrong in trying to keep as close to natural conditions as possible when dealing with the business of trying to breed first-rate queen bees. I believe that other things being equal in every way, naturally reared queens are healthier, hardier, and longer lived than those raised by artificial methods, especially in climates such as ours where the weather is apt to be unsuitable for the work during a good part of the season of bee-breeding.

When finished, the cells may be removed from the building colony, if desired, and placed in a second story of a strong queen-right stock over an excluder until they are wanted for introduction to nuclei. If a couple of combs of brood are placed one on each side of the cells, it will keep the bees from deserting them in case of a cold night late in the year; but if you use this method, take care not to leave the cells too long, for if you do that a virgin may emerge and destroy all the others.

Finished cells may also be placed in an incubator, where they can be allowed to emerge into small cages stocked with honey and pollen or with queen-cage candy. In some ways this is the best plan of all as by it we are able to use cells or virgins at will; but it is well to remember that no virgin should be kept caged in an incubator for more than a short time without having workers put into the cages with her, in fact it is quite a useful plan to put a few workers into these cages before the virgins emerge. Cages should be large enough and have a good supply of food (see illustration). But very few beekeepers will be able to use an incubator, and completed cells will, as a rule, be given direct to nuclei when within a few days of the expected emergence of the queens.

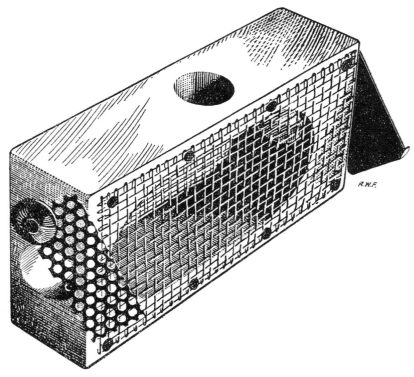

Figure 4

NURSERY CAGE SUITABLE FOR USE IN AN INCUBATOR

It saves a good deal of valuable nucleus-time if the cells are introduced just before the virgins are ready to emerge; more still, if virgins are given soon after fertile queens have been taken from the nuclei; for it is important, if the best is to be made of our equipment, that each nucleus shall mate as many queens as possible in the season, and this entails 'keeping the pot boiling'. A fertile queen is removed from a nucleus: twenty-four hours later a cell from which a virgin is due to emerge in two days is given to it, or a virgin is caged in it, thus saving some days that would be lost were a newly sealed cell given. Personally, I like the method of introducing virgins to nuclei better than that of giving cells. It is slightly more trouble to cage a virgin than to put a cell in place; but it seems to me to have the following advantages. The virgin is seen, so we can be sure that she is a good one, at all events so far as appearance goes. A virgin introduced will usually be mated from three to six days sooner than one emerging from a cell placed in a nucleus at the same time. Also, there is no trouble from the destruction of introduced cells by the workers of the nucleus.

In the early part of the summer queen-right cell-building colonies are quite satisfactory. Besides building our queen-cells they should be rearing large numbers of choice drones all the time, and in addition should provide many combs of stores. As these colonies must be fed a good deal they will continually fill and seal combs of stores, which may be removed from time to time to be replaced by empty ones or by foundation. These combs, containing as they will a mixture of honey and syrup, should be used to supply winter stores to nuclei, where required.

If one of these colonies is not sufficient to provide all the queen-cells we need, it is easy to use two of them, or more, and much simpler, in my opinion, than to start the cells in one colony or swarm and have them finished in another; but for extensive commercial queen-rearing the latter method is probably the better.

Many, perhaps the majority of beekeepers, have their cell-building done in queenless colonies which are constantly supplied with combs of brood in order that there shall be a continual supply of young bees. In many ways this is the most satisfactory plan of all, so long as the necessary brood can be obtained without much difficulty. It is the only way by which good cell-building energy can be got continually in one colony right through the season, and it is certainly the best method for work late in the summer, its single drawback being possible difficulty in maintaining the supply of brood. Towards the end of July, just when in most seasons bees tend to be less and less inclined to build queen-cells, the queenless stock, if well supplied with brood, will show no inclination to reduced energy in supplying relays of grafted cells with royal jelly, but this is far from being the case with queen-right colonies. These are almost useless from this time onward, and should never be used on any account; for even if they build queen-cells, these will be sure to be poorly supplied with food and poor queens will inevitably result.

Apart from the queenless stock plan described above, there are others that will produce fine queens late in the year. I don't set up to know all about it by a very long way, and the reader should remember this when considering the following additional plans which I have found useful.

For those who have only one apiary it may be best to adopt the following. From a strong stock remove the queen and all the unsealed brood, placing the removed combs in a second brood-chamber and setting this on another stock over a queen-excluder. The queen should be caged on a comb in one of those push-in cages already described, so that the bees of the stock on which the combs are placed shall not harm her when they rise through the excluder to care for the brood. Now we have to arrange the colony from which the queen and brood have been taken. There must be two or three combs of honey and pollen, the pollen being important. Usually there will be two or three combs in the hive containing pollen and honey which can be left, and if a comb or two are left containing sealed brood as well, so much the better; but on no account must there be any unsealed worker brood. These combs should be flanked by one or two dummy feeders, and spaces should be left for one or two graft dummies or prepared combs. A good arrangement is as follows: starting at one side of the hive, we first have a dummy feeder, next to it a comb of stores is placed, then a comb of sealed brood, then a graft dummy, then another comb of sealed brood or stores, then a second graft dummy, if two are required, ending with more combs of stores, or stores and sealed brood. The feeder should be filled at once. In a short time this colony, which is, in fact, just a queenless shaken swarm, will be showing great distress, the bees will be running in and out of the entrance and all over the hive in a frantic search for the missing queen whose loss is far more severely felt when no unsealed brood is present in the hive. Now is the time to give them grafted cell-cups, which they will accept eagerly, and will supply with ample quantities of royal food. A strong colony such as I have described will be in exactly the right condition for building queen-cells, because when taken from the brood which they are engaged in feeding, the food-secreting glands of the nurse bees are in full action and are gorged with the required material, just as the lactic glands of mammals become gorged when milking suddenly ceases.

Such a colony may build as many as sixty cells at once; but I much prefer to give about thirty at first, a second thirty when the first batch is sealed and removed, and finally a third smaller batch of about fifteen. When these have been removed after being sealed, the brood with the queen must be returned to the bees.

A good plan for those who have out-apiaries, is to take a well-ventilated hive and fit it with a temporary sliding cover of plywood having a large slot in its centre. This slot should extend to the full length of the hive so that a comb can be passed down through it. At an out-apiary, having found the queen of a strong stock, in order to make sure of not including her with the shaken bees, two or three combs of bees are shaken into the prepared hive, or swarm-box if we prefer to use one, by holding the combs down through the slot in the cover and giving them a sharp jerk or two. If the end of the top-bar should hit the floor it will be the more effectual, but care must be taken that the blow shall not be hard enough to crack the comb. It is better not to shake the bees from more than two or three combs of any one stock because one does not want to weaken the honey-getting colonies unduly; but if the job is done with circumspection very little harm will come of it. This process should be repeated several times, taking two or three combs of bees from each stock until we have accumulated a very large artificial queenless swarm. It will be found that if about fourteen combs are shaken (British standard size) it will be sufficient. Our shaken swarm is now taken to the breeding apiary and in the evening is allowed to fly and is given combs of honey and pollen and furnished with feeders as before described. It can be given the grafted larvae as soon as the bees show distress, when these will be readily accepted. Such a cell-building swarm will provide royal jelly in exactly the same manner as the bees that have their brood and queen taken from them.

This last plan is the one I like best when the season is getting late, and I find that these shaken swarms, if given a fertile queen when their cell-building usefulness is over, will, if well fed, build up into excellent wintering colonies. But they must have pollen combs given to them unless they have been able to gather and store a good deal of this before the close of the active season.

I have hit on another very good plan for getting late queen-cells built which often saves the bother of making these shaken swarms, a job that takes up a good deal of time. It is a common occurrence in August to have a few swarms issue with virgin queens. When all queens are clipped, as they must be on a honey-farm where out-apiaries are the rule, supersedure frequently causes a swarm to issue with a virgin if the stock be a strong one, as is usually the case at this season. Now while we lose some of these late swarms through their coming out after we have long ceased to carry out periodical examinations, we do usually find a few each year. This is partly because swarms issuing with virgins late in the year tend to hang longer, often for days, and partly because they frequently issue in wet weather, and getting wetted, are less inclined to move. Sometimes these swarms are very large and can be made to build a large number of very fine queen-cells which produce magnificent virgins that are usually able to mate satisfactorily as late as mid-September.

To make use of these swarms, they must be de-queened, and to do this, it is necessary to hive them just as they are and to leave them alone for forty-eight hours or so, after which the virgin must be hunted up and got rid of, for by that time there will seldom be more than one present. In any case, the virgin being killed, the bees will show distress within an hour if they have only the one. If they show no uneasiness it may be taken that there is still a queen with them and she must be caught. These swarms are treated in exactly the same way as the shaken bees, and will be found, if anything, better for our purpose. They will also make good wintering colonies if managed rightly.

Towards the end of the breeding season, about 1st August, the colonies that have been used through the summer to provide our drones must have their queens taken from them. These queens should not be destroyed, of course, as they are extra fine ones, but should be preserved in strong nuclei. The purpose of removing their queens from the drone-breeding stocks is, to keep the supply of drones in being so that those virgins which we rear in August and early September shall be able to mate satisfactorily, for unless they are de-queened, those colonies would make short work of their drones at the end of the natural breeding period.

Three or four days after the removal of the queens from these drone-breeding colonies, they may be given grafted larvae and will be found to rear a large number of excellent queen-cells for three weeks or so, after which they may either be allowed to rear queens themselves from the cells they have built, or may have a fertile queen given to them.

It is constantly asserted in the bee-press and elsewhere that queens from cells built in colonies that are fed with sugar syrup are inferior to those produced in colonies having only natural stores. Whether this is so or not, I do not know; but no positive evidence has so far come to my notice that proves the contention. There is no doubt that very good queens can be reared while the cell-building colony is being fed syrup, and I am afraid that this is one of those evils, if an evil it be, for which there is no remedy in a breeding apiary, because one must raise queens rather out of season if one is to rear enough of them, and to feed honey in a breeding apiary would be a very dangerous proceeding indeed. The whole question is difficult, but for my part I am satisfied to use sugar syrup and natural pollen at such times as I must, for I have reared hundreds of excellent queens while supplementing natural stores with sugar. Theoretically, the finest queens should be those reared in the flush of the honey-flow under the swarming impulse, and in fact such queens are hard to beat, but as we cannot rear all our queens under those conditions, we must just do the best we can.

To breed a considerable number of fine queens is impossible without sacrificing some really good stocks and much time and labour just at that season when we are busiest on a bee farm. To rear queens costs money as well: a considerable capital outlay being required for the plant. The principal expense, of course, is for the mating nucleus hives, the bees, and for a grafting room and an incubator, if one can be afforded. A good deal of sugar will be needed in poor seasons, too.

The Mating

When the queen-cells have been sealed over for about eight days the virgins will emerge, and by the sixth day the cells should be distributed to queenless nuclei so that they may emerge and fly to mate. If an incubator is used, however, they can be allowed to leave their cells in it by the use of nursery cages into which the cells have been inserted. The virgins are kept apart in these cages so that they cannot fight or get at occupied cells to kill the virgins in them. They can then be introduced to nuclei; but they should not be held in these nurseries for more than two or three days, I think, even if well supplied with suitable food and with a body-guard of workers.

When the virgins emerge in our nuclei, or are introduced as virgins, they should mate and be laying fertile eggs in around ten days, and may be used as needed a few days later. All of which sounds simple enough and very easy; but like so many things connected with bees is not entirely plain sailing. There are snags that the inexperienced are not prepared for, and I will try to point out some of them; but first I will describe the mating nucleus hives generally used, with special reference to those used in our own breeding apiary.

Theoretically, the smaller the nucleus the better, because it requires less material to make and less bees to stock it; but in our climate I feel sure that nothing is really gained by using anything smaller than British standard frames, or any nucleus that will not hold three of these and a dummy feeder. What are known as 'baby nuclei' of various patterns are nothing but a delusion and a snare. I have tried them and am satisfied that this is so. Folding frames and sectional frames of varied types such as are commonly advocated, and all such complicated nuisances should be avoided; but the use of shallow standard frames has some slight advantage in respect to cost, though this is, in my view, more than offset by the fact that they are not very satisfactory for wintering and must usually be united at the end of the breeding season.

The Sladen mating arrangement is about the best I have used other than my own; but it has serious faults. It is a square hive of British 'National' size, divided into three parts by sliding divisions. Each compartment takes three standard frames and the whole is provided with a metal feeder supplying all three compartments simultaneously, being filled from outside the hive through a small covered funnel. In practice, this feeder is almost useless, as it very soon gets blocked up with rubbish; dead earwigs, dust and

BREEDING BEES

dirt generally, and is very far indeed from hygienic. I have six of these mating hives in use; but have long since removed the feeders and now use only two combs in each compartment together with a dummy feeder. But queens mate from them very well.

My own plan, brought into use after many years of trial of various equipment, is as follows: the unit consists of a long-shaped hive divided into two equal parts permanently. Each of these halves is of the correct size to take nine standard frames with ordinary metal-end spacers, and is fitted with a division-board which slides in grooves to separate it into two, so that the whole provides four mating nucleus hives, each of which has an entrance on one side of the hive, the four entrances facing in different directions. These nucleus compartments will hold three standard frames and a dummy feeder each, and to commence with are set up in the usual way by taking combs of emerging brood and bees from stocks, and are in due course given a queen-cell each. We also use mating hives with two compartments with a movable division, as illustrated.

The stocking of mating nuclei is a rather tricky business, as bees, when moved from one hive to another in the same apiary, will return to their old home after flight, unless they are under the age when bees first fly from their hives. This difficulty may be got over in two ways: if a comb of brood about half of which has emerged, is taken, bees and all, and placed in the nucleus and the bees from two more combs are shaken in with it and the entrance stopped with a bunch of grass for twenty-four hours, it will be found that enough bees will be retained to cover the brood, and as young bees are continually emerging on the comb transferred, our nucleus is safely established from that time. It should be given a comb of stores and a queen-cell and left to itself for a week. Another plan that is good when we do not care to use many bees from our breeding apiary is to bring home combs of brood and bees from out-apiaries. These placed in our nuclei will stay put all right. Again, we may use a swarm to stock nuclei by first placing a comb of brood in each and then dipping a cupful or two of bees from the swarm into it. The swarm must, of course, be made queenless a short time before being used in this way, and before the bees are dipped into the nuclei, they should be sprayed with thin syrup to stop them from taking flight. Such nuclei of one comb of brood and one of stores, if given virgins or queen-cells soon have fertile queens. They are quite strong enough to start with and rapidly become much stronger if the young queen is allowed to lay for a few days.

Once formed, these nuclei are permanent, barring accidents, and are really very little trouble to maintain. At the close of the breeding season the pairs are united, one of each pair being allowed to retain its last queen. The pairs are united by pulling out the sliding division-board and leaving a dummy feeder between them for a day or two, after which the feeder is removed. In my experience they virtually always unite peaceably, provided that one nucleus has been deprived of its queen twenty-four hours before the amalgamation takes place. After uniting, two combs of stores are added to the six of the united pair, making eight in all, and feeding should be done for a time by filling the remaining dummy feeder about twice or three times a week. The dummy feeders we use are made from blocks of wood hollowed out with a morticing machine: they are the same thickness as a comb and will take the place of one. Thus, if I have made myself clear, it will be readily seen that each of our compound mating hives contains during winter two eight-comb stocks of bees with a dummy feeder in each.

About the third week in March we begin to feed these colonies, and find that it is usually possible to have them build up into strong little stocks by the beginning of May, and as soon as they reach the maximum strength that these small hives can accommodate, I make a nucleus with the queen from each. These nuclei can be sold or taken to another apiary and used to build up into honey-producing stocks. We now have remaining in each of the two halves of our mating hives four combs containing brood and stores, and these we divide into two nuclei by sliding the division boards down so as to leave two combs on each side. These divisions should be well greased with vaseline at their sliding edges, of course. The two nuclei tend to be rather uneven in strength, although both entrances have been open all the time, for the flying bees always use one much more than the other; but this soon rights itself, and we can assist matters by placing the oldest brood on the side where there are least bees. A dummy feeder and a third comb or frame of foundation is added and a queen-cell given next day.

The making up of the nuclei should be synchronized with the

cell-building so that when our nuclei are ready to take them, cells will be available. Nuclei will accept the cells twenty-four hours after being made up. If all goes well, we may have young queens laying in the nuclei about fourteen days later, and if each young queen is allowed to lay for four to six days before being removed, the nucleus will be self-maintaining so far as brood is concerned, but feeding will most likely be required at such times as no honey is being gathered. Foundation is added to make up the three combs, and this will soon be built out if there is a honey-flow or bees are fed well. I find, myself, that these nuclei, once established, usually require hardly any feeding during May, June, and July in moderately good seasons.

When the young fertile queen is removed, a queen-cell may be given the next day, and this will nearly always be accepted, whether feeding is being carried on or not, and irrespective of honey-flows, until late in the season, but it is better not to give very ripe cells, i.e. cells from which virgins are due to emerge in a few hours, because the bees are rather liable to kill the virgins as soon as they emerge in that case. Later on, especially towards the end of August, or in early September, feeding is really necessary when cells are given to nuclei, for unless fed the bees are very likely indeed either to destroy the cells at once, or to build cells on their own brood and to kill the virgin of the given cell as soon as she emerges. In fact it is well worth while to remove all self-reared cells before the given cell is due to hatch out, even when feeding is being done. Bees seem to sense that the cell introduced is alien and to prefer one of their own production, and it is worth while to take every precaution to prevent their destroying it, for it is extremely annoying, late in the year when cells are scarce, to have one of the specially raised virgins destroyed in favour of an inferior one reared in a small nucleus, possibly the progeny of a mis-mated queen. One advantage of giving ready-hatched virgins is that cell-destruction is avoided thereby.

Mischances

In queen-rearing things don't always go as smoothly as one could wish. Occasionally virgins are lost while flying, though this is not nearly as frequent an occurrence as is usually supposed. When it does happen, the nuclei, being left hopelessly queenless, are liable to produce laying workers, and these are real pests in a breeding apiary, making it rather difficult to have cells accepted by their nuclei, and producing drone-brood of altogether inferior type which must be completely destroyed before emergence.

Another trouble met with by the queen-rearer is the loss of virgins with mating swarms. These swarms are rather difficult to prevent in very hot weather when the nuclei have become too strong, for they are prone to hang out in bunches from their entrances. Now if a virgin should fly while such a cluster is hanging, the whole lot will sometimes join her and form a cluster on some bush nearby, in which case the bees never return to their hive, and if not found quickly, will eventually fly away as a small swarm. The way to stop this little game is to see that the nuclei do not become too strong. If each young queen, when fertile, is allowed to lay only for about four days it will usually be found that the nucleus will maintain itself at about the correct strength; but judgment must be used in this, and it is always a simple matter to give a comb of brood from an over-strong nucleus to one that is not strong enough. A good deal depends on the quickness of mating; the longer the interval between the removal of one queen and the commencement of laying by the next, the longer must the new queen be allowed to lay; but in no case is it of any use to allow a queen to remain longer, once she has supplied as much brood as the bees can cover.

Another trouble of the breeding apiary is robbing, the risk of which is obvious, with many of these weak colonies being fed as they must be. Feeding MUST be done at dusk, so that robbing is unlikely to begin. When the feeders are open dummy feeders that are quickly emptied, the syrup will be stored in the combs long before morning and there will be no robbery; but it should never be forgotten that these nuclei are very liable to be robbed if the beekeeper is not careful, for they are all small colonies, and many will always be in somewhat abnormal conditions; some queenless; some even broodless, and they are constantly being opened and upset.

I have found, quite by chance, a plan that goes a very long way to prevent this nuisance of robbing in the breeding apiary. Our buildings are situated in such a way that they surround the breeding apiary on two sides and I have found that if a little out-door feeding be carried on now and then through the spring and summer on the side of the buildings away from the hives, the bees will form the habit of keeping watch on this side of the buildings and the moment a drop of syrup is put there they are on it in a moment. Now should there be any upset in the breeding apiary on the other side of these buildings during feeding or otherwise, the bees instead of attacking some luckless nucleus, immediately hurry to their usual feeding ground and a very little syrup placed there will keep them busy until all is consumed, when they return home quietly. This has been very useful to us.

When we wish to remove a fertile queen from her nucleus, care is needed in catching her. I prefer to take her by the thorax, if possible, rather than to pick her up by her wings, but if lifted by the wings it is rather important, I think, to take hold of the wings on one side only, leaving her free to twist round. These newly-mated queens are very active, and when lifted by both pairs of wings they curl their bodies forward in such a way that the tip of the abdomen comes into contact with the hinder legs. Now when a queen is in this position her sting is almost always protruded and is rather liable to prick the leg which happens to contact it, and when this happens the queen frequently suffers. Usually little or no damage is done; but at times this self-stinging has serious results. So frequent has this occurrence been with me that I am now very cautious about picking up queens by their wings, especially newly-mated ones, for older queens do not struggle so much or twist about so violently, and I have no recollection of any queen other than a young one in a mating nucleus stinging herself.

When this does happen, the sting will sometimes hold firmly, so that the leg is tied to the abdomen. If this connection is not immediately broken I gently part the sting from the leg with a pair of clipping scissors or other pointed instrument. Sometimes, even when the sting has entered the leg or foot sufficiently to require such aid to release its hold, the queen after release, shows no sign of disturbance, and behaves as if nothing had happened; but she usually falls over and seems to be quite paralysed. All that can be seen to show that life still remains is a slight breathing movement and an occasional tremor of the antennae. Sometimes queens stung in this way die, but by far the greater part completely recover after a time, and seem none the worse. The length of time during which they lie inert before recovery or death, varies, but rarely lasts more than an hour and seldom more than thirty minutes. A self-stung queen that recovers, is as good as any queen whatever, so far as my experience goes, and I have used a good many, all of which have turned out perfectly satisfactory mothers.

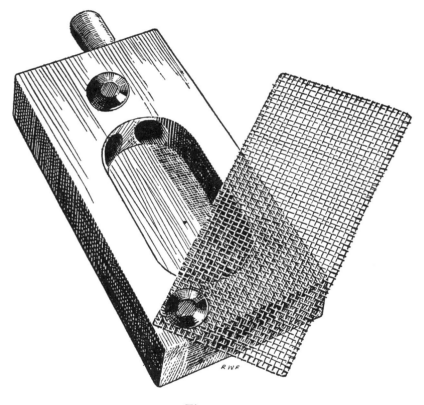

Figure 5

CAGE FOR CATCHING AND CARRYING QUEENS

First and last, I have not had more than three or four queens die of this mishap. If you do take up a queen by both pairs of wings, it is wise to hold her so that her legs can grasp something, a finger or anything whatever, so that she will not put her tail-end up to meet her feet.

For carrying fertile queens to apiaries we use a small home-made cage of which I give an illustration. It is made from a single piece of very soft wood, much as an ordinary mailing cage is made, but instead of having a hole at each end and a large food compartment, it has two rather long tunnels side by side at one end. One of these is filled with candy and the other is stopped with a wooden plug. When catching the queen and her escort, the plug is removed and the bees are run into the cage through the tunnel and the plug replaced.

Young queens that seem all right in appearance and that lay eggs correctly, occasionally turn out to be drone-breeders, or partially so. This may not be discovered until after such queens have been introduced into colonies, for it is only by the cappings that one can tell. It is therefore wise to keep a record of which nucleus has supplied the queen to any colony so that in case we find that the brood in the nucleus from which she has come is not satisfactory, we can destroy and replace her at once. Drone-breeding young queens have failed to mate with any drone; but those which produce a mixture of drone and worker larvae in worker comb have probably mated with immature drones, or with drones that are the progeny of laying workers. In rare cases a young queen will lay either all drone eggs or a mixture of drone and worker eggs for a short time and after that become normal. I have had one such case; but in the main it is best to destroy any young queen whose brood does not show the characteristic compact appearance of all-worker cappings.

On very rare occasions queens will mate, assume the appearance of fertile queens that are laying, but never produce an egg. The cause is probably some physical defect that prevents egg-laying. Such queens are useless.

I have known a queen to mate on 30th June, and still retain the organs of the drone on 4th July. There was certainly no second mating. The drone attachment disappeared after that time and the queen turned out to be a normal mother.

Queens returning from mating are sometimes stung on their legs. It is difficult to account for this, but there is no doubt of the fact. When a sting enters a leg joint, the limb becomes totally paralysed and withers up, being either dragged during the rest of the queen's life or lost altogether, presumably being broken off. One of the four anterior legs may be spoiled without much apparent inconvenience to the queen, and I have seen many queens live out their lives normally when so injured; but when the withered limb is one of the hinder pair, although the queen will as a rule lay normally and as well as any other queen, the bees are likely to supersede her before long. Of course, in the ordinary way, it is best to replace injured queens as soon as possible, except when a queen is very badly needed and no other is available, or when the injured queen is an unusually good one.

Why a sting from a worker should destroy a queen's leg while a self-sting has no such effect, I cannot guess; but such is the fact. Maybe self-elaborated poison has less power over its producer than over others. I don't know whether when a queen is stung on the leg by a worker she becomes temporarily paralysed or not, as I have never seen a worker sting a queen, though I have many times seen the dried-up sting fixed in the queen's leg. I imagine that if a queen is stung on the body by a worker she dies, but I don't know. This would account for the disappearance of queens that are expected to mate, which sometimes happens, for it does not seem likely that stinging of a queen is confined to her legs when her body presents so much larger an object.

The balling or stinging of young queens on their return from mating is quite common, and is not very easy to account for. I have seen the thing happen several times. The queens are rarely interfered with by the bees when returning from flight previous to successful mating, in fact they are often no more noticed by the workers as they pass in or out than if they were drones or other workers; but every now and then a queen carrying the organs of the drone is attacked on entering her nucleus and is frequently crippled and occasionally killed altogether. The fools of bees throw her body out and then kick up a most awful fuss because they have lost their queen. One gives them a queen-cell and they have to bring another along. I have noticed that this trouble is more common with nuclei that have been rather newly made up with emerging brood and young bees. I have wondered if this unbalancing of the colony may have something to do with it.

A good deal has been said at one time and another about injury that a queen may sustain through having her wings clipped, some profess horror at what they call a 'barbarous practice'! Of course if she should be roughly handled she may be damaged, but that is not what is implied; but rather that the cutting of the wing tissues must cause injury through bleeding and shock. Well, there is some bleeding when a wing is cut, but unless the amputation is made close to the body, I am sure that the alleged injury is imaginary. I have my own opinions on the proper way to clip, and like so many more of my notions, they are not the same as they used to be, and they are not orthodox. I think that clipped queens may be very slightly more difficult to introduce to alien colonies than unclipped; but the advantage of the latter over a properly clipped queen is extremely slight. There is not much doubt, however, that a queen having her wings on one side clipped down hard, say two-thirds of their length taken off, is really more likely to be rejected in introduction, and is more liable to be superseded than a normal queen. I myself have taken to removing about one-third of the long wings on both sides with a single scissors cut which usually takes just the tip off the short wings as well, but sometimes misses these altogether. Queens so treated do not seem to be objected to by the bees at all, and are virtually never superseded. It may be nonsense, but I have a feeling that it may be the asymmetry of the wings when cut on one side only that motivates the instinctive action of supersedure. Queens with one back leg gone are usually superseded, so why not queens with one wing cut off? I know, of course, that this does not meet with the approval of many experts and authorities, on the ground that a queen so treated can sometimes fly a little way. So she can, but only a few yards, which is not altogether inconvenient, sometimes, on a bee farm. Herrod-Hempsall strongly advocates cutting the wings on one side only, and the removal of two-thirds of their length, but immediately after this he says that he does not recommend clipping because queens mutilated in this way are liable to be superseded; but since the removal of one-third of one wing will effectually prevent flight, why cut off more?

Another bother in breeding apiaries is that of freak bees of various kinds. On rare occasions you will have a young queen that produces extremely yellow and very small workers. I cannot imagine the cause; but this is one of those curious things that do happen in queen-rearing. Such queens must be killed, for they may produce dwarf drones later on: I have never kept one to see. Then there will be every now and then, maybe once in five or six years, a queen that breeds what are known as gynandromorphs, or, less accurately, hermaphrodites. These are bees that through some genetic mix-up are partly male and partly female in structure. You may find worker bodies with drone heads, or vice versa; or the body may be divided between the sexes in other ways. These monsters are interesting to the biologist, but to the queen-breeder they are anathema, and the queens that produce them should be got rid of at once. Some queens will produce these freaks by hundreds, and it is only such that are a nuisance. One may see an occasional freak bee without needing to worry about it.

Introduced virgins are much more liable to be balled when returning from flight; so don't open their nuclei for about ten days after safe introduction. It is all right to open the day after releasing them, but not, apparently, after they begin to fly.

Very small virgins should be destroyed; but it requires some judgment to say just where the dividing line comes. Of course, ill-nourished dwarfs are always to be rejected on sight, but short fat virgins that look very small are often really good, so don't destroy these. In fact, to judge the probable quality of either virgin or fertile queen by look is difficult. Very large queens are sometimes poor in performance, while I have had very small ones do well. Cell building varies greatly with the strain of bee. Italians tend rather to build smallish cells, and in some cases very small indeed, while Carniolans build their cells like great acorns; but the virgins that come from them are much of a size.

Italian bees are not very good for cell-building because this variety, when of a good strain, tends to construct very few cells for swarming and is reluctant to build many when we are asking them to do it: Dutch, on the other hand will build cells by the score. I once took seventy-eight from quite a small stock! Generally speaking the more a strain is inclined to swarm the more cells they will build for us, and conversely.

What are now so regretfully referred to by some people as 'the good old English Blacks' were good in some ways, but not in others. They are extinct now, I suppose, so *de mortuis nil nisi bonum.* But as I remember them, it seems to me that those who extol their memory might be none too pleased if they had to use them to-day. They made very good sections and used little propolis. They consumed very little food in winter. This, by the way, is the reason for the orthodox thirty pounds for winter stores. The old blacks really would live from flow to flow on that. They were very nervous, and would sometimes almost clear right out of the hive when smoked. The crops of honey they gave were rather small as we should think to-day.

The pure race I liked next after Italians, but coming a long way behind in my affection, were Caucasian bees—the grey kind. These wintered on very little, came through as quite small colonies and built up more rapidly than any other kind I have had to do with. They swarmed to no great extent, and no more than Italians, I think. They made some very good sections, but with rather thick cappings, although these were white and not without the air-space. Good selling combs, but not up to exhibition. They put about a pound of propolis into each hive, binding down the frames to the floor all along the front of the hive, but not using very excessive amounts elsewhere. They had one fault that I could not tolerate at all. While pure, they were the easiest bees I ever handled, but their crosses were, some of them, the most vicious brutes I have ever had to put up with. So I 'liquidated' them. Some people seem to get on with them, but I didn't.

Italians and their crosses for me every time. You know, whether we like or not, we have most of us to use cross-bred bees, and the Italian crosses are the best crosses in my opinion. My counsel is to aim at pure 3-banded leather-coloured Italian bees of a good strain. You won't hit the bull's eye every time by a very long way, but you may come near it even when you miss. All over the world honey producers use Italians and it would be foolish to suppose that they do it because these bees have pretty coloured tails. More people use Italians than you would think likely. I remember when I was younger and more innocent than I fear I am now, I was much surprised on visiting the apiary of one of our notables who was never tired of holding up for our admiration the great qualities of the English blacks, to find all or nearly all the hives stocked with Italians, and very yellow ones at that.

I do not claim to know all about this interesting problem of breeding bees; in fact it will be clear enough to all who may read what I have set down here that I have a lot to learn; but I do know something about it: enough, anyway, to show me what a lot more there is to it. I am keen to learn always; but there are so many difficulties one runs against that short-cuts to knowledge have not come my way. I have myself had to learn chiefly by trial and error, but it may be that some who read this may be helped, if only through seeing my mistakes. Breeding bees is not simple and easy, though one might suppose so who only read the 'slick' writings of those who really do know all about it, you know. It is a work of great interest and considerable difficulty, and the most important branch of honey farming and beekeeping. There is no doubt that any one of us beekeepers can greatly improve the stock with which we have to do if only we are prepared to go to some trouble and to overcome obstacles. It requires patience and perseverance; but it is really the mastering of difficulties that makes life interesting, and the beekeeper who sets out to breed an ideal strain of bees will not find the enterprise monotonous.

CHAPTER VI

THE PASSING SEASONS

I think all of us who have lived by any sort of production from the land must realize how great an advantage we have in being constantly in contact with Nature. To me this is what makes out-door life so interesting. Farming, gardening, fruit-growing, bee-keeping, all these ways of living have an attraction for those who are adapted for that kind of life. Some people hate it, and I have had men toy with the idea of running a honey farm for a time who have soon shown by their attitude that they would never make bee farmers. They don't want their feet on the soil; they don't care to face the elements; they want to be able to control every side of their business. This is all quite understandable. I once knew a young man who thought of starting up in our line, and who had good business ability, enough capital, and plenty of energy; but I knew almost from the start that it would come to nothing. He was interested in bees in a way; but what he was almost entirely out for was profit. And you can't get profit just like that. He said he could not stand it because in beekeeping you are always worrying about the weather. There you have it. Bees pay well, but you have to take a long view and have faith and patience. Same with all businesses that are concerned with production from the land.

But to the man with the right psychological bent, it is just this uncertainty that lends the charm to the thing. Besides, if you who read this are in the least like me that way, which I think you must be if you are to get any good from beekeeping, the out-door life and the scenes that are continually changing as the wheel of Nature turns, are of enormous interest.

> *Autumn to winter, winter into spring,*
> *Spring into summer, summer into fall,*
> *So rolls the changing year.*

If you go in for honey production for your living, you must be prepared for extremely aggravating behaviour on the part of the weather; but it's not a scrap of use to worry: you just have to take what comes and try your best to be thankful it is no worse. No one can tell me anything about that, I'm sure. You have to remember that in our country most of the fine, settled weather comes in the winter, and at that time bees take little advantage from a spell of fine weather. The time when honey is supposed to be plentiful and we are supposed to be sweltering in a heat-wave is nearly as often as not, cold, wet, and windy. Sometimes all our honey comes in May; sometimes in August; often July gives no good yield— very often. June is supposed to be the height of the honey season, but it very often isn't. All we can do is to keep everything going in good order so that when Nature smiles we are all ready for her.

We generally reckon that the bee-man's year begins with September, but in actual practice, we shall find that no sharp line of division can be drawn between summer and autumn. We shall see in Chapter XI how the honey is harvested, and it should be all off the hives by September. That is, all but heather honey, which will seldom be harvested before about the middle of that month. The year for each colony, we may quite correctly say, begins the day after its supers have been finally taken off. When supers have been removed from an apiary it is time to begin autumn operations, and we should go to our apiaries as soon as this has been done.

The harvest is all in; hives are stripped of supers and look curiously squat and unfamiliar at first. It seems a real relief to be able to open them up without first having to take off the supers, and we must now start a proper examination of each colony to see how the food situation stands, especially if there has been no late honey-flow. It is not uncommon to find stocks with hardly any honey when this has been the case, particularly those that have had very prolific queens and have given heavy crops of honey. This is especially the case when the brood-chamber has been limited to ten or twelve British standard frames, and is even found to be so, sometimes, when the larger Dadant hive is used. If the queen has occupied almost the whole comb-area during the height of the season, and no honey-flow has occurred since then of sufficient volume to do more than meet the current requirements of the bees, the brood-combs will contain little or no honey.

Some beekeepers manage their bees on the double-brood-chamber system, and in that case there will generally be quite a lot of honey in the two chambers; but I'm afraid the temptation to take the top one away and extract the honey is too much for a great majority of them. You see, in a poor season, if both these bodies of combs are left for the bees, there will often be little or nothing for the bee-man, and he can't stand that. So the hive is shorn down to one brood-chamber, and the immediate problem is feeding, unless the bees are to be starved. When shallow frames are used with ordinary British ten-frame hives, you will do well to leave one super on the hive and keep it there all the winter. I don't like this plan, but when only shallow supers are used, it is better than letting the bees starve; but if you must starve your bees to death through grabbing almost all the honey and neglecting to feed them, better far destroy the bees and take the whole of it. In this way you will get some for yourself, and you may as well kill the bees at once as leave them to starve to death some time during the winter. You can't have it both ways, you know; if you take honey out of a hive when there is not enough in it to keep the bees, you might as well take the lot and be done, unless you are ready to feed about double the weight of sugar back for winter. Some people seem to forget that the more they take away the less there is left; as the Duchess said to Alice, 'The moral of that is, "The more there is of mine, the less there is of yours".'

Early Feeding

So the first autumn job is to supply stores to all stocks that need help, in order that they shall not starve quickly, or even be short of stores of liquid food. Bees on the verge of starvation are apt to restrict their breeding, and although I don't believe in what is called 'stimulative feeding' either in spring or autumn, it is certainly wise, I think, to see to it that ample food is present right through from the removal of supers. Of course, bees do sometimes get a little honey in September; but it is rare for them to get more than a negligible quantity, except where heather yields. One can manage this food supply either by giving combs of sealed honey or by feeding sugar syrup, and there is no question in my mind that the latter is the correct procedure, because food given by feeding syrup at this early season will be stored well and sealed securely, making it as nearly equal to honey as it is possible for sugar syrup to be, whereas if we give sealed honey, the bees will use this up quite soon and it will not then be available to them for winter stores and for spring supplies.

September is the best month for feeding bees up for winter, and if possible we should get right on with this job as soon as the month is in. Feeding earlier than September should be looked upon as simply a necessary proceeding when there is a serious shortage of stores which might injure the colony, for early autumn feeding is very apt to result in too heavy breeding and consequent consumption of the syrup fed, which makes it necessary to begin feeding all over again in the middle of September. I have in years gone by had to feed to avert starvation quite early in August, and thinking that I might as well save time by completing the feeding while I was about it, have fed enough sugar to, as I thought, carry the bees through until the following spring, with the result that I have had to feed all over again in October. That is how we learn.

Re-queening

At the first examination of the colonies after harvest is the time to see about re-queening where necessary. If young queens are not ready just then we must make a note of which colonies want new mothers, so that we can introduce these without any loss of time when they are to be had. All queens that have proved at all unsatisfactory in any way should be listed. In my case a reference to the record books will give the data in most cases, but unbooked undesirables are often found. There are several important faults that must be taken into consideration when deciding about whether a queen ought to be superseded or not, and if we can't get enough young queens to replace all those that we would like to get rid of, why, we must replace the worst first, so that if any have to be left alone, they will at any rate be the least objectionable. The queens that should be replaced without fail are all those that head colonies that have shown any sign of paralysis or abortive (addled) brood. All those whose colonies have for no clear reason given distinctly poorer yields of honey than the average of the apiary in which they are situated. All those whose workers are nervous, excitable ('runners', we call them), for such bees are nothing but a nuisance. All those whose workers are excessively vicious: called 'wicked' bees in Ireland and 'cross' bees in U.S.A.

Now we come to a more debatable question. I always used to

systematically replace all those mothers that had served two full seasons in a honey-producing colony. I used to say that we ought never to hold a two-year-old queen for a third term of office unless she is a very specially good one required for use as a breeder next year, when she might be tolerated until spring, or even allowed to head the stock into summer; but even in this case I used to think it best to give her to a nucleus, and to introduce a young queen to her stock. This advice is, I think, good on the whole, but I am sure that it is necessary to modify it a bit. It is true that these old queens are rather liable to fail in their third year, and I suppose it is hardly necessary to say that nothing but the very best should be carried over, but when we come to those very best, I have come round to the view that they must be left. Some will fail us, of course, but unless we give them a chance, how are we to know whether they have stamina for three years' work or not? And I have found that some at least of these very good queens will do as well in their third year as in their second; but these are few and far between with me, as yet. Still, if they are bred from, they should improve the stock very much.

I have never had a queen that gave a good account of herself in her fourth year; in fact I have never had a queen that lasted through her fourth summer in a honey-producing stock. All those that have lasted through their third summer with me have either been superseded by August or have become so obviously worn out and feeble that I have replaced them.

This is the place to mention that when you have seen some thousands of queens of all ages, you get to be able to judge pretty well by her appearance how much vigour is left in a queen. The queen that is breaking down has a very distinctive look. I think the best way to describe it is to say she looks shabby and dull. She has lost the strong, active movement that is the hallmark of a queen in her full vigour, however old. Don't attempt to winter any queen like that; and if you decide to re-queen any such, mind what you are about, for there is very often a virgin in the same hive with her. How long queens live in the most favourable circumstances I am not sure. It is said that in some rare cases a queen has been known to live for six years, and it has even been claimed that one has reached her ninth year, a regular Methuselah among queens; but I don't know that I quite believe it. At all events, you and I will do well not to rely on our queens reaching any such ages as these: our queens will be pretty sure to go the way of all bees long before that, and we should act accordingly.

Supersedure

I think that this will also be a good place to mention supersedure. This is quite a common action of bees, and every autumn we find, on a good-sized bee farm, that young queens are present in colonies where, according to the register, we should expect to find old ones. Supersedure seems to be a more or less normal instinct. It has even been said that every queen would be superseded if she were left alone by the beekeeper. This is certainly not the case, however, as I know from my own experience. I expect, all the same, that a big majority of queens would be superseded if left to grow old. This instinctive act by bees is a capital thing when it is successfully effected. A really successful supersedure should take place at or soon after the close of the honey-flow, and what happens is this: while the old queen (she need not necessarily be very old, or even worn out, for I have known quite young queens to be superseded) is still laying well, and is showing no sign of decrepitude, a queen-cell, or more often two or three queen-cells, are built and from one of these a virgin emerges, mates, and commences to lay eggs while the old queen is still present. That is supersedure *par excellence*. The young queens so bred are generally good, and the re-queening is done without any bother at all: I only wish it occurred oftener.

But supersedure does not always come off quite so nicely as that. Bees often postpone it until their queen is laying practically all drone-producing eggs, or until the season has advanced so far that the young queens fail to mate. They very frequently omit it altogether, and then, if the old queen dies during the winter when no brood is in the hive, we have a 'dud' stock in spring. Good queens can only be reared in favourable circumstances, as I have pointed out in Chapter V, and unless supersedure should take place when the conditions are favourable, poor queens will be the inevitable result.

Now when a colony is headed by a queen that has passed through two summers in a honey-producing stock, we naturally take particular notice of the mother concerned, for in about two cases out of three she will not be fit to undertake maternal duties through another season. If she is not one of those extra good ones I have mentioned, we ought to replace her. But supposing that supersedure has already taken place, how are we to know it? There may be a virgin present, as well as the old queen; there may be a young laying queen. How can one be sure? Well, you can't be *sure*, especially in the case of a virgin, and there will always be this small risk in replacing two-year-olds.

There is, however, one fortunate circumstance that in very many cases has served to avert the disastrous consequences that follow the introduction of a young fertile queen into a colony where a virgin or fertile queen has already established herself. If there are eggs present, there is a queen. In nineteen cases in twenty, when you have found the queen she will be the only one in the hive; but if there are two, and if queens are always kept clipped, a glance shows whether the found queen is the old one or another. If unclipped and obviously fertile, we may just forget it and write in our record that that stock has a current year's queen by supersedure; but if the queen we find is clipped, it is wise to look carefully over the comb she is on, and over the two combs on each side of it, for if there is another fertile queen present she will almost always be on one of those three combs; in fact, of all the scores of cases in my experience where two queens, both fertile, have been present in the same stock, I can hardly remember one case in which the two were not close together on the same comb, or else one on each of two comb-surfaces that face one another. The commonness of this occurrence is shown by the number of published photographs of two queens almost in contact on the same comb. This is not nearly so general in the case of virgins, but when these are in question, unless they are seen by chance, the given queen will be lost. It is of no use looking for hypothetical virgins.

At this point I must refer to one thing I usually do at the end of July. I make increase every year by removing from colonies that are strong and can spare it, one comb of brood with the adhering bees, as described in Chapter VII. If there is not already a dummy in the hives so treated, one should be inserted now, and this is a good time to place a bottle of methyl salycilate in position, as described in Chapter XII. As the dummy will not entirely fill the space made by removing a comb, the whole of the remaining combs are pried over a little towards the dummy with a hive-tool, so that most of the space formerly occupied by the removed comb will be filled. This is quite a good thing, for it follows that the outside comb, farthest away from the dummy, will be spaced well away from the hive wall during winter, and this helps to keep the comb from getting damp, in case the hive side should become so, as is sometimes the case.

At this time of year we are now making it a rule to introduce methyl salycilate into all our hives. We lift out the dummy and set a bottle of this material on the floor of the hive at the rear corner, and replace the dummy, which, as will be shown in Chapter XII, has a recess or notch cut out of its lower corner. If flat tins are used for methyl salycilate, this is the time to put them on the floors of all hives.

In the case of Modified Dadant hives, I am not at all sure that it will not turn out a sound plan to work the hives constantly with ten combs and a dummy instead of eleven combs, and in any case there is certainly no need for eleven combs in these hives at any time except the summer.

There is one method that can be employed to re-queen colonies that have really good, but old queens; queens, that is to say, that are quite desirable breeders. I have used it many and many a time, and have rarely had any occasion to regret it. Just remove the old queen at the close of July or early in August. About six days later examine all the combs with care. You will find queen-cells; sometimes a great many; sometimes only very few. You will very likely find some sealed or almost sealed. Destroy every one of these, and all others, if possible, except one or two that are unsealed and lavishly stocked with royal jelly. Forget all about it for three weeks, when, if you examine the combs, you will almost always find a very fine queen laying. If you care to remove one or two of the cells just before they are due to hatch, you can make use of them in mating nuclei or otherwise. I have found such queens very good; but it is necessary to see to it that only selected unsealed cells are allowed to mature.

Feeding for Winter

Apart from emergency feeding, mentioned early in this chapter, there is no time like September for the general feeding up of all colonies that are judged not to have enough stores to winter on, and the sooner we get on with this job the better. If there is any serious shortage of stored honey in the brood combs, feeding will be a long and heavy job; a dirty, sticky task, which must be carried on in all weathers. I think every bee farmer must hate it. I do, anyway, and aim to get it over just as soon as ever I can. In small garden apiaries, where the owner is living close to his bees, stocks can be fed about a quart of syrup every day or every alternate day until enough is stored. That is the ideal way of getting bees into winter quarters in good order; but one can't possibly do that on a large farm where the bees are scattered about in different places miles from home.

All feeders for use on a bee farm of any size must be so made that the syrup can be poured into them from a honey tin; at least, that is what I think. And another thing—you need a large number of feeders so that a great many stocks can be fed at one time. Some large honey farmers carry the syrup round to the bees in a large tank mounted on a lorry and run it off into cans at the apiaries. We fill it right away into 28-lb. honey tins at home and carry it to the bees in these. It seems to us to be less trouble and labour, and is certainly less expensive, I think. But opinions differ. In pouring the syrup from the tins into the feeders, full tins should not be used as this causes waste of sugar and makes a mess through splashing. One empty tin should be carried, and the first tin of syrup partly emptied into it, after which it will pour well. This avoids making a mess on the hive sides to attract robbers, which is important in September, particularly so if we are introducing queens in the apiary, because robbing bees are excited, and excited bees will very often kill a queen that is being given to them.

Making syrup is a very simple process, but different bee-men have different ways of doing it. Some use large tanks and heat the water in independent boilers, which is convenient, and if the boiler is a fixture, set up for other purposes as well, it may be the best plan; but whether it would be profitable to set up such a plant solely for making syrup I rather doubt; however, hot water is useful for many purposes on a bee farm central plant. Here, we are all behind the times, I am afraid, for we make all our syrup in a 20-gallon boiler, using wood as fuel, and this is how we do it: seven gallons of water are put into the boiler, and as soon as it boils we shoot a 1-cwt. bag of sugar into it and stir well until the sugar has all dissolved and the resulting syrup is clear and transparent. The syrup is then dipped out into 28-lb. tins (with handles to them) until only about a gallon is left in the boiler. Then another seven gallons of water is poured in and the process repeated. One man can dissolve from fifteen to twenty hundredweights of sugar in a day.

If thymol is used for autumn feeding it should be added to the syrup just before filling the tins, which should have their lids put on immediately. I need hardly say that the thymol must be well stirred into the syrup. The addition of thymol to syrup for winter stores was first, I think, recommended by the late Dr. Killick. I have a long letter that he wrote to me about this in which he explained his reasons for advising the use of this substance. He considered that the bees were able to transform thymolized syrup into a food more nearly approximating to honey than is the case with plain sugar and water; but I really believe that its principal value is due to its power to prevent the growth of ferments. Syrup that has had a minute amount of thymol added to it will not ferment, and when there is any likelihood at all of any syrup fed to bees being left unsealed, I think it is a very good thing to use thymol. I once hid a 28-lb. tin of thin syrup containing thymol in a hedge near some bees, intending to feed it at my next visit: I forgot all about it, and it was only found after eighteen months: it was then perfectly good; there was not the slightest sign of fermentation, and that syrup was fed to the bees then and there.

The use of thymol has been condemned by some writers in the bee-press, who have given hair-raising accounts of the dreadful things that follow feeding it to bees; but I am bound to say that although I have fed thymol in my syrup for six or seven years, it has done my bees no harm whatever, and it has been of some assistance, in my opinion at all events, in helping bees to winter well. I propose to continue its use until there shall appear to be some reason for not doing so. Of course, if one could always feed slowly, a pint or two a day, the ferment trouble would not arise, but in bee farming on any scale it is not possible to do this, and heavy feeding does sometimes result in leaving some stores unsealed in the outer combs, in which they are liable to ferment. A slight addition of thymol will quite prevent this. Thymol is made up and used as follows: dissolve one ounce of thymol crystals in five fluid ounces of surgical alcohol. Use half a fluid ounce of this mixture to 112 lbs. sugar in seven gallons of water.

One must use judgment as to the amount of syrup to be given; but it is always better to give too much rather than too little. There is no use in overdoing it, however, though I believe we may largely discount the gruesome stories of the result of overfeeding with what Herrod-Hempsall calls 'artificial food'. It is true that if you are foolish enough to restrict your bees to ten British frames during the season when supers are off the hives, you have to choose between insufficient stores and too little brood, for the simple reason that there is not room for enough of both in such a brood-chamber. It is the old problem of making two plus two come to five. I don't know exactly what the solution of this difficulty is in the orthodox circles of beekeeping: I suppose, however, that this determination to fit a quart into a pint pot accounts for the almost universal use of candy in winter and for advocacy of black bees that don't need much winter stores. The tradition of the elders in this country is that bees need thirty pounds of stores for winter, and like the Ironsides of Oliver, these people are apparently ready to 'prove their religion orthodox by apostolic blows and knocks', and the bees come off second best.

The late John Anderson used to say that bees need eighty pounds or more of stores. I don't for one moment think that there would come any harm to the bees if every stock had as much as that in its combs at the beginning of winter, provided there were enough combs to hold it, and also to receive the brood that would be reared on it during the following spring. I have never owned a stock myself that had too much stores—for the bees; but to leave eighty pounds of honey for winter is entirely unnecessary and it would hardly be profitable to leave so much. At least, I think so. Still, there is no doubt that heavily stored colonies go ahead in spring at a great rate and get extremely strong quite early, which sounds all right: but does it pay the owner to have such stocks? In some seasons, when the flow comes abnormally early, and in very early districts, I expect it does; but I don't think it would pay the average bee farmer in the average district. You know, it's a curious thing, perhaps, but almost every first-class honey season I have had in my time has followed a bad winter for bees, when colonies have come through weak and have taken until June to build up to full strength. Of course we should try to have our bees come through the winter in good order, but the rather disconcerting fact remains that when they come out extra well, there is more often than not a short crop of honey. Anderson was one authority; but there are others who think quite differently. Probably, after all, the bees themselves are the best authority for us to follow. They say (to me at all events) that they like to have about fifty pounds of stores in a hive that contains at least 50 per cent more comb area than is provided by ten British standard frames. That is what my bees have been telling me for about thirty years, and I believe them.

There is really no satisfactory way of estimating the amount of stores in any hive other than by making an examination of the combs. If you know pretty much what the hive weighs and what the combs in it are like, and how much pollen there is in them, you can guess fairly accurately how the food situation stands; but this is necessarily an unreliable method. It is much better to look inside. Of course you may find hives so heavy that there is obviously enough food; otherwise examine combs. And don't forget that *a little honey stored over a lot of pollen may be very deceiving*. If you will take a number of stored brood-combs in September and extract them, you will probably be greatly surprised, if you are at all inexperienced, at how little honey you get out of them, and I recommend this experiment to all beginners, just once.

In most cases, probably forty to fifty pounds of sealed liquid stores, in addition to five or six pounds of sound pollen stored under it, will carry a good healthy colony through an average English winter from October to April inclusive, and most stocks of brown or Caucasian bees will be safe enough on much less. Italian bees do undoubtedly require more winter stores than the dark-coloured bees, but I think they also give a larger money profit, so I don't mind about the extra bit of food. I believe that about 80 per cent of all the bees wintered in this country, and very likely in other countries too, do not really have enough stores in their combs, when they are finally settled for the winter, to carry them through until the earliest honey-flow in spring, for, in spite of the lines we have all heard so often, spring is generally a good deal farther behind than the average beekeeper is apt to calculate on.

When you are feeding your bees, remember that it is the weight of the *sugar* that counts: it is of no use to feed thirty pounds of syrup and imagine that your bees have stored away thirty pounds of stores in their combs. This is an illusion that not only beginners, but quite old hands are sometimes caught by. The water does not count at all: I doubt if more than two-thirds of the sugar counts either, as winter stores, for some is consumed in producing wax for sealing the fed syrup, and some for the extra brood that feeding always causes bees to raise. In fact there are times when hardly half of the sugar fed is actually stored as winter food. This is especially so when feeding is done in August, or when the syrup is given in little daily doses, continuing for some time. It is not really wasted, of course: it is turned into young bees, but it is not there for winter and spring food supplies. I have many times known twenty or thirty pounds of thick syrup fed in August to be completely consumed by the end of September.

In autumn feeding the rule should be to feed plentifully if the bees require it, but there is no use in overfeeding; in fact, with ten-comb standard hives one may even feed to such an excess that the brood-nest may be temporarily choked and the queen checked in her laying; but I don't believe that this temporary check is harmful unless it takes place so late in the year that, there being little comb area occupied by brood, the combs become solid blocks of syrup. This is bad for the bees, for they need open cells inside the cluster. This cannot happen while breeding is going on, no matter how fast or heavy the feeding may be, because bees never displace brood in favour of stores, and as soon as feeding begins a queen always expands her brood-nest. Very little harm ever comes of feeding in that way; but whether beekeepers as a body have got to be too reliant upon sugar as food for bees is a question that has been very seriously raised of late. I rather incline to the opinion that it is a true bill. I think that pure sugar-syrup makes a very good substitute for honey as food for bees during that part of the year when they do not breed, or breed very little; in fact there can, I think, be very little doubt that good syrup is better for bees at that season than a good many kinds of honey. Heather honey, for example, as I know by my own experience, is a poor winter food unless the season happens to be a very mild one. Good honey is the best of all food for bees when it keeps liquid, and when I say 'good' honey, I mean good in the sense that it is of such a nature that it does not tend either to granulate in the hive or to put extra strain on the digestive tracts of the bees, as heather honey seems to do.

In some districts, mine for one, where charlock and other flowers of the *cruciferae* family are plentiful, a good deal of the honey stored granulates solid, causing waste in consumption through the rejection by the bees of the coarser crystals, which they appear to be unable to use in the winter. Probably the best kind of stores in such localities, or possibly in any district, would consist of twenty pounds or so of good sealed syrup, fed over twenty or thirty pounds of honey and five or six pounds of pollen, and there is an advantage in having even more food in any hive if it can be managed.

Preparing Stocks for Winter

When all our bees have been sufficiently fed and all feeders have been removed and stored away, we are ready to arrange the hives for winter. In reasonably dry situations the roof is lifted off and across the inner cover are laid two quarter-inch plaster laths and the roof is replaced. If the roof happens to be a shallow one, under five inches deep, a string is tied right over the hive to hold it on; otherwise, nothing more is needed, except to fasten some sort of guard across the entrance to keep out mice. We use a strip of perforated zinc fastened by two drawing-pins in such a way that its bottom edge is low enough to prevent a mouse from entering, while still being high enough to allow bees to remove their dead without hindrance.

This is all I do now. It sounds very shocking, I dare say, after all the talking and writing about how bees require to be insulated, packed, and wrapped up snug and warm to keep in the heat that the cluster generates; but I have been wintering bees quite a long time now, and wintering them in considerable numbers. I have tried every imaginable kind of packing and protection except actually putting the hives into a cellar: I have spent, I suppose, hundreds of pounds on it—and—well, I have to get my living out of my bees or else starve, and I winter them as above.

About one year in twenty in this country we have a winter that might justify packing, but capital cannot profitably be employed for a purpose restricting its usefulness to 5 per cent of the time. In the great majority of British winters, I think bees winter best unpacked in any way. I don't think it would pay me to pack them.

In countries having a continental type of climate, such as the northern United States and Canada, where winters are very severe, where long spells of bitter frost are the rule, and where the temperature falls far below zero, steps must be taken to protect the bees in order that they may be able to move on the combs to follow up their winter stores as these are consumed, for unless they can do that, they cannot live for very long. I have little doubt that the ideal plan in such climates would be found in properly built cellars, electrically ventilated, wherein the temperature would be automatically controlled by a thermostat; but no such thing is needed in our equable clime. Of course cellars are used in the northern States, and many other troublesome methods, and still their losses are very heavy in some years, and too heavy in all. It only shows what a wonderful country they have for honey, over there, when we consider that, in spite of these troubles, they do make money, even at the low prices their product brings on the market.

Our advantages from this view-point are great, but we lose too many bees in Britain in winter all the same. I don't believe that one stock in five hundred that dies during winter here is lost from the direct effect of cold weather. Starvation and disease are the principal causes of such losses, with queenlessness as a good third. Starvation is usually brought about by carelessness or ignorance on the part of the beekeeper in allowing his colonies to start the winter without enough stores to last them until spring, but may be caused in other ways.

On bee farms that are well managed losses from starvation are very small, and when bees do starve it is virtually always through excessive food consumption caused by irritation of acarine mite infestation, or by unsuitable stores causing indigestion, or else through depletion of stores by wasps, or even robber bees. Both wasps and bees will sometimes, quite late in the fall, after the bees have clustered in most colonies, practise a kind of furtive robbery without attracting the notice of the robbed bees.

It may be objected that with good management there should be no disease; but very few of us are good enough beekeepers to completely eliminate these troubles from our apiaries, though, of course, a lot may be done to that end. Here I am trying to deal with realities as I see them, and I think we must always expect a certain amount of disease, however much we try to keep it at bay.

Every spring a certain percentage of stocks will be found to be queenless, and I think all bee farmers find this queenlessness one of the chief vexations; at least that is how I have found it. I never have been able to ensure that every stock shall have a queen in spring: I only wish I knew how that could be brought about. This, however, has nothing to do with cold weather.

In this country healthy bees well supplied with sound stores and situated in sheltered apiaries will, I believe, hardly ever be found to winter badly in the hardest winters. In exposed apiaries, where the winter gales strike the hives without restraint, bees do die in severe winters; but not, I think, from the direct effect of low temperature. In these cases the bees are immobilized on their combs and are unable to reach their stores, and so starve. Also there is little doubt that in apiaries that are at high levels, and are not sufficiently protected by suitable wind-breaks, bees die at the margins of the cluster, especially when the stocks are somewhat weak; but this is not really because the thermometer is low so much as by reason of the convection caused by the play of the cold wind upon the hive. Stocks will stand many days of sub-zero temperature when protected from wind, better than they can tolerate a few degrees of frost while exposed to a gale.

One of the most trying winters we have had for many years was that of 1939–40. The Thames was frozen over for weeks, and one could go skating on it; but with the exception of two or three exposed apiaries, and particularly one of these where the bees were wintering on heather honey, losses were quite small. In one place, however, where I was stupid enough to leave the apiary unsheltered at a height of 700 feet above sea level, I lost about one-third dead, and more than another third were reduced to mere handfuls of bees: none was strong. The weak ones built up through the summer in time for the unique flow that lasted throughout August and into the second week of September; some of them giving eighty pounds of surplus honey: but none of the dead stored anything. In this case at least some of those that died were found, by examination of the dead, to have been infested by mites, but most of them were healthy enough and died from the effect of the cold winds, to which they were exposed. Most of the dead had plenty of honey in their combs in spring, and when I went to that apiary on the first warm day after the great frost, almost every stock was flying freely: it was later on that those colonies dwindled and died out.

In beekeeping you should always be ready to learn, and I learned a lesson that time. I have never attempted to winter bees in high-up exposed places since; we just move the whole apiary away to a more suitable wintering site, and take them back in the spring; for these places where bees winter badly are usually very good for getting honey. I don't think it would pay to pack bees even in such a winter as 1939–40, or to use double-walled hives either, for stocks in sheltered apiaries at lower levels where the winds are not so rough, wintered quite well. But apiaries should always be sheltered from the north and east winds. If there is no natural break, an artificial one can easily be made, as shown in the photograph.

I used Roots' 'Buckeye' hives for years, but they never wintered the bees as well as the single-walled ones, though they are packed with cork-dust between their walls. W.B.C. hives are considered good by many, and it would seem that the outer walls must help by breaking the force of the wind and reducing convection, but I can't say that when I used them there was any apparent advantage. That is only my opinion, of course; I don't want to persuade anyone against using W.B.C. or any other fancy type of hive, but one thing I feel sure of is that you won't get any more honey by doing so.

How Bees Winter

I don't know for certain how bees arrange themselves for winter, or just what their method of feeding may be. Lots of people do, though; but their views are so far from being in agreement that I think my guess may be almost as good as anyone else's. Pellett says that the colder the weather the more active the bees are inside the cluster, and the colder the weather the tighter and closer the cluster becomes. He says that the centre of the cluster is hollow, too. All you can do with a statement like that is 'do the best you can with it'. It reads to me like a contradiction in terms. Hawkins and Atkins say (*How to Succeed with Bees*), that if you could peek inside of the cluster, which of course you can't, you would find the bees there less compactly crowded together, and that there you would see that the bees are consuming honey, and moving about with greater rapidity as the temperature falls: meaning, no doubt, that as the outside air gets colder, bees raise the temperature of the cluster. Pellett also says that the colder the weather becomes, the more active the bees are inside the cluster. Hawkins and Atkins say that when the bees at the margin of the cluster become chilly they move inward, the inside bees taking their places. Phillips says much the same.

Now, while I don't feel confident about it, not having seen the inside of a cluster in winter any more than anyone else, yet I do think that the general teaching with regard to this wintering of bees, that has been accepted almost without question for a good many years, and has, in fact, come to be looked upon as more or less authoritative, may not be true after all. It is a plausible theory, no more. How do I know? Well, I don't know for certain; but the doubt arises from the fact that this theory does not fit facts. Bees do not agree with it. They don't winter as if it were the true explanation. Phillips goes so far as to state that during times of low temperature bees expand the cluster and actually fan with their wings. At least I can't see how they could fan unless they did relax the closeness of the cluster. Bees are wonderful insects, but not quite as remarkable as all that.

One guess quite likely being as good as another, I will give mine. I think that when bees first cluster they very probably fill up their honey-stomachs with food, honey or syrup. This seems to me to be an extremely likely instinct to be produced by evolution in such an insect as the hive-bee. Bees fill up when about to swarm; why not when about to cluster on the combs? If this is so, it will be seen that, once clustered, the bees are in a position to stand a long period of weather cold enough to prevent ready movement on the combs, and we may well suppose, as Darwin used to say, that while they can move about pretty easily, they keep their bread baskets full. I believe that, once clustered, bees do not move very much, right through the 'dead' part of the winter, the part which in this country may be roughly reckoned as mid-November to mid-February, but varying with different seasons. During this period, I believe that bees respond to changes in the temperature outside the hive by the simple act of contracting or expanding the cluster as the air gets colder or warmer. The movement of any individual bee in this process would be very small, and could be extremely slow.

I have seen it stated that bees take nourishment during winter, while clustered, by means of the central bees passing food out to those farther from the centre; but surely this must be wrong, for it is practically always the case that the stores are at the margin and not at the centre of the cluster where the bees occupy empty cells. This would entail the passing *inward* of food by those bees that in a cold period would be least able to do it. I think this idea is probably a mistaken one. It is well known that bees will almost always winter well, *if healthy*, no matter how cold the weather, provided that cold is broken by warm intervals. I don't know how frequent these intervals must be, but I suspect that if investigators could find this out, they would be able to say with some certainty just how much honey bees habitually carry in their stomachs when a cold spell begins. Conversely, I think it not unlikely that if we could know just how much food the bees carry in their interiors, and what the quality of that food is, we could predict the length of time that bees can go without an interval of weather warm enough to enable them to re-stock their stomach larders.

Some very interesting, and in my view, important experiments have lately been made that are confirmative of the theory I have here advanced. The matter can be seen in the issues of the *Scottish Beekeeper* for November and December 1944. By means of a highly sensitive microphone connected with head receivers, Mr. Sutherland was able to show that fanning and other activities can be heard during mild weather, but that as the weather cools the sounds from the cluster gradually decrease, until with severe frost absolute silence prevails. This appears to be fact at last, and I think my theory fits it; but I may well be mistaken.

I have dealt with the theory of wintering at some length, and I hope I have not bored those who take up this book; but wintering is an important phase of honey production, about which we none of us know enough. Now to return to practical work.

I must explain the two laths that we place under hive roofs. Under flat roofs, particularly those covered with metal, as all roofs on a bee farm ought to be, there is a tendency for damp to accumulate. Moisture is also liable to collect on the walls of the hive itself unless some arrangement is made to allow it to pass away. It is a winter problem that is troublesome if not dealt with. In nice warm, airy sites, where the sun shines in during winter, I have found that hives keep dry if these laths are used. They raise the roof a little above the inner cover, and the laths contacting at only four small points, a free circulation of air can pass continually over the inner cover and will carry away any damp that would otherwise accumulate. Moisture from the cluster appears to pass through the inner cover boards, especially if these are of that porous wood known as red cedar, but if it seems necessary the feed-hole may be left slightly open by moving the covering block a little, so as to leave a slit about one-eighth of an inch wide at its side; in fact there is no harm in leaving the feed-hole entirely uncovered, but where some kind of fibre-board is used as the roof top under the metal, bees will gnaw this badly if allowed access to it.

In damp places it is necessary to employ another method. Of course it is far better not to keep bees in places that are not exactly right, but needs must when the devil drives, and bee farmers find themselves driven that way more often than is exactly convenient. So if you have bees so situated, take a lot of bits of wood one-eighth of an inch thick, or less, section wood will do, or matchsticks, or even some two-inch wire nails, place one of these small objects under each corner of the inner cover, and your hives will usually keep dry enough. This question of dissipation of the moisture thrown off by the bees is a very important one; much more so, I believe, than packing and double-walled hives, for in my opinion bees do not need to be insulated, packed or cockered up in any way in Britain. After all, they winter perfectly well in chimneys, roofs, and all sorts of cold, draughty places. I remember one lot in an old pollard willow when I was beginning to take an interest in bees. The combs were all of four feet long, the tree was split from top to bottom, and the combs could be seen in half a dozen places. It had been there for many years, the farm men said, and might have been there much longer had I not come along.

Again, I saw some of Madoc's hives in Norfolk one winter, when woodpeckers had made large holes. In some cases the holes were big enough to put your fist into, and the clustered bees could be seen through them, but the bees wintered all right, I believe. I have seen bees come through the winter well when housed in old cracked boxes that were about as airtight as a colander, which brings me to another matter: the dressing of hives.

The orthodox thing is to paint hives with lead paint, and to paint them white. Apart altogether from the prohibitive cost in material and labour, bees don't winter so well in painted hives as in unpainted. At least I have found that this is so in this locality, as Dr. Miller used to say. But hives need some sort of preservative dressing, and creosote is good in some ways. It has the great advantage—disadvantage, some people would say—of making the wood porous after a time, but it is smelly and sometimes it attracts robbers if you are so silly as to put bees into a freshly dressed hive at robbing time. Creosote is not too permanently useful, and as on a bee farm repetitive dressings are practically impossible, we have for two or three years been trying 'Cuprinol' as a preservative. It seems to do very well, though time will be needed to prove its worth. It is a rather expensive dressing compared with creosote, but may be good value all the same. It has the advantage of not making hives conspicuous, which I think a good thing when they are in out-apiaries. Besides, a brown colour allows the hives to be warmed up quickly by the sun during winter when it comes out for a short time.

Maybe I ought to say a word about top entrances for wintering. The trouble is that I have never tried them. I'm always intending to; but when the time comes we are all so dreadfully busy that it gets put off until next year. All I can say is that it seems well established that bees winter well with these entrances arranged at the top of the hive, combs do not get mouldy and hives keep dry and sweet. I *must* try some—next year. The difficulty seems to me to lie in the changing over, at the time of putting bees into winter shape, from the bottom to the top entrance, and in the reversing back again in the spring. I think, too, that as in most cases it is recommended that we should have a special entrance gadget, like a shallow super, to place on top of the brood-chamber and under the roof, a good deal of expense would be entailed. But I'll try— next year. If only some dodge could be found so that we could simply close the ordinary entrance and open another, all would be easy, and, in fact, if I do try it, it is my intention to do something of that sort. I cannot quite see, speaking without actual trial, of

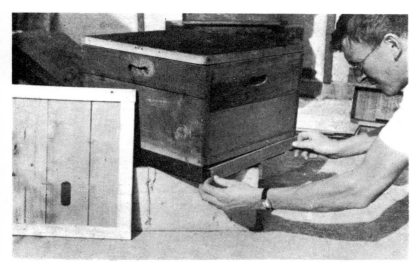

14. Placing an entrance guard in position on a screened hive

15. Stapling brood-chamber to floor ready for moving

16. Using a 'Signode' strapping machine on a screened hive

17. Heather honey, showing the super we use

course, why it is necessary to close the bottom entrance at all. I think it likely that if we left it alone at, say, five inches by three-eighths inches and made a hole about two inches from the top of the front wall, boring with a half-inch auger, no harm but much good might result; but there is always a dislike of mutilating hives.

Tough Old Combs

There is just one other point I would like to make. Bees always winter better on old combs than on new, and I think it matters not at all how old the combs are so long as they are in good condition otherwise. Really good old combs are one of the greatest assets a bee farmer can have. Some people have been foolish enough to advise the regular and systematic scrapping of brood-combs to the extent of 20 per cent per annum, and in so far as good worker combs are concerned, this is just silly advice. My counsel is, get rid of combs that have too many drone cells or are otherwise imperfect, but hang on tight to all others. The older they are the better bees will do on them. This is not theory, or some cracked idea of my own, but a fact which any intelligent beekeeper can prove for himself in a very short time. The only qualification it requires is this. In very extreme cases (you or I will never have one) the cell bases may become so much thickened by the accumulation of larval refuse through continuous breeding over long periods, that unless the bees destroy the comb down to the septum and rebuild the cells, the depth of the available part of the comb may be so much reduced that breeding will be interfered with.

There were great arguments over this in bygone years in the American bee-press, and various ideas were put forward; but the usual theory appeared to be that as the bottoms of the cells thickened, bees extended their mouths. There would, of course, be a limit to this; but it takes very many years to have the cell bases thickened to such an extent as could not be compensated by a slight lengthening of their walls. Don't worry, however, you and I will be exceedingly lucky if we can keep our brood-combs otherwise in good order for one quarter of the time it would take to have them put out of action by any thickening of the cell bases. It has been stated in America that bees will strip down the combs, clear away the refuse that causes the thickened bases, and rebuild the whole comb from the septum; but I have rarely known them to do it.

There is another curious notion that is current in some beekeeping circles. It is believed that breeding cells are progressively reduced in *diameter* by the gradual accumulation of the silken cocoons left adhering to them by the pupae, so that in time the cells get so narrow and small that the bees bred in them cannot grow to their full size. I think this is a mare's nest, myself, for I have seen many very old combs in derelict hives, black as jet, yet the bees were full sized. I think it has been shown (in America, as well as I recollect) that when, if ever, cells do become thus contracted, bees will normally clean out the remains of the cocoons. Personally, I don't see how they possibly could, but I can tell how they often do it in my colonies when combs get rather old: they tear away the part of the comb affected and rebuild from the base.

When the hives have all been arranged in the way I have described, all that is needed is to pay them a visit about once a month to see that nothing is amiss with them, to make certain that apiary fences are in good order, and to put them right if they are not. It is really very important indeed that these fences shall be kept up, for if horses or cattle should get in among the hives in winter they might do a good deal of damage to the bees; while in summer the bees might seriously injure the stock. Bees have enemies, too, as we shall see later, but their worst foes in winter are, in my experience, members of our own species. It is thought a great game, apparently, to poke over a few hives, or to take off their roofs, and to throw bricks at them beats coconut shies all to pieces. I have had boys tie a long wire round a hive and then go back into an adjoining copse, out of the way, and pull the whole thing over.

The aggravating thing is that you never catch these gentry at work, but sometimes, when they try on the trick in summer or other time of activity for bees, they get a lesson. Some years ago I was being rather badly tormented by the boys out of a neighbouring industrial school who used to come round and do mischief of this kind. One day I had shut in three or four colonies of those horribly spiteful French black bees in the evening, and had carried the hives to the gateway ready to be carted away to another apiary in the morning. For some reason I could not get to them before ten or eleven o'clock the next day, which was a warm one; and when at last I came for them I found that two of the roofs had been thrown off and the inner covers moved aside so that the bees could pour out. I got well stung as soon as I showed myself. Afterwards I found that these boys had been into the apiary and taken several roofs and inner covers off. This they probably did with impunity as the bees were Italians and there was a honey-flow. They then saw the bees by the gate and thought what a jolly game they would have by treating them in the same way. I wish I could have been near to see; but I can imagine it. I should not have cared to let loose those devils of bees without a veil and smoke. Anyway, I never had any bother there after that. My friend Wadey says it's a good plan to have one or two of these vicious stocks in every out-apiary; but I don't like them.

Sometimes a good deal of damage is done if a spell of bad weather comes on before hives that have been upset are put right, but it is wonderful what colonies will stand. I have had a stock turned over and its combs exposed for weeks, the floor having come off and the hive being upside down, and in spring that stock was none the worse, being strong enough to go to early fruit pollination. But sometimes a stock so treated is destroyed.

The winter work on a honey farm consists in packing honey, making up hives, frames, etc., and in doing various other jobs as they turn up. There is no leisure at all, except, if one is lucky, two or three weeks' holiday. A moderate crop of honey, if bottled for the retailer, will occupy the staff of a bee farm for about three or four months.

Early Spring Work

About the end of February or early in March it is time to begin the first job of the year. Each apiary is visited in turn and the floor of every hive is cleaned. We take two or three spare floors with us, together with our tools, smoker, etc., for, although smoke should not be needed for this work, one can never be certain and it is as well to be prepared for anything. We also take as many combs of honey as are available so that if any stock is found to be short of stores, a comb of food can be given immediately. We usually have a good many combs in store that contain sealed food, for it is generally the case with us that at the time when we are making the final preparations for winter a few stocks are found to be queenless, or to be too weak in bees to be likely to winter, and the often heavily-stored combs of such stocks, after the bees have been shaken into another hive, are put away for just such a contingency as this.

On reaching an apiary we first gently remove the hive-staples from all hives that have their floors fastened on, so that the brood-bodies can be lifted. Then one assistant takes a clean floor and stands ready to place it in position on the stand. Two more then, having loosened the hive from its floor, lift the whole to one side, holding it between them for a moment. The first man immediately sets the clean floor on the stand and the two who are holding the hive then allow the floor to drop off and as quickly and gently as possible, place the hive-body upon the clean floor. The entrance-block belonging to the clean floor is placed in position before the hive is set back in its place. At this operation the mouse guard is taken away, for mice rarely, if ever, get into hives as far on in the year as this. The whole thing can be done with very little disturbance of the bees and takes only a minute or two for each hive.

It is important that those who lift the hive should note its weight, and it is wise to take off all roofs when doing this job as this allows a more accurate estimate to be made, for some roofs are much heavier than others unless you have an absolutely uniform outfit, which I have not. Of course any such estimate must be very loose, but if any hive strikes the lifters as unusually light, it is wise to raise the inner cover and have a look inside. No need to do more than give a quick glance at the combs in nine cases out of ten, for if sealed stores are seen on two or three combs, there is almost certainly enough food to last until the apiary is visited again; but a note should be made of any stocks that seem lighter than the average, even so.

If no sealed stores can be seen we must do something about it. What I usually do is very gently to pry apart two of the combs nearest, but not actually occupied by the cluster. If sealed stores can be seen farther down between the combs, I let well alone, for it is not good to upset bees at this early date unless absolutely necessary. Here I may point out that one advantage given by taking one comb from each hive in the autumn and substituting a dummy is that it makes it very much easier to move combs without much jarring or disturbance. If little or no stores are to be seen, it is best to take out one or two empty combs and replace them by the stored ones that have been brought with us, or by some removed for the purpose from over-heavy colonies in the same apiary. Usually nothing of this kind need be done if the bees have been properly attended to in the fall; but we do sometimes find bees very short of stores for some reason or other, and we try to save them.

It may be argued that bees that consume too much food are probably diseased, or are at any rate inferior, and that they would be as well out of the way. There is sound sense in that contention and it is a matter for the owner to decide according to his lights; but if it is decided that such bees should be got rid of, don't let them die of starvation and so clog up their combs with their dead bodies, which ruins them, but kill the bees and after brushing the combs clear of the dead, store them away. If the bees have acarine disease, this will not make the combs dangerous to other bees, provided they are stored away for a few weeks so that stray mites may die.

As soon as the hive is back in its place on the clean floor we clean off all dirt, dead bees and other refuse from the dirty floor by a thorough scraping; but not before we have had a good look at the debris on that floor, for a good deal can be learned in this way. We sometimes find dead drones or drone pupae, indicating a drone-breeding queen: also we may see a few worker pupae lying there. This indicates a fertile and rather prolific queen that has extended her brood area rather too rapidly. We occasionally find a dead virgin, and this shows that supersedure has taken place at the wrong time of year. Such facts are all noted in our book for future action. Besides all this, it is possible to judge, with a very considerable degree of probability, from the appearance of the circle of fragments of cappings lying on the floor, what the size of the cluster is. As soon as clean, the floor is used for the next hive, and so on.

About a month after the floor changing, I like to get around to the apiaries on a warm, sunny day when the bees are flying freely so that I can see if pollen is being carried in plentifully. I have found that at this time of year, about the end of March or early April, there is seldom anything wrong with stocks that are taking in pollen rapidly and in large pellets; but when a colony is seen to be idle while the rest are busy, that colony should be inspected at once. It is wise to open it there and then to see what is wrong, and in nine cases out of ten it will be found to be queenless, for this is always the chief cause of winter loss on a bee farm.

Queenless Colonies

Queenless colonies in spring are generally of very little use as they are usually weak, and when this is so it is best to destroy the bees altogether rather than unite them to another stock. In any case the bees will be old and worn and will not help the other stock if added to it, and they may introduce some disease, too. Such stocks very often have a good deal of honey in their combs, and this can be used to assist other colonies as above mentioned, provided always that such combs are seen to be free of foul brood. If that is present, I need hardly say that the combs should be burned forthwith.

If a stock is found to be without a queen, but at the same time strong and having large numbers of obviously young bees, it is a case of loss of the queen late in the winter, and just before breeding begins, unless, indeed, a virgin is present. In cases like this, the best plan is to close up the hive and remove it to the next apiary to be visited, where, unless you are a remarkably lucky or unusually efficient beekeeper, you may find a queenright stock that is weak in bees and to which the strong queenless stock may be profitably united. To unite these all that is required is to give the queenright one a little smoke and a few smart raps on the hive sides, then set it aside and on its stand place the queenless lot and release the bees. Now open this and, after removing enough of its combs to make room for the brood of the queenright colony and shaking off the bees, just place the combs of the weak, queenright lot bodily into the space made, being sure that the queen is between two of the middle combs so that she shall not contact the old queenless bees immediately, while they are frightened and excited. To make doubly sure of safe acceptance, the queen may be caged on her comb, the cage being arranged for automatic release by candy. Smoke slightly and close the hive and in about 99 per cent of cases all will go well.

While I am on this subject of uniting bees, I may as well say that in my opinion more nonsense is found in bee guides about this than about most matters, and that is saying a good deal. It is almost always recommended that very weak stocks should be united, with the idea that they can in this way be made strong enough to store surplus honey. Well, unite them, and you will not have a stock worth much. I have tried that often enough to know, too. A stock that is too weak to build up is of very little use for uniting or for anything else. Also we are told that bees must be sprinkled with flour, sprayed with scent, and the rest. This is all footle: I have united plenty of bees in the last thirty years, but have never used flour or scent or anything at all. Any time it is a simple matter to unite two poor stocks by caging a queen, preferably in an automatic release cage, and alternating combs after some smoking and general frightening of the bees. Or two large stocks can always be united simply by standing their brood-chambers one over the other with a sheet of newsprint between them. Swarms, casts, and driven bees require nothing at all except to be hived together. But you will find that very little uniting of bees will be required on a bee farm if you know your job.

Spring Feeding

About the middle of April, if it is necessary, general feeding can be started. If the bees have ample stores in their combs, and those stores are not seriously granulated, it is much better to let them alone and not feed at all; but if there is not an abundance of food, or if the stores are granulated much, it is a very good thing to set to work and feed to each colony a gallon or more of good, thick syrup. Don't have anything to do with stimulative feeding with thin syrup: bees that are any good at all don't need any encouragement to breed in spring if they have plenty of liquid stores in their hive. This stimulating fad is nothing but a hobbyist's amusement, and is a waste of valuable time, for it is much more likely to do harm than good. No bee farmer need bother with that sort of thing.

A good deal depends on the district and on the season as to what feeding may be required in spring. Where there is an early flow, giving honey in April, no feeding at that time is needed, but these early flows act as a strong stimulant to breeding, and thus to honey consumption, and unless there is a good income of nectar later on, it may be necessary to feed heavily then. In the various localities of which I have had personal experience, May is the month of all others when it pays to feed, if there is the least short-age of food in the hives. In no case should bees be allowed to run short of stores in May. There is hardly anything on which money can be so profitably spent, as sugar for May feeding, if feeding is needed at that time: there is hardly ever a season when it is not a good investment.

Speaking of early flows in some districts: I was visiting some beekeepers in Sussex a few years ago, and was shown, in April, stocks of bees crowding two ten-comb Langstroth bodies. There had been a flow from the willow, but there was certainly no great weight of stores in the hives. The owners were very proud of these stocks; but my reaction was—thank goodness my bees are not like that or I should be ruined buying sugar by the ton to keep them alive, and those who may read this should note that when I write of May, I do it in reference to my own district. What I mean is that it always pays to feed bees, unless they have ample stores, during the month previous to the first main honey-flow.

Supering

Except in seasons when the bees are in an unusually advanced condition, in which case many supers go on in April, we usually have a super on every stock during May, except for a few backward ones, and we try to have the bees occupying them before nectar is brought into the hives freely; but this does not always come off. We should like to have all stocks like that, but they never are; and if we manage to get the bulk of our colonies into supers in May we are pleased with the way things are going; but ours are Dadant hives, you know, and we are not in an early locality.

The first supers put on are always full of drawn comb, and are placed over queen-excluders when first set on the hives, for we find this more satisfactory than the plan of allowing the bees to enter the supers at first, and putting on the excluders later on; for one thing, it keeps drones out of the supers altogether, and pollen also to some extent. Bees are a little slower in rising into the supers when excluders are in position, but not seriously so, especially when the super combs have been stored away wet from the ex-tractor.

During April each stock should be carefully examined once to make sure that no brood disease is present, and also for the purpose of clipping such queens as are not already clipped. Every queen should be seen, whether she is believed to be already clipped or not, for sometimes supersedure will have taken place during the autumn, and when out-apiaries are worked on the clipped queen system of management, it is necessary that *all* of them shall be known to be unable to fly.

In the foregoing account of seasonal work I should point out that its background is necessarily my own procedure, that we use only two kinds of hive and frame, of which the Modified Dadant is the chief, being used in the ratio of about ten to one as compared with British standard. The M.D. is distinctly a single-chamber hive, and is intended to be used as such, but I also use some British standard frame hives as single brood-chamber hives, simply supering the twelve-comb bodies in the same way as the Dadants, and with the same pattern of supers. These stocks are inclined to swarm rather more, and are very liable to end the season almost bare of stores in their brood-combs; they are also more bother to handle and manage; but otherwise are not too bad. I should not care to run a large bee farm with British standard frames and metal ends, no matter how modified and rationalized the hives and equipment; but it can be done, as witness Mr. Gale.

Many beekeepers who wish to carry on the business in a fairly large way will decide to use British standard frames, and these should work to some system suitable to their equipment. One of these is that of 'doubling'. As soon as colonies begin to get strong in springtime, a second brood-body full of good combs is placed under the original one and without any excluder. The queen will soon go down into this, and later on may be kept down, if desired, by putting an excluder between the two bodies and seeing that the queen is in the lower one. Supers are, of course, set over all as needed. I do not care for the plan myself, but some men do. It entails extracting from brood-combs full of pollen unless, indeed, both bodies are left for winter. It is necessary to allow the drones to fly from the top story after the queen-excluder has been put on, for otherwise they will be unable to leave the hive, and in their struggles to pass the excluder, will be caught in it and will die there.

I am not myself in love with any double brood-chamber system, for several reasons, of which the chief are that they make it so troublesome to locate the queen; they allow more breeding room than is necessary for any queen; they practically always lead to the use of brood combs for extracting, and this, among other things, is, I feel sure, one of the causes of the spread of foul brood in many cases.

Pollen Substitutes

Before leaving this account of work to be done in spring, I ought to mention one other matter. For many years it has been a traditionally correct procedure to stand a box of shavings near the bees and sprinkle flour on them. Bees will carry this flour into the hives. It is one of those fads that amuse amateurs, and the fun might, I think, be increased by adding colouring matter to the flour, and pretending that the 'pollen' is that of different plants. As for any good it does the bees, it is pretty well known that it does none. It is true that it has been found that when dried skimmed milk is used in this way, bees can breed on it; but if there is doubt as to whether bees reared on sugar syrup and natural pollen are as robust as those reared on honey and pollen, there can, I think, be little doubt that those brought up on skimmed milk in place of pollen are likely to be quite inferior. No bee farmer or serious beekeeper need concern himself with supplying pollen substitutes, at all events in these Islands. Pollen is rarely in short supply here; in fact, it is much more common for our bees to gather more than is required for the rearing of the brood, the result often being combs full of mouldy pollen.

In America a good deal of research has of late been done on this matter. Reports in the American bee-press have been of interest. Soya bean flour has been used with some success, combined with the feeding of natural pollen trapped as the bees carry it into their hives. It seems that in some experiments more brood has been raised by the bees so fed than when they have reared their brood on natural pollen. Personally, I think we should wait and see whether the bees so reared are equal in stamina and other qualities to those reared in the normal way. My own belief is that it is far better to feed our stock, so far as is possible, on natural diet. Sugar we must use to some extent in modern beekeeping, but there is, in my opinion, not the slightest need to use any kind of pollen substitutes in this country.

CHAPTER VII

SWARM CONTROL AND SUMMER WORK

In some ways this will be the most difficult section of this essay, and I shall take the position that during the eight or ten weeks following the onset of the first honey-flow the primary work on a bee farm is the control of swarming. This has always been the case with me and I cannot see how it could be otherwise. I must point out, however, that opinions differ about this; some say that the swarming of bees is, in fact, an unnatural act brought about in all cases by mismanagement: they say that if you will only give the bees plenty of room for storing and breeding at all times, they will not swarm; but I have not found it so. The late Dr. Anderson was inclined to take this line, and so have others, and at the present time its best known exponent is Mrs. M. H. Hooper, authoress of a book called *Common-sense Beekeeping*. Mrs. Hooper has advanced a theory of swarming in her book, and appears to be satisfied that her hypothesis is complete and unassailable. This lady holds her view confidently, and is inclined to be dogmatic on the subject; but whether she would continue in the same mind were she obliged to make her living from four or five hundred stocks of bees, I rather doubt.

Passing to the opposite extreme, we have the ideas of Wilder, an American beekeeper who has successfully run what must have been one of the two or three largest honey-producing businesses the world has so far seen. Here is a quotation from his book, *Wilder's System of Beekeeping*: 'Anywhere bees swarm naturally. In some sections of our country bees swarm but very little unless they become crowded for storage room.' Wilder's system was intended for use in his own, or any other locality where bees are rather inclined to swarm, and consisted in extensive manipulation. 'My system', he says, 'involves a great amount of manipulation.' I have always thought that he might well have carried on quite as successfully without so much of this constant handling of the bees, which must have required an immense amount of labour-time; but I am extremely diffident about criticising the methods of a man who can write: 'The dream of beekeeping on an extensive scale, and this method to be used, soon materialized after I had started out with my first colony; and by its adoption, coupled with energy and sane knowledge, I have been able to establish a very large bee business, consisting of fifteen thousand colonies in three hundred apiaries, all well equipped, with seven central points where leading apiarists live, and where I have up-to-date packing houses and workshops suitable for the business. . . .'

So there is another side to the manipulative swarm control question. None but very amateurish beekeepers want to handle bees more than is necessary, but I think there are times when a certain amount of handling pays well. Some time ago I came across a manuscript in pencil in an old unbound copy of *Gleanings* which appears to be a rough draft of an article written by E. S. Miller, commenting on an article by A. C. Miller. In it he says: 'In regard to the "needless" manipulation of bees, I believe there is no work connected with the industry more profitable than the proper handling of the colonies in spring and summer. There are times when an expert operator can earn twenty-five or thirty dollars a day, or more, in such manipulation. Furthermore, it would be foolish to invest in equipment and then not to work that equipment to its fullest capacity, when it is possible to do so. . . . While useless operations are often carried out by incompetent bee-men, manipulation pays big. There are too many slovenly bee-keepers who work their bees on the let-alone plan to save the cost of manipulation, a penny wise, pound foolish way of doing. . . .' So you see, doctors differ.

Causes of Swarming

Before dealing with the summer management of bees and the proceedings that have been found necessary, in my experience, to prevent the loss of swarms, I had better say something about swarming and its probable causes. Theories that purport to account for the swarming of honey-bees are many, and I will list a few of the more plausible. Meanwhile I give my own ideas for what they are worth.

The hive-bee community has as one of its principal basic facts the phenomenon known as parthenogenesis, or I should rather say, partial parthenogenesis. In the great majority of animals produced by sexual union, male and female births are equal in numbers, an inevitable result of the fusion of the chromosomes of the male and female gametes, but in the beehive quite a different state of affairs is found. There we have one pregnant female to produce the eggs required to keep the population going, and tens of thousands of sterile females to do all the rest of the work. In the breeding season a number of males are generated from eggs laid by the queen, but deposited without having first been impregnated by a sperm cell. Such eggs, of course, produce drones only, and the queen, influenced by stimuli that are not completely understood, regulates in this way the number of males in the colony. This fact, it must be fairly apparent, makes necessary some manner of increase by honey-bees which is radically different from that of most animals.

Most of the theories that have been advanced to explain the swarming of bees are, I think, merely contributory stimulants, and I believe that if we are to understand the fundamental urge that underlies this peculiar instinct in this species, we must realize that swarming is nothing less than an instinct of reproduction, a force upon which the continuity of all living creatures depends. It has been argued that, since no sexual urge influences the act of swarming, reproduction can have nothing to do with the matter; but not all reproduction is sexual, nor is there any inherent reason why it should be, and the honey-bee having evolved an almost unique way of living, there should be nothing very startling to our intellect if we find, as we do, that provision for the perpetuation of the species is procured in a virtually unique manner: reproduction by colonization, or swarming.

The hive-bee differs from other social insects in that none of the individuals which make up the community can at any time or by any means continue to live alone, so that, unlike humble-bees, wasps, and many other insects, a pregnant female cannot hibernate. Those insects raise a number of queens each year in each community, and these mate before hibernation, each, if it has luck, starting a new colony in the following spring, so that by increase the race is kept in being. All the individuals forming a honey-bee colony are produced by sexual union but, since none of these can survive alone, there is only one possible method of increase—swarming, which is analogous to increase by budding off in plants, or by division as in unicellular organisms.

Since the individual bee cannot live alone, it is necessary to regard the whole community as a single being, compounded of a large number of highly specialized members which act togetl.er as one organism, a single self-sufficient living entity whose whole economy is governed by stimuli which, acting on motor nerves, produce all the various activities of the hive-bee colony, swarming included. Those who set out to manage bees and to control and influence their actions will do well to bear always in mind that they are dealing with non-reasoning organisms, for that is what honey-bee communities are. We so often read in literature devoted to beekeeping long discussions about bees and their ways while attributing to them almost human faculties, that we are sometimes led to lose sight of this fact. I do not think that any arguments based upon any such premise are of very much value. *Bees do not think, nor have they ideas of any kind.*

If it is correct that the fundamental cause of swarming is as I have stated it, we are in a position to consider what steps can be taken in the management of the bees, that may be expected to have the effect of controlling or reducing the tendency to swarm unduly. There are variations in all animals, both in bodily structure and in habit, and I think that the best way to go about reducing swarming in our bees is to take advantage of this fact. In some seasons swarming is well known to be very much more prevalent than in others: some strains are much more addicted to swarming than are others; but as things are, the bee farmer must treat all colonies in all seasons as if they may be expected to swarm. It is the only safe way, until by selective breeding a completely non-swarming strain has been produced; and that time is not yet. I know very well that many a beekeeper will tell you, in all good faith, that his bees never swarm. 'My dear sir, I have kept bees for ten years and never had a swarm.' What you are to understand is that no swarm has been seen.

I don't always agree with Herrod-Hempsall, but I think he is quite right when he says, on page seventy-four of his *Beekeeper's Guide*, in richer language than I could aspire to, that the only way to prevent swarming is to breed bees that are not prone to swarm. He considers that in this way swarming may be reduced to 3 per cent. Well, I won't contradict him. It may be possible to reduce swarming to 3 per cent in this country by breeding, but I very much doubt if it has ever been done. I have no doubt myself, that the best hope of reducing the incidence of swarming lies in breeding from non-swarming strains, strains, that is, that show much less addiction to swarming than is the case with the average colonies. I believe that if we systematically breed from queens and drones of strains that have swarmed little, and have produced much honey, and have not suffered from disease, we shall in that way lay the foundation of successful honey production.

Consider the case of the wild honey-bees, quite uncontrolled by man. It would be absolutely necessary that there should be swarming, for otherwise the species would soon be extinct; but it would be equally necessary that there should be neither too much nor too little swarming. Should a strain of wild bees develop a decided tendency towards either extreme, that strain would very soon die out. Swarming, therefore, with bees in a state of nature, must be sufficiently frequent to counterbalance natural attrition; but too many swarms, especially in a poor season, would mean the weakening of the parent colony and its probable extinction, and the loss of the swarms too, very likely. In this way natural selection would weed out the unfit, as it always does, and only such strains as reproduced themselves in a manner that conformed with natural requirements would survive.

Now in our hives, under our control, this process of natural selection no longer operates and, after a time, unless we are careful how we breed our stock, strains are liable to arise that have the swarming tendency too highly developed, especially as we ourselves have a propensity to breed for prolificacy, sometimes without paying enough regard to other traits, and that is why I, basing my opinion upon personal observation of many thousands of colonies, have come to the conclusion that the character of the bees themselves is the most important of all the stimuli that set in motion the swarming instinct.

Apart from the character of the bees used, I feel pretty sure that first and foremost of the causes of undue swarming is the character of the season. Everyone who has had any extended experience of managing bees knows very well that swarming varies very much from one season to another, no matter what the strain of bees. My own experience is fairly long and quite extensive, but for all that I don't know one bit just why it is that bees will swarm hardly at all in one season, while in another they will swarm a great deal; but this I do know: non-swarming seasons are always poor honey seasons, and the converse is usually, but not always the case. Probably the reason for a good deal of the swarming in some years is due to constant intermittence of the honey-flow, for I believe that this is the greatest of all the secondary factors that induce bees to swarm.

Here I give some of the 'causes' of swarming suggested by bee-keepers at different times.

Overcrowding of the hive. Too many drones.

Lack of adequate ventilation. Congestion of the brood-nest.

Overheating of the hive in hot weather. Lack of shade.

Superfluity of larval food. Poor queens.

Reduced feeding of the queen as laying space is restricted.

Disease in the bees. Opening the hive while drones are present.

Dislocation of the brood-nest by inadvisable manipulations.

These are some of the principal stimuli, to one or other or to a combination of several of which, swarming has at one time or another been attributed by various writers on beekeeping in different countries. That most of them may and do help to induce swarming no one will deny; but anyone with fifty or so colonies can easily satisfy himself that no one of these conditions, or, indeed, all of them together, can at any time be relied upon to produce swarms.

Dealing with the listed causes of swarming: overcrowding, lack of ventilation, congestion of the brood-nest, and overheating are all easily avoided, and are avoided on all well-managed bee farms —but swarming takes place, nevertheless. They all, combined or separate (and they are seldom found alone) undoubtedly tend to influence bees to swarm; but I have known any one of them or all combined, completely fail to prevail upon a colony to swarm: yes, many and many a time, and I have also known bees to swarm when none of these conditions was present.

The theory of Gerstung depends on the assumed inability of the nurse bees to modify the secretion of larval food as the number of grubs is reduced by the queen after she has passed her laying peak. I think we have something very near definite proof that this assumption is unsound, and that larval food, on the contrary, is

19. Scooping heather honey off the septum of a comb

18. How we arrange the wooden strips under the roof for wintering

20. Heather honey press, Raynor type, as used by us

21. How we arrange methyl salycilate bottles
in a notched dummy

produced in exactly the correct quantity required at any given time. Were this not so, what would be the position at the close of the breeding season? I have gone into that question, as I see it, earlier in this book. In any case it would in all probability be a matter, not of any individual bee suspending the action of its brood-food glands, but of the glands of newly mature bees not being stimulated to begin secretion, just as is certainly the case at the close of the breeding season. We have seen that it is very probable, indeed in my opinion almost certain, that the period of activity of the brood-food glands in any bee is short, and that the production of larval food is maintained by a succession of young bees taking up the work as the glands of their predecessors go out of action. I suggest, therefore, that young workers come into service as feeders of brood in exact proportion to the amount of food required; in other words, to the number of larvae that need food, and that there is never at any time in any colony an excess of active brood-food producers, and, consequently, that Gerstung's idea falls to the ground.

Poor queens are undoubtedly a cause of swarming—supersedure swarming only. When the instinct of supersedure is aroused by the presence of a failing queen during the swarming season, the supersedure is often converted into swarming.

As for reduced feeding of the queen as laying space is restricted, I find myself unable to see any logical argument here. When bees have ample brood combs and plenty of supers as well, they do not restrict the laying space by filling it with honey. It is true that when there is a very heavy flow of honey the bees will hastily place some of it in the unoccupied cells of the brood-nest, but this is very quickly removed to the supers, so that the queen is able to lay all the eggs she likes. We must remember that swarming takes place, as a rule, fairly early in the summer, and not at a time when the rate of breeding is on the decline. We all know, or ought to, that when we find that a colony is extending its brood area to new combs, it is very unlikely indeed that we shall find queen-cells; but that if during the swarming season no such extension of the brood-nest is taking place, we are very likely to find some in the hive. But surely it is putting the cart before the horse to suggest that the contraction of the breeding nest is the cause of the cells; on the contrary, I think it is the fact of preparation for swarming that has caused the restriction of the queen's activities. Just as soon as queen-cells are begun in a colony, the queen eases off laying and, presumably, takes less food, or is fed less if you like it better. To stop off laying when queen-cells are present is, seemingly, a powerful instinct whose purpose is to have the queen light, active, and able to fly with the swarm, which she could not do without this preparation; but that this slacking off of egg-laying is in any sense a *cause* of swarming I don't for one moment believe.

There is one disease of bees that can and does cause them to swarm. When bees are infested by the mite Acarapis woodi, their power of flight is greatly affected, even when they have not entirely lost it, and it seems to be true that almost the entire population of a colony may reach this state without, in summer, showing any clear external signs of the fact. Such bees probably feel disinclined for flight and hang around in the hive feeling very sick and fed up. This staying in instead of going out to forage, causes overcrowding and consequent discomfort; cells are started, and the bees swarm. Then may be seen a sight that was familiar to those of us who were in the game in the days of the 'Isle of Wight' disease devastation. The swarm will always cluster near the hive it comes from, and under it will be seen thousands of sluggish bees crawling feebly about and bunching on the grass or lumps of earth. In front of the hive they generally lie thickly, showing very clearly where the swarm came from. These swarms generally have virgin queens, for the old one will often have disappeared, at least that is how the few typical swarms of this class that I have seen have behaved. Such swarms should be destroyed at once; they are loaded up with mites and as likely as not the young queen is also; but I have saved the parent stock in most cases by giving it a new fertile queen after destroying the virgin or cells, and placing on the floor a large bottle of methyl salycilate.

Regarding other diseases; bees suffering from brood ailments seldom swarm unless this happens before the trouble has gained sufficient hold to reduce the colony's strength, and at no time are brood diseases in any sense a cause of swarming; in fact nothing that reduces a colony's population is a cause of swarming, but rather the reverse. My experience has been that bees of good characteristics do not swarm unless strong, and rarely until the combs in the brood-chamber are completed, and that diseased stocks, except those suffering from acarine disease, do not attain to great strength.

Mrs. Hooper has an idea that the opening of hives and examination of combs during the time of year when drones are present is a serious cause of swarming. I do not think that this can be so, because I have never been able to trace the least tendency in bees so handled to swarm more than others. However, since drones are present all the summer, there is no help for it, even if it is so, unless we decide to leave our bees completely alone during the swarming season, which might be all right for those whose bees can be relied upon not to swarm at all, but would be lunacy for those of us who have not yet succeeded in attaining that state of perfection, and do not expect to. We can't afford to risk the loss of swarms and therefore must act in such a way as to prevent the escape of such as issue.

That we can tip the scale in favour of swarming, by dislocating the brood-nest by foolishly changing the places of the combs, I think is probable; but I am almost sure that it is not an important cause. It is more likely to have the opposite effect in most cases, I believe, by increasing the area of empty cells in the immediate neighbourhood of the queen; in fact several methods of swarm prevention are based on some such interference.

The Prevention of Swarming

So much for the alleged causes of swarming; what of the means of preventing it? At intervals, ever since I can remember, there have been published in books and journals a number of suggestions for the attainment of complete control or suppression of swarming, and some have been very popular, at all events for a time. If you consider the causes of swarming, as usually accepted, they will be found to be various aspects of frustration, and those methods of averting swarming most generally advocated, to consist in removing the cause of that frustration.

One of the more generally used of these methods is that known as the Demaree system. The queen and one comb of brood and bees are placed in an empty brood-chamber, which is then filled up with drawn combs. This new body is then set on the floor of the hive with an excluder over it, and the original brood-chamber is placed over this. The supers, if any, are placed over all. There are a great many variations of this plan, but all are based upon the above operation. I believe it works well as a swarm preventative if the weather continues favourable, which it rarely does in this country in my experience. I tried it extensively many years ago and found it a failure in my hands. Should the weather turn cold and unfavourable for honey soon after the 'demareeing', the bees simply ignore the comb, or if foundation is used they gnaw it to bits. The queen, also, is liable to disappear, for if it turn cold the bees may retire into their upper story through the excluder, leaving the unfortunate queen trapped below it. This plan usually ruined the stocks when I used it, though occasionally it was very successful.

There are very many different plans for averting swarming, such as using complicated gadgets like the Snelgrove boards that have been so popular among amateurs of late; de-queening and introducing a queen of the current season that has just begun to lay. This must, of course, be done before there is any sign of queen-cells, in which case it is often a rather successful operation. Sometimes, early in the season, when we find a very powerful colony at the first examination during the flow from fruit blossom to be building queen-cells, it is possible to end the whole business by transposing it. Find a medium, but not a weak stock, and just exchange its place with the swarming one. This has the effect of diverting the very large population of foraging bees from the swarming lot into the medium one, and having them replaced by the much more moderate number belonging to the other, which causes the bees to abandon cell-building. This is in my opinion one of the best plans for preventing the issue of swarms in the early part of the season, when it is probable that the early flow that may have helped to bring on this swarming attempt, will be succeeded by total dearth for a time. Besides, it equalizes the colonies, which is good at this early date. This May flow from fruit and other early-flowering plants greatly stimulates breeding. Stocks seem to double their populations in no time, and the queen covers combs with brood at an almost incredible rate; then the flow ends as suddenly as it began, either because the early blossom is over, or more often through an adverse change in the weather. Usually only a few stocks offer to swarm during the flow from fruit, and these can be dealt with by the transposition plan; but when the sudden end comes to this honey-flow, as it nearly always does, in this locality at any rate, we sometimes have quite a minor spate of swarming. We usually make increase from this, for it is early, and both swarms and their parent stocks may be reasonably expected to yield good crops of honey later in the summer.

This early run of swarming is usually very small and soon dies out, and colonies that have done nothing amiss go on building up their strength until the next flow begins. This may be any time that the weather turns hot; but the last few days of May and the first two weeks of June are as a rule the first main honey-flow here in Oxfordshire. Swarming may be expected in some colonies at any time now, but a stop in the flow in early June produces more swarms than any other incident in the year. This is generally the last of the serious swarming season, and a *heavy* flow of honey will bring it to an end in all hives simultaneously. Nearly all later swarms are, I believe, in reality, supersedure swarms.

Wadey, in *The Bee Craftsman*, says: 'Probably one of the soundest plans was that long ago advocated by Simmins. This consisted in putting a box of foundation beneath the brood-chamber, and then when built out, to place it above the excluder and place another box of foundation at the bottom of the pile. The drawback to this is that the combs built below the brood-nest are less perfect than those made in an upper story.' Well, I tried that plan long ago and found that the drawback was that the bees would not in any circumstances build out the foundation below the brood-chamber, at all events so long as there was any room at all in their supers, and it did not entirely stop swarming, either. But there is no doubt whatever that a set of frames of foundation kept below the brood-chamber, and between it and the entrance, does help greatly to discourage swarming, though the foundation will probably be ruined by the bees tearing it to pieces. Query: would not a super filled with empty frames do just as well; or maybe a very deep floor fitted with a rack as used by the late Dr. C. C. Miller?

Given a good strain of bees, bred carefully for non-swarming proclivities, we can, by taking reasonable care during the critical season, count on not having any excessive swarming in any but exceptional seasons; but I have not yet come across a breed of bees worth anything at all as honey producers, that did not swarm to a certain extent, and I am not sure that I should care to have a completely non-swarming strain. I think a reasonable amount of swarming, say 15 or 20 per cent, is rather a good thing; but I have no doubt that this will be regarded as a very silly sentiment by some of those who are really in the know on the subject of producing honey.

Periodical Examination

On bee farms where the production of honey with a minimum of labour is the object, it seems to have become generally accepted that there is only one practicable method of management. This is the system of periodical examination every nine, or possibly ten days. Amateur beekeepers frequently write to the bee-press pointing out how foolish the bee farmers are to go to all this labour when there are so many much more simple and easy methods that might be employed. It does not, seemingly, occur to them that the reason we do it is that we know of no better way. We don't open our hives in regular rotation eight or nine times every summer for the fun of it. On a bee farm you must have a method which provides for the management of distant apiaries that can only be visited at stated times: every kind of scheme must allow for considerable intervals between visits, and the biology of the honeybee practically forces us to make the intervals nine days in length.

I have found that when I have mentioned the usual methods employed on bee farms, quite a lot of beekeepers seem to misunderstand what is implied. The late Dr. Anderson was a case in point, and he used to become quite facetious when dealing with those of us who spend a good deal of our time over what is known as swarm control. Anderson, of course, had no experience of large-scale beekeeping, any more than have the great majority of those who read the bee-press, and he seemed to be unable to understand the reason for our routine work; seemed, in fact, to think that every colony dealt with was a swarming colony, and to consider those who practised it, little better than fools. Like so many others who are greatly interested in beekeeping, Anderson never got beyond the stage of the enthusiastic amateur.

Some years ago, after reading some of this sort of stuff in the bee-press and elsewhere, about how simple and easy swarm control can be without having recourse to periodical examinations, I really did begin to wonder whether, after all, I could have been altogether mistaken through all these many years; so I wrote a line to the two most extensive bee farmers I know at all well, Gale and Madoc. I asked the simple question: 'Is there any other way of control that will certainly prevent the loss of swarms?' Gale replied, 'I know of none'; Madoc said, 'I do not know of any.' Well, I don't know of any other way, either.

Before I describe our methods of management and control I may as well say that when a day is spent on this work in the summer, we do not usually find more than about 3 to 5 per cent of colonies building queen-cells. When we spend a day in apiary work, we take both lunch and tea with us, boiling the kettle on a primus stove for much-needed refreshment for the latter meal, and we may go through several apiaries, opening every colony and doing the needful work its condition calls for. Supers are put on where required, frames of foundation are added in the brood-chambers if needed, and about six combs of brood are taken out and examined. The queen is seen more often than not, and from her appearance and from indications presented by the combs, together with the general aspects of weather and honey-flow, we are able to decide with a very high degree of probability whether the bees are likely to swarm or not. If there is no clear indication that all is well, the examination is carried further; otherwise the hive is quickly closed and will remain unmolested for nine clear days.

I had better say at once, to avoid misunderstanding, that the purpose of regular examinations is not to prevent the bees from building queen-cells, but to preclude the loss of swarms when the bees do build them. If you want to get your living from honey production you will be wise to ignore the theories of those who say bees ought not to swarm; that they will not swarm if properly managed, etc. The reality, well known to every bee farmer in the world, is that they often will. We can never in any circumstances, under any management, in any climate, at any time during what we call the swarming season, *rely* upon absence of swarming in any strong, healthy stock that has not already swarmed. With well-bred bees we may expect that the incidence of swarming will not be much greater in most seasons, than 10 or 15 per cent, but in some years no method of management whatever will prevent swarming from being more prevalent than that, no matter what the strain of bees. On the other hand, in some seasons swarming will be almost absent, even if the bees are of a 'swarmy' breed, and in spite of bad management.

Every now and then there may be seen in the bee-press an account of some new dodge for the prevention of swarming, triumphantly written up. Don't take these reports too seriously, for they are always coincident with what we may call a non-swarming season. The writers are, no doubt, quite honestly of the opinion that at long last 'the whole discovery has been found out', but success has been due to the season, which has been one of those that, for reasons not yet clearly understood, inhibit swarming, and has little or nothing to do with the new plan recommended.

The interval of nine days is, as I have pointed out, dictated by the biology of the bee. From new-laid egg to fully matured virgin queen a period of fifteen to sixteen days is all that is needed, and from the sealing of the cell, only eight. If, therefore, a colony is left without queen-cells in any form and the queen is clipped, no swarm can abscond within sixteen days. If only unsealed queen-cells are present, no swarm can abscond within nine days, even if such cells are on the point of being sealed. If only cells in an early stage are present, no swarm can get away within ten or twelve days. These facts are basic to our system of periodic examinations.

When queen-cells are destroyed in a colony that is preparing to swarm, the bees almost always immediately start a new set, and these may be begun over larvae as much as three days old, so another reason for making our intervals nine days long is that in such cases a virgin may emerge before we can do anything about it, if a longer time has elapsed, and she may take off a swarm which will probably be lost.

Another reason for not allowing a longer time between examinations is the necessity, if we are to get through the work quickly when dealing with cell-building stocks, of attending to them before the virgins in the cells are too far advanced, for should they have reached a stage within a day or two of emergence, the workers will have ceased to feed the queen and she will have become small in appearance, and active like a virgin, and queens in that state are extremely hard to find. Besides, the stock is likely to have already made an attempt to swarm, in which case the clipped queen may be lost, though in my experience she seldom is, but is generally still present in the hive, having either refused to leave it with the bees when they issued, or else having managed to get back into it again. Another reason for the nine-day interval is that an unsealed queen-cell cannot produce a virgin within that time, and thus, if all sealed queen-cells are destroyed on any given date, no swarm can get away before the apiary is again visited.

Before entering upon a description of the methods of summer management employed in the apiaries of Chiltern Honey Farm, I will point out that we make no attempt to prevent swarming by any mechanical device, such as the boards advocated by Snelgrove; nor do we make use of any of the various manipulative operations, such as have been advocated by Wilder, C. C. Miller, Demaree, and others. We do our best to keep down the incidence of swarming by breeding and by avoiding the causative stimuli referred to a few pages back. This may surprise some readers, but I have tried all these things and have come to the conclusion that, all things considered, none of them is worth the labour entailed when it is extracted honey that is being produced. After we have done our best to have our hives stocked with bees that are not very much inclined to swarm, we rely on periodical examinations to obviate the loss of such swarms as would otherwise abscond. I hope I have now made it clear that this system of routine examinations of colonies is in no way swarm-prevention in the sense of being an attempt to restrain the bees from building queen-cells for the purpose of swarming, for it is no such thing.

I suppose it is needless to say that the routine examinations are not begun before they are really necessary, which is about the time of the first honey-flow. The first supers, as we have seen, are in place on all but backward colonies; spring feeding is over, and feeders have been removed. It is at this stage that the inspections begin. Taking one apiary at a time, each hive is quickly opened and a few of its combs taken out and looked over, when, if there is any sign of an inclination to swarm, this will be noticed at once and the stock dealt with. In the great majority of cases there will be no sign of queen-cells, and the hive is quickly closed. Very little disturbance is caused when this is done in fine weather during a honey-flow, and if more disorganization results from carrying it out in less suitable weather, it does not in practice seem to have any evil effect. I know that it is sometimes said that this disturbance will so upset the bees (demoralize is the word generally used to describe this supposed effect on the bees) that they will stop gathering nectar for the rest of the day; but this is just nonsense, and if you want to know how little effect disturbance has in putting bees off acquiring honey, try to stop a colony from robbing by disturbing it.

During these inspections a good many other matters must be attended to. An experienced beekeeper is always on the look-out for brood disease, and will also notice any combs that should be replaced on account of having too much drone comb or other irregularity. Such combs should be placed outside the others if they contain brood, so that as soon as their brood has all emerged they can be removed; but do not put brood right at the outside of the hive, away from the brood-nest unless the colony is a very strong one. If bad combs are found without brood at this first examination, it is best to remove them, even if they contain a good deal of honey, and replace with frames of foundation; but be sure not to denude the hive of necessary stores when doing this. If there is a shortage of stores, condemned combs containing stores, if placed at the outside of the brood-chamber, will be emptied by the bees and the combs may then be replaced at the next inspection.

Keeping Records

It is very important that notes be made of every circumstance that should be remembered and acted on at the next visit. I keep my notes in a book; but some beekeepers prefer cards attached to the hives. The book plan suits me best because I can take it home and there refer to it at any time. Each hive has a number and a page of the book is numbered to correspond. I make a practice of keeping a few pages at the end of each book on which to make a note at each apiary of everything that will be required there at the next visit, so that when next we come there we shall not find that something needed has been left behind. All the same, I'm afraid we do leave things behind more often than we should, for the flesh is weak. I have even known our men leave their dinner behind, but perhaps that was because they did not make a note of it! These record books are interesting in many ways, if you keep them. Among other things they enable one to trace back the swarming proclivities of queens for many generations—if you have been at it long enough.

We should always work in couples, one of each pair being an experienced man who does the handling while the other manages the smoker. On our farm we go to the apiaries four or six strong, so that the whole of the colonies in an apiary can be dealt with quickly. This has the advantage that in case of need there are plenty of us and all our kit is available. We find this better than for two to go to one apiary and two to another: it saves time in the end. I once spent a day with my friend Gale, and he worked that day in a rather different way from ours. He had four men besides himself. It was quick work. Two men smoked a stock and removed the supers; then Gale examined the combs, or at any rate enough of them for his purpose, made his note, and passed on to the next hive, which by that time was opened ready for him. Meanwhile the other two men replaced the supers and closed the hives. It all went smoothly and rapidly, except when cells were found: then a hunt began for the queen, and in one case it took quite a time before she could be found and her stock treated in some way, the details of which I forget. By these means an apiary of fifty stocks was put through in short order, and we went right on to the next. I forget exactly how many apiaries we got through that day, but four at least were done, and we only started after midday. These inspections are really only a matter of moments when the stocks are found to be behaving properly; it is when swarm-cells are found that time is required.

When examining stocks in this way it is very necessary that we should know exactly what to look for, what indications to pay attention to, and how to perceive them. This is the kind of thing that can come only by experience; but it is really surprising how quickly an observant boy who is intelligent and keen will pick it up. Some of the indications are subtle and hardly to be described in writing; but others are very plain. If you find your bees are building out foundation it is hardly necessary to trouble further, so far as possible queen-cells are concerned. If the queen is spreading out on to new comb and covering it with eggs as fast as the workers build it out ('laying out', we call it) there will rarely be cells. If the queen is very swollen and heavy with eggs, it is very unlikely that cells are present, at any rate cells with larvae in them, though there may be cells with eggs. (I may say here that 'cells' in this connection means queen-cells.) If foundation is not being drawn and the brood-nest does not appear to be expanding, look carefully over most of the brood-combs, for you are likely to find cells. The same if the queen is looking light and as if she is slackening off in her laying; but when the indications are that all is well we do not usually take out more than four combs. When the whole trend of the season is in favour of little swarming we can generally tell if all is well by looking over two or three combs.

I have now come to the place where I must try to describe the various methods used by different bee-men to deal with those colonies found to be making preparations to swarm. There are two distinct aspects of this question of swarm control: is it to be with or without increase?

It may be well to point out that there is no question here of simply hiving a natural swarm in another hive. That is the best of all if increase can be accepted, and the swarm is an early one, but in apiaries visited only periodically it is exceptional for the beekeeper to be present when a swarm comes out; if, however, he does happen to be there at the time, the right plan, I think, is to try to pick up the queen from in front of the hive where, being clipped, she will often be found, or else to catch her as she issues if the swarm is actually seen in the act of rising. If the bees cluster, the queen may be placed with them, and the swarm hived as soon as it has settled quietly. Such a swarm is, of course, the same in every way as a natural swarm, and can be hived in the same apiary, if desired.

The stock it came from must next be attended to. All brood combs should be examined with great care, and all queen-cells but one destroyed. The bees should be shaken off these combs, to make it more certain that no cells are missed; but the comb which has the selected cell on it, the cell to be left to provide a virgin, should never be shaken for fear of injury to the embryo queen: the bees should be brushed from it, if necessary. This comb should be marked to save trouble next time, and the hive may then be closed.

At the next visit, nine days later, a virgin should be present, and another examination of all the combs must be carried out, the bees being shaken from each comb to make certain that no queen-cells are left. I may mention here that the cell the virgin has come out of will be easily seen, and will often be open and the virgin obviously properly hatched; but in about one-third of these cells from which virgins have emerged the caps will be found in place just as if no queen has hatched at all, but if you pull these cells open you will find a dead worker in each: I have found two dead workers many times. If the time for a queen to have matured has passed, one ought always to open the cell if not already open. Occasionally a dead virgin is found, probably due to chilling or jarring at the previous handling; but this is quite rare. The presence of a worker is a sure sign of the normal emergence of a virgin, which in that case may be safely assumed to be in the hive. There should be a laying queen a few days after this operation, and a stock treated in this way, if strong when the swarm issued, and provided the time of swarming shall not have been later than early June, will be very likely to give a good crop of honey.

It is far better to manage the matter in this way than to attempt to return the swarm without its queen, an operation which almost always leads to the complete ruin of the colony; for unless the swarming impulse be satisfied in some way once a colony has built queen-cells which have reached an advanced stage, hardly anything will prevent the issue of a swarm in some form or other, and if the swarm be returned without the queen, the bees will in the majority of cases swarm with the virgin when she flies out to mate, leaving the colony, not only without any queen, but without the means of rearing one. It is understood, of course, that before returning a swarm without its queen, all cells but one will have been destroyed; otherwise two or three swarms would probably issue and get away, leaving practically nothing behind them in the hive.

In some cases the swarm does not cluster when issuing with a clipped queen. In that case the hive from which it has come may be set aside for a few minutes and a box, skep, or other hive set in its place, when the queen, if found, may be allowed to run in with the returning bees. When, however, the queen returns to the hive after running out on to the alighting board and finding that she cannot fly, we must just allow the swarm to return and, after half an hour or so, go through combs in the ordinary way as described below.

When, in the normal routine inspection, a stock is found to have started queen-cells, the treatment varies to some extent. If nothing more than eggs or very young larvae are in the cells it is usual to destroy them and to leave the colony alone until the next visit, for very often, if a little manipulation of the brood-chamber is done to relieve any congestion there may be, and more room be allowed by giving another super, perhaps, the bees when again seen will be found to have abandoned their swarming preparations: it depends very much on the weather.

Once the bees have queen-cells containing advanced larvae, it is usually quite useless to attempt to prevent swarming by any method that does not satisfy the impulse. This is fully recognized by all who have any experience of the management of bees in out-apiaries. To destroy queen-cells will have no effect whatever, except to start the bees off building a lot more. Two of the silliest notions that have ever got into the heads of beekeepers are that destroying queen-cells will stop bees from swarming,. and that clipping queens will do the same. Neither action has the slightest influence on the bees as a deterrent to swarming, except in rare cases, when some sudden change in weather conditions happens to coincide with the breaking down of queen-cells by the bee-keeper.

Control without Increase

There are several plans that can be used with fair success by which the loss of swarms may be prevented, and yet increase avoided. The swarming urge can be allayed in three ways; by taking a swarm, by removing the queen, and so compelling a break in brood production, or by replacing the old queen by one of the current season that has just begun to lay. This, if done before a colony has shown any inclination to build queen-cells, will very commonly obviate swarming altogether for the season. The difficulty in this case is, of course, the provision of young queens early in the season, for it is next door to impossible to rear them in this country. In times of peace, queens can be got from Southern Europe, but one needs to be very careful as to the strains so purchased. Very fine queens have been reared in Italy in the past; but much rubbish has also been sent into this country from there.

The method of replacing an old queen by a young one is not as easy as it sounds. To simply remove the old queen and introduce a young one in her place would be very liable to lead to disaster, for in a large percentage of cases the introduction would be a failure, the young queen being rejected, cells being built, and swarming precipitated instead of prevented. But there is a better plan of action for achieving the desired result. Have a small nucleus hive ready. Any small roughly made one will do, provided it will hold about four frames. Have ready, also, four frames fitted with foundation. Now open the colony to be treated and having found the queen in order to make sure that she is left behind, remove from two to four combs of brood, bees and honey and place them in the nucleus box, shake the bees from two or three more combs into the box with the combs of brood, and close up the nucleus thus made. Push the combs that remain in the colony over to one side and fill up the brood-chamber with the frames of foundation provided.

In making nuclei in this way, it is probably best not to take more than two combs of brood, but when the treated colony is very strong and occupies two brood-chambers, one may take three or four with advantage. It is necessary to note that a very large number of bees must be shaken into the nucleus because all those that have flown from the parent colony will return to it.

We now have a colony strong in bees, but having been robbed of a part of its brood, unlikely to begin cell-building for some time at least: also a nucleus without a queen. This latter should be left alone for twenty-four hours, by which time the older bees will have rejoined the parent stock, leaving only quite young ones to care for the brood. These young bees will readily accept any queen given to them, and a young queen may be introduced in a semi-direct cage. When she has had a week or so in the nucleus, and has developed her full laying capacity, the queen of the parent colony may be removed, either with a comb or two of brood to form a nucleus, or not, and the entire nucleus with the young queen may be placed in the centre of the colony, room having been made for it by the removal of frames. See that the young queen is between two of the combs of the nucleus when uniting, so that she shall not immediately contact the workers of the stock. There should be no need for caging when this is done. It is best to remove the old queen about twelve hours before the uniting is done.

The above plan is for use before a colony begins to build swarming cells. Its advantage is that it does probably prevent swarming altogether; but as it is not by any means every colony that will attempt to swarm, it is not in the majority of cases necessary;

besides which, queens are expensive and difficult to obtain early enough in the season to be used in this way. We most of us, therefore, wait until we find a colony actually constructing queen-cells before we put any control methods into practice.

One method of swarm control without making increase is to make an artificial swarm on frames of foundation on the stand occupied by the colony treated, moving the combs of brood away to the rear. As soon as a young queen has commenced to lay in these combs, the old queen is done away with and the whole reunited after about fourteen days. When it is intended to reunite in this way, the combs in their hive should not be moved far, but placed close to the parent hive, though well to its rear.

Another plan is to make a nucleus with the queen when queen-cells are found. Have ready a nucleus box and take two combs of emerging brood together with the queen and some stores and place these in the nucleus box. Shake the bees from several combs into the nucleus so that enough bees will remain there to care for the brood after all the older ones have returned to the parent hive, as nearly all of them will. The nucleus is then placed close beside the parent stock, but with its entrance facing a little to one side, and it is as well that it should stand right on the ground so that the hive being on a stand will be a different level. Unless this precaution is taken, the queen will sometimes leave the nucleus with the returning field bees and enter the hive from which she has been taken.

Here I ought to point out that when bees are shaken from their combs in making the nucleus, the combs should be shaken hard so as to dislodge nearly all the bees on them, because it is the young bees we want to take away, and young bees are those that require the most shaking. It is surprising how much more easily forager bees are jarred off combs than are young bees that have never flown. So decided is this difference that I believe by gentle shaking, one could divide the population of a hive according to age, with a fair degree of accuracy.

Having made the nucleus, all queen-cells except one are destroyed in the parent stock, and also in the nucleus, though in the latter the bees themselves will usually tear down any that are on their combs.

Nine days later a virgin should have emerged from the cell left, and we then destroy all queen-cells. This queen should be mated and laying when the colony is next inspected, and if so the nucleus may be united to the parent colony minus its queen. This plan often works quite well; but like most other beekeeping operations, not always. In some seasons, not even in the majority of cases.

Here we come up against that greatest of all stumbling blocks in swarm control, the mating swarm. When a virgin queen is left in a strong stock, mating is most uncertain. Virgins always take longer to mate in strong stocks than in weak ones, and when they do fly out to meet a drone, it very frequently happens that the bees come out with them as a swarm, never to return. This means the complete ruin of the colony if the swarm gets away, for no brood being left, the bees cannot, except in very rare cases, produce another queen. To avoid this, it is a very good plan to place a push-in cage with an excluder slot, as described elsewhere in this book, over one good cell, so that a virgin can emerge normally, but cannot escape from the cage where she will be quite safe and well tended by the workers which can reach her through the excluder. At our next visit this virgin can be destroyed or removed and a fertile queen given in her place. As the safest of all methods of queen introduction is by replacing a virgin with a fertile queen, this plan is nearly always successful. The nucleus may be united after a further interval of nine days, or can be used for increase, as desired; but on no account unite until the new queen in the parent stock has fully established herself, or she will very likely be destroyed by the bees. Once this operation has been successfully completed, the colony will rarely give any further trouble for the rest of the season.

A system that has a fair measure of success is that of removing all queen-cells when first found, except those containing very young larvae or eggs, and at the same time removing the queen. After nine days again remove all queen-cells and give a young laying queen *in a semi-direct cage*. When this does work it is the best of all plans for control without increase, and I have had fine yields of honey by its use; but it doesn't always come off. What *should* happen is that the bees, having no unsealed brood and no queen of any kind, accept the queen presented to them, and at once start her off laying. This is ideal, for there is only a brood-break of nine days, and the young queen soon makes up for lost time. However, while a queen given in this way is rarely killed or even injured, the bees will quite frequently begin to raise queen-cells on her first brood, and will then swarm with her; or if she is clipped, will, after making one or two attempts to get away with her, allow a virgin to emerge and swarm with her. This is fatal for the honey crop, and a considerable proportion of the stocks I have treated in this way have so acted. Perhaps I have been unlucky or unskilful; in any case I have given up that plan.

Apart from the nucleus plan described, I have given up all attempts to control swarming without making increase, except in the case of colonies that are found to be making queen-cells late in the summer, say from 1st July onwards. By this time the season is becoming so far advanced that in normal years we must expect the honey-flow to end before very long, and, consequently, colony strength must be maintained. I need hardly point out that I am writing with a view to my own district, and readers will be readily able to adjust their proceedings to suit their localities, whether these are earlier or later. It is at this period of the year that it is wiser to try the de-queening plan rather than that of making an artificial swarm as described below, but even then it is probably better to make a nucleus with one comb of brood and the queen, and to reunite nine days later. This is probably the best plan for late work, for at that time it is above all things desirable to keep up the colony strength for a week or two, after which it does not matter so much, as the season will be over. But it requires a nucleus box for every stock treated.

Here I may as well note that these nucleus boxes need not be at all elaborate or expensive. All that is needed is to make a box to hold four to six frames and a dummy. Four frames will be enough for large combs, such as the Dadants, but for British standard equipment, five or six combs should be provided for. Always make your nucleus boxes roomy so that there is an extra half inch beyond the actual requirements of space for the appropriate number of frames. Also make them deep enough. A full inch under the combs is not too much. Arrange the bee-space over the top-bars, that is, have the walls of the box about three-eighths of an inch higher than the frames. Then the roof can be just a flat board, or a piece of thick waterproof plywood, well painted and cleated at the ends, but not at the sides. This is all that is required for these temporary homes.

Control with Increase

The control of swarming when increase can be accepted is quite a different business from that of checking it without adding to the number of our stocks. As already stated, I have given up all methods of control without increase except those I have described, and for dealing with swarming early in the season I now feel sure that it is better and more profitable, if increase is not absolutely inadmissible, to allow the bees to have their way. Since they cannot swarm naturally on account of the queen's inability to fly, we have no fear of any swarm being lost, although the queen may disappear should the colony attempt to swarm between routine inspections.

On finding queen-cells in a stock, I now generally make a shaken swarm. This is a simple operation. A well-ventilated empty hive, or better still, a travelling box, is set down by the colony to be treated. In cool weather we sometimes use a hive with its entrance closed with perforated zinc; but if it is hot a properly ventilated travelling box should always be used. Of course, if no travelling box is available, it is easy to make a ventilated cover for a hive, but travelling boxes are easily made at home, as was that shown in the illustration.

When making the artificial swarm, the cover of the receptacle, whatever it may be, is held by one person while another does the shaking. First of all the queen must be found and the comb she is on held down in the travelling box or hive and shaken, while the cover is moved aside. Having thus made sure of the queen, the bees are rapidly shaken from several combs until we have what is judged to be a moderately large swarm, such as might be expected to come from a colony of the strength of that being dealt with. And in making swarms in this way it is necessary to use a good deal of discretion in deciding as to the number of combs to be shaken, for a good deal depends on whether most of the bees are at home at the time, or whether the greater part of the population is away foraging. The middle of a hot day during a honey-flow is not a good time, as one does not get enough of the older bees, but I have not experienced any serious difficulty through this, for it is not usually in heavy flows that we are much troubled by cell-building.

When enough bees have been shaken, the swarm is fastened in

and removed to some shady spot until we are ready to go on to the next apiary, for no artificially made swarm can, of course, be released within bee-flight of its original home. The swarmed colony is then attended to. When taking the swarm, it is important that one comb with a queen-cell on it shall not be shaken, and it is wise to find such a comb and mark it before commencing to shake bees. All other cells are carefully removed and the hive closed up and left until the next visit, when a virgin may be expected to have emerged from the cell left. At the second visit all queen-cells are destroyed, after we have ascertained that a virgin has in fact emerged from the cell left. At this stage we may either kill the virgin, if we can find her, and give a young fertile queen, or the virgin may be left to mate.

Virgins in these cases usually mate satisfactorily, and do not often go off with mating swarms. That is to say that stocks so treated show little more inclination to throw off mating swarms than colonies do after normal natural swarming. The swarm taken, however, should be of fair size, such as would be expected to come from a stock of similar strength, swarming naturally, but it should not be too large or the parent stock will be seriously depleted, and its prospective crop of honey greatly prejudiced. Of course, any swarming will reduce the immediate increment of honey, for we are taking away large numbers of foragers, but stocks that swarm, or are artificially swarmed, will very often give excellent yields of honey before the season's end, and in years when the main honey-flow comes very late, they may even give a larger yield than unswarmed stocks. In such years, too, the swarms will often give heavy crops of honey.

Swarming, thus, does not always result in a reduction of the honey crop. A great deal depends upon how quickly the virgins mate in the swarmed stocks, and upon the season also. The ideal method of management by artificial swarming is to have plenty of young fertile queens on hand at the time, so that when shaking the swarm the cell left to emerge can be caged on the comb, as described a few pages earlier; then, at the second operation, when all queen-cells are destroyed, the caged virgin can be killed and a fertile queen substituted for her. This, as I say, is the ideal plan; but the trouble about it is that it is very difficult to get the necessary fertile queens. We used to be able to get them from Italy; and may again some day, but at the time of writing this is impossible. It is, unfortunately, equally impossible to rear queens in England early enough for the purpose.

The success of this plan of swarm control by artificial swarming also depends a great deal upon the strength of the colonies that give the swarms. It is not of much use to treat in this way stocks housed in the ordinary ten-comb brood-chambers of British orthodoxy, for only the most miserable little swarms can be got from them (which accounts for the orthodox dogma that swarmed stocks will give no honey), but when the colonies that provide the swarms are housed in double brood-chambers of standard size, or are in Dadant hives, why, you get swarms that you can do something with.

When too many stocks build queen-cells, and we wish to reduce the ratio of increase caused by this, we can, while still making artificial swarms, make the increase a matter of 50 per cent instead of doubling the number of hives. To do so, we simply shake two swarms together and so have one very large swarm. Such double swarms will give an almost immediate return in surplus honey if a strong honey-flow immediately supervenes the making of the swarms, but if a period of dearth should follow, such swarms are no better, and often less useful than single ones. No queen, you understand, could fill up a sufficient brood area to replace the natural losses of the population of such large masses of bees, and it will usually be found that after a few weeks such double swarms will be no better than single ones made at the same time. Besides which, I have found that double swarms are very apt to supersede their queens about a month after being made up.

Here, again, I come to another of the snags we beekeepers all have to be prepared for. I have found that swarms made in this way are on the whole much more liable to supersede their queens than are natural swarms. I don't know why; but so it is.

There is an advantage in giving a fertile queen at the first operation nine days after taking the swarm; but I don't recommend it, because, while it is a fine thing when it goes right, it does not always do so. If a fertile queen be given at the end of the nine days, while there is still a great quantity of sealed brood in the hive, there is grave danger that the bees will raise queen-cells on the new queen's brood and swarm with her. On the whole, if the breed is a desirable one, it is probably better, I think, and safer, to let the virgin alone over the second nine-days' spell, at the end of which time, if she has not mated, she should be replaced by a fertile queen.

Here we are up against another of those snags so often found when we are dealing with bees. It is easy enough to say that the virgin should be replaced, but it is generally a much less simple thing to do it. Like the proverbial hare, the virgin must first be caught, and to find a virgin queen in a powerful colony is not at all an easy job; furthermore, should we fail to find her, it is no proof that the colony is queenless. We can't be sure, and without certainty we dare not expose a valuable fertile queen to the tender mercies of a possible virgin; there is, therefore, only one thing to be done, and we place in that colony a comb of unsealed brood so that at our next visit we can tell at once the state of affairs. We call combs so used 'Test' combs. It is because of this difficulty, and also because of the risk of the issue of virgins with mating swarms, those bugbears of all bee-farmers, that the caging of the cell and subsequent introduction of a fertile queen about the eighteenth day after swarming is recommended, if queens are to be had.

Here I will point out that by the use of bees of Italian origin, whose queens are much more readily noticed than those of the brown or other dark varieties, the saving of time in hunting for queens, both fertile and virgin, is immense. It is not necessary to have very yellow queens, but it is a great advantage to have queens that have a good deal of colour. They catch the eye much more readily, and this is especially the case with virgins; for a dark-coloured fertile queen, even if somewhat reduced in size through the shrinkage of her ovaries, is yet much more easily spotted than a virgin, for a fertile queen, except in an extreme stage of abdominal contraction, displays some colour at the joints of the segments, whereas a virgin shows little or none. While dealing with this matter I would mention that when swarming has been frustrated for several days, that is to say when sealed queen-cells are present, and the bees have attempted to swarm once or several times, and have returned to their hive through their queen being unable to fly, queens are often so greatly shrunken through not having been fed for egg production that it is sometimes even more difficult to see them than to see good-sized virgins.

SWARM CONTROL AND SUMMER WORK

This is an important reason for dealing at once with colonies found to have started swarm-cells, rather than postponing treatment to another visit, after destroying the cells. Only experienced beekeepers can have an adequate idea of the great decrease in size that a fertile queen sustains when her workers cease to care for her, and it is hard to realize that a miserable-looking shrivelled little creature that we see being hustled around the hive to-day is the identical insect that we saw a week ago when in full lay, walking over the combs with a great swollen abdomen; but just make an artificial swarm with her, and in a few days she will once again be her old self.

Making double swarms presents no difficulty. Just shake first one and then the other into your travelling box or other receptacle and the bees will unite quite peaceably. All swarms should be fed as soon as they have been placed on their permanent stands. It is usually better to hive large swarms on foundation, plus one drawn-out comb; but the foundation should not be given until the swarm has reached its final resting place. I usually start a new apiary each year with artificial swarms made in this way, and in some seasons such apiaries give very good crops of surplus honey. In a favourable season I have known such swarms hived on eleven Modified Dadant combs and with a super of Dadant shallow frames, all fitted with foundation only, to virtually fill the whole in nine days; but such performances are very exceptional.

When making examinations of colonies, especially those that have been dealt with to control swarming, it is well to know what to be on the look out for, and I here give a few hints.

If you find an egg in a queen-cell in a stock that has no other brood at all, that colony has a laying worker in it, and unless a normal queen-cell or a comb of young brood is given, at your next visit you will find laying workers both active and numerous.

If a stock is without brood and it is not known for certain whether a virgin is present or not, and you find a queen-cell with pollen in it, you may bet your last dollar that there is no queen.

If you have given a new queen at your previous visit, and find no brood when you inspect the combs to see if the introduction has been successful, there may be a virgin in the hive; but if you see the worker bees standing about buzzing and fanning, the colony is certainly without any queen, and either a queen-cell or young brood should be given to it: in fact it is best to give both, for a couple of combs of unsealed brood and a queen-cell, if given at once, may save the situation. But don't try to introduce a fertile queen in these circumstances: you will lose her if you do, almost every time.

If you suspect queenlessness, but find that the bees have a patch of comb all cleaned and polished up ready for eggs, there is almost certainly a virgin in the hive; in fact there is quite probably a mated queen that has not yet started to lay.

There is no known plan of swarm control that can in all circumstances be depended upon to work without fail: at any rate I don't know of one, and have not yet met an experienced man who claimed to do so. I have read plenty of books and articles dealing with this matter, and some of these writings are quite pathetically artless, so much so that one feels rather sorry for the writers on account of their obvious inexperience. Dogmatism in beekeeping usually, I think, indicates inexperience, for I cannot imagine a man with really extensive knowledge laying down the law about bees and their actions.

I should like, here, to mention one very interesting circumstance that all beekeepers are almost certain to meet sooner or later. It will happen sometimes, even in the best regulated of apiaries, that queens or virgin queens will be lost, leaving their colonies, generally speaking, hopelessly queenless. Now although such stocks, unless assisted by the beekeeper who may give unsealed brood, a queen-cell, or even a fertile queen, are in a completely hopeless condition in nine cases out of ten, yet every now and then there will be found in one of these queenless colonies a perfectly normal queen-cell from which a normal virgin will emerge and mate quite successfully. The same thing does occasionally happen in colonies that have laying workers in them. Now where does the egg that produces the queen in such cases come from? Many theories have been put forward from time to time, including the (to my thinking) quite preposterous one that worker bees that are without the means of raising a queen will go out on a robbing expedition, and entering the hive of some queen-right colony, carry off an egg from it to their own home and there rear a queen for themselves. That bees will move eggs from one part of their hive to another is quite credible, but that they should enter the hive of another colony for the purpose of stealing an egg seems to me to be extremely unlikely, and to assume an altogether impossible degree of intelligence, courage and restraint on the part of an insect.

There are other ways of accounting for this phenomenon. It seems to me that such queens may sometimes be raised from eggs that have been lying neglected in some chilly corner of the combs, until found and tended by the workers. I do not know for certain, but I think it likely that bees' eggs may remain inert when neglected in this way, but may well retain their viability.

There is another way of accounting for the presence of good queen-cells where we should not expect them to be possible. The laying worker is a very common occupant of queenless stocks, as I have mentioned earlier in this essay, and it has recently been shown that on rare occasions—perhaps not so rare either—these bees can and do lay eggs that develop into females, and will produce queens if fed for that purpose. It has also been proved that queens that have been confined to their hives so that they have been unable to mate, have laid eggs from which queens and workers have been raised. I do not know just how this can be accounted for, but I see no reason why an occasional diploid ovum should not for some reason miss its reduction division and so, without conjugation with a male cell, be furnished with the full set of thirty-two chromosomes and consequently develop into a female bee.

Although these female cells are occasionally found, let no inexperienced beekeeper, should he find cells that look like queen-cells in some colony that is believed to be hopelessly queenless, conclude that all must be well. These cases are comparatively rare, and in the great majority of cases such cells will be built over male larvae, and their contents will be quite useless. Such cells are very common indeed, but they can generally be distinguished from genuine queen-cells by their appearance. They are smoother, and have thinner walls; in fact, to the experienced eye are usually unmistakable. I have known drones in these cells to reach the stage of becoming coloured; but have never known a drone emerge from one.

Towards the end of the summer we usually have a few colonies that are in this hopeless state. Often they have laying workers in them. The only safe way to treat such stocks is to give a comb of brood with a queen-cell on it. Of course, you can let a newly emerged virgin run on to the combs, and she will often be accepted, but the cell is the best thing to give. Never attempt to introduce a fertile queen to a stock in which laying workers are active, for you will lose her in nearly every case. But if no laying workers are present and the bees seem distressed and are fanning on the combs when their hive is opened, a fertile queen may be allowed to run on to a comb among the bees. If these seem friendly and allow her to run about among them unmolested, or if they touch her with their antennae, you may fairly safely lower the comb she is on into the hive and close it. If you see bees actually feeding the new queen, then you may be practically certain that she will be accepted at once.

It has been asserted that colonies with young queens are less liable to swarm than others, but apart from stocks that have been re-queened with mothers of the current season's rearing, after a short broodless period, I can't say that I have ever been able to confirm this claim. I don't think it makes a bit of difference what the age of the queen may be so long as she is in full vigour. A failing queen, of course, is well known to act as a stimulus to queen-cell construction at all times, and when this happens in the swarming season the stock, if strong, will swarm. At other seasons this leads to normal supersedure which may or may not be successful.

It has also been claimed that the presence of many drones will lead to swarming, presumably through the crowding of the hive, but I must confess that I have never been able to confirm this either, and I have yet to learn that a large number of drones in a stock does any harm at all; in fact, when we are harvesting our honey we are always struck by the fact that the stocks that have the most honey almost always have a large number of drones. I don't say that it is cause and effect, but I say that we have found the fact as stated.

There is one factor, however, that I had better mention while dealing with this question of drones and swarm control. In all plans that rely on dividing the brood-chamber with queen-excluder, as in the demaree system, a great deal of trouble is sometimes entailed by the trapping of drones above the excluder. Sometimes a drone-hole is provided (just a small hole bored through the wall of the upper story or something of that sort) so that drones can leave at will; but in my opinion the place for drones and queens is the brood-chamber, and there they should be kept.

We have seen that on a large bee farm the greater part of the summer work consists of operations connected with swarm control, but there are other matters that have to be attended to during these eight or nine crucial weeks. Supers have to be given as required, and for my part I would always recommend that what is known as 'top supering' should be the rule. Each super needed should be set on top of those already in position. Don't lift a super that is three parts full and being worked on by the bees and place an empty one under it, as is so generally recommended. It may be all right in some climates, but I am pretty clear that in this country it is not. Of course, when honey is needed and the bottom super of a pile is full and sealed, that super can be taken away; but the rest should be returned in the same order as before.

Sometimes it is desired to transfer bees from British standard to Modified Dadant or Langstroth equipment. If the bees to be transferred are a small lot with brood on only three or four combs, it is best to fasten the entire frames of comb inside the M.D. frames, as shown in the photograph. If we wish to transfer to Langstroth frames it can be done in the same way by removing the bottom bars of the Langstroth frames. If the stock to be transferred is a strong one that fills a brood-chamber, it should be placed bodily over a set of drawn combs of the size desired, so that the bees can transfer themselves. This is rather complicated by the fact that the bee-space of British stuff is under, and of American, over, the frames. However, it is an easy matter to get over this difficulty by making a rough box for the purpose of transfer and afterwards discarding it.

Making Late Increase

Towards the end of the summer, about the third or fourth week of July, before the honey-flow is altogether over, it is a good plan to make up any increase that may be desired. I described this operation in detail in my other book, and need only say here that by taking one or two combs of brood with their adhering bees from each of enough stocks to make up nuclei of five to seven combs, being very careful to see that the queen is left behind in every hive from which brood is taken, we can remove these nuclei (they are really quite strong stocks) to another apiary and introduce a queen to each forthwith. When the combs are being taken for this purpose, they are placed in the hive in such a way that there is a good space between their faces, for this prevents the bees from starting to fight before we can unite them properly. As soon as all are in the new hive, they are just shoved up together by means of a hive tool and a dummy placed next to them and fastened by a couple of small wooden blocks tacked to the hive sides. The hive is then well jarred and knocked to frighten the bees. Bees treated so won't fight and by the time they have travelled to their new home will have settled down quite happily. Queens introduced to these nuclei by the cage I have described are only very rarely rejected. New stocks made up in this way will turn out to be among the best next year. I know of no other way of making increase which entails no reduction of the honey crop in any shape or form. This proceeding can only be carried out by those who have out-apiaries or can arrange for a temporary site for their new stocks until they shall have become established.

Apart from making actual increase in the ordinary meaning of the term, it is a rather good plan to make up a number of colonies as described above, and to winter them in rough boxes made of stout but rough and inexpensive boards to hold eight or nine frames. These boxes must, of course, have good waterproof covers, but the whole thing can be made for a trifling outlay. Bees winter very well in these, and in the spring the stocks so carried over can be used to restock any hives in which colonies have died or become queenless during the winter. In this way we can to a great extent avoid having a lot of empty hives on our hands, and there is nothing much more unproductive than an empty hive. This hint may be useful to those who have not thought of it and who lose stocks during winter, though it will not be of any interest to those fortunate people who always have their bees come through without loss.

Summer work on a bee farm is strenuous, but interesting, and usually very pleasant. Hours are long, but there is no need to begin the day very early now that summer-time and double summer-time have replaced Greenwich time. It's no use changing the clock so far as bees are concerned: they take no notice of that, and as it may be late before we are able to leave off in the evening it is better to start rather late in the morning. The double summer-time helps a lot, we find, when we have bees to move, for the earlier in the morning that is done the better, and it pushes the whole job forward to pretend that it is six o'clock when it is really only four.

There is a sort of tradition that keeping bees is a light and easy job: so it is; but if you want the bees to keep you, you will find it necessary to do a great deal of hard and heavy labour. However, it is good, clean, healthy work, this summer care of bees, and quite enjoyable unless the weather is very bad, and I know of no more comforting sight than hundreds of supers full of new-sealed honey. We don't mind lifting them!

Before I conclude this chapter on the work of the summer season, it may be advisable for me to try to give a few hints on queen finding. Every queen on a properly managed bee farm should be seen at least twice every year; once in the spring at the first examination of the stock, when we must make certain that she is properly clipped. It is not enough to know that the colony in question was headed by a clipped queen when settled for winter the autumn before, for we can never be certain that such a queen has not been superseded. Every year I find many such queens, and were they left unseen, swarms might easily be lost.

Apart from this routine queen finding, it is necessary to see queens for many reasons during the summer, and unless the bee-man is fairly experienced in the art, much time may be lost in vain endeavours to find queens when time is very precious on a honey-farm.

In the first place, if you want to find a queen quickly, look for her; concentrate on looking for the queen and for nothing else. If you wish to find a queen in any stock, don't smoke the entrance before opening the hive, and don't smoke more than you can possibly help at any time. One reason why it is easier to find queens in good-tempered stocks is that the search can be carried out without much smoking, for the less bees are excited and frightened the more quietly they stay on their combs and the more readily the queen is seen.

When it is desired to find the queen in a large supered stock, the way to go about it is this. First remove the supers in a body, without much smoking. If you have smoked the entrance, tip up the supers and look under them, for queens are very apt to get up on to the under side of the queen excluder when this is done. If she is not there the frames should be taken out one by one, the first being leaned against the hive in order to allow plenty of room; in fact it is a good plan to remove two frames in this way if the weather is warm. The first frame will seldom have much brood on it and it will not matter if it does get cold. As you lift out the combs, take a good look at the face of the next comb in the hive, for, as most people know, the queen will immediately run down the comb as soon as it is exposed to light, and slip under its bottom edge like a shot. While she is running down, she is very conspicuous to anyone who is looking down into the hive, especially if the light from the sun is shining right into it. I think quite a quarter of the queens we find here are found in that way. If no queen is seen there, examine the comb you hold in your hand, and if no queen is on it, put it back into the hive and repeat the operation with the next.

Contrary to the general belief, it is much easier to find a queen while the hive is full of bees: I mean while most of the foraging bees are at home. When nearly all are in the fields and the combs are only thinly covered, queens will run about all over the place in a way that they hardly ever do when the combs are crowded.

In April and May queens are much more commonly found towards the outside of the hive, especially on newly occupied combs. In summer there is no guessing where a queen is most likely to be, but in the autumn queens are generally to be found towards the centre of the brood-nest.

It is a great help in searching for a queen to know just what she looks like. If you are under the impression that a queen is yellow or light brown, you will very often fail to see a black queen. Light-coloured queens are, of course, much more easily spotted than are blacks; but there is one type of bee that has queens that are quite difficult to see, albeit are light in colour. These are those Italian crosses in which the queens and workers are almost exactly the same colour. The easiest of all queens to see is a bright-coloured Italian among black bees, or a black queen among light Italians.

Every now and then we fail to find a queen after going through her combs twice, and in that case it is always best to close up the hive and leave it for a quarter of an hour or so, and then have another try. In five cases out of six the queen will be found at once when the second examination is carried out.

Many a time have I failed to find the queen, and have then looked around me on the grass and there found her. Twice I have stepped on such a dropped queen; so be careful of this. Heavy clipped queens easily drop from combs, especially when they are rather old.

Sometimes when we are dealing with very nervous and excitable bees, it is almost impossible to find the queen, for she will rush off the combs with the bees, and the whole tribe will run from one side of the hive to the other as if the devil were after them. In such cases as this I usually take all the combs out of the hive and can as a rule find the queen running around on the floor or on the sides of the hive; but I need hardly say that when caught it is as well to remove a queen like that altogether and introduce another of more amenable strain.

The late C. C. Miller, who used to give so many good tips in the American bee magazines and who died in 1920, gave this method for catching difficult queens. Remove three or four combs to a spare hive, making sure that the queen is not on one of them. Then arrange the remaining combs in pairs with a good space between each pair. After a short time you will find the queen in the seam of bees between one of these pairs of combs. I never tried this myself, but Miller was no fool where bees were concerned, but an exceedingly able beekeeper.

I tried using the marking plan years ago, thinking it would make queen finding easy, but although I tried gold, silver, and several colours for the marking discs, I did not find it much help for I nearly always saw the queen before I noticed the mark. The fact is that after a man has been finding queens by thousands for many years, he becomes rather adept at the job; but the marking may help others. It is applied by means of a small instrument known as the Eckhardt marking set, and once the queen is marked and safely established it seems to work all right, but such queens are very liable to be superseded soon after being marked. Personally, I would not mark queens now.

CHAPTER VIII

THE INTRODUCTION OF QUEEN BEES

The introduction of queens to alien colonies is the most difficult and uncertain of all beekeeping operations. That is my opinion, in spite of all that has been said and written by those who have from time to time explained, and who continue to explain, how simple, certain, and easy the whole business is for anyone who will only follow their advice. The plain fact is, so simple and straightforward is this job, that for many years a considerable literature has been published in the bee-press of nearly all countries to explain how to do it, and finally we have an entire volume of two hundred pages devoted exclusively to this single operation: *The Introduction of Queen Bees* by Snelgrove.

I have been introducing queens for more than thirty years and have introduced thousands, and I still find queen introduction an exceedingly tricky business. I have been trying to find some method that will ensure safe introduction during all this time, and I find myself to-day far from satisfied with any plan tried. This can hardly be attributable to some peculiarity in my personal make-up, because several other men who have to manage large numbers of stocks of bees have told me that they are in exactly the same boat; in fact one extensive bee farmer of long experience wrote to me in 1943: 'I have been experimenting with queen introduction for more than twenty years, and am as completely in a fog to-day as when I began.'

I remember my own experiences very well. It was not until after I had been keeping bees for some three or four years, as well as I remember, that I bought my first queen. I forget whether it was one of Sladen's 'Goldens' or one of Simmins's 'White Stars'; but in any case I had read *A Modern Bee Farm* in which is given the author's method of direct introduction, and this was the plan I tried first. The queen was accepted quite satisfactorily, and so were the next three or four introduced, and I thought to myself that those who made such a fuss about so simple a matter must be stupid indeed. Why bother with cages and other gadgets when it was so easy to give queens direct?

However, like all beginners, I wanted to try Italians, Carniolans, and other varieties, and these ambitions soon provided me with experiences which resolved that puzzle, for a very serious percentage of queens introduced thereafter were rejected by the bees. I tried the mailing cage which was even less successful; and after that a Raynor cage which was worse again, so I reverted to direct action. I think I must have lost about 30 per cent of the queens in those days, and I believe that this is very generally the case with beginners and amateurs who buy queens. A dealer in imported queens once told me that at least 50 per cent of the queens sent out were lost in introduction, adding that he reckoned that most of the rest were afterwards spoiled by wrong methods of management.

So, while I will try to give some information based on my own experiences of the more successful ways of persuading bees to accept alien queens, I am afraid I don't know of any method that is even 90 per cent safe at all times. I should be very glad indeed to find one, for losses of queens in introduction, after all the care and work of breeding them, are very trying; but these losses seem unavoidable in at least a small percentage of cases, no matter what system is operated. Hardly a month passes without the appearance in one or other of the bee magazines of some article on introduction. Most of these are so very artless that one cannot help a feeling of pity for the authors of the efforts, so confidently given, to assist others in an operation with which the writers have pretty evidently only a very limited knowledge themselves. We are told that if only the job is done in some particular way, all will be well.

But what is the right way? What are we to make of such a fact as this? Thirty-six queens are removed from the mating nuclei at nine a.m. They are introduced to three apiaries later in the same day, apiaries situated in similar country and quite near together. Twelve queens are introduced in each apiary to stocks that require re-queening for the purpose of replacing two-year-old queens. All are given in exactly the same way. In one apiary all twelve are accepted; in a second, all but one; in the third, seven out of the twelve are rejected. I am not suggesting that there is no valid reason for it: there *is* a reason; but what it is I cannot tell. I only wish I did know why rejection is sometimes the rule in one apiary while all, or almost all, the queens are accepted in another. There was no robbing anywhere. It could hardly be because the apiaries were dealt with, necessarily, at slightly different times of the day, because all queens were caged in push-in cages allowing access to the queen only after an interval, and through excluder. That is the sort of puzzle we are up against, and I am tempted to think that those who tell us so confidently of methods whereby introduction may be made virtually 100 per cent safe, are really basing their confidence upon insufficient experience.

Condition of the Queen

Before going into the various methods of introduction, it may be well to consider the different conditions under which we have to give the queens, the various purposes which the introduction is intended to serve, and the condition of the queen that is to be introduced.

Taking the last point first: the condition of the queen is of far more importance than we are apt to think. In the matter of giving a virgin queen it is of great consequence, for it is a well-known fact that a newly emerged virgin will be accepted by almost any colony, even if that colony already has a fertile queen of its own. But the virgin will only be tolerated for a short time in the latter case. As soon as she passes from the soft state in which she emerges from her cell, the bees cease to treat her with indifference and, recognizing her as the alien she is, set upon her and destroy her. Such a virgin will sometimes be permanently accepted if run on to the combs when the old queen is removed at the same operation.

The theory of this is that on emergence from the cell all bees are in soft, immature condition, in the sense that they are not in a state to take any active part in the community of the hive (just as newly emerged butterflies and moths need a short period to harden up and mature before beginning their active life), and that while in this state they are completely ignored by the other bees; treated, in fact, like any other newly emerged bees. As soon, however, as they take on full maturity they are no longer ignored, but are either killed by the workers or accepted by them as their new mother.

Two or three times in my experience I have known a stock of

bees of an undesirable strain in which a black virgin was known to be present, to be re-queened by the simple process of dropping into the hive an Italian virgin that had just emerged from her cell. The bees, apparently, made no distinction between them, but accepted the survivor of the inevitable battle between the two. An account of such a case was given by H. Wickens in *Bee Craft*, March 1944. It must be emphasized, however, that the virgin used in this way must always be one that has newly emerged *at the completion of her pupation* and not one that has been held imprisoned in her cell by the workers; for a queen that is kept confined in this way, as is very frequently the case, is no more likely to be allowed to run about on the combs of an alien colony than a fully matured virgin that has been free in her own nucleus or colony. Hundreds of times I have seen queens that have been confined by the workers for days, emerge from their cells, on the comb being taken out, and many have taken flight immediately.

As for fertile queens, generally speaking it is fairly easy to introduce those that are taken straight from the colony in which they are laying normally, while introduction becomes more and more hazardous the longer the queen has been removed from that colony. Thus, a queen taken straight from her own colony and forthwith introduced to another in the same apiary has a very much better chance of acceptance by direct introduction of any kind than has one that must be caged and carried to another apiary, even if the caging lasts only an hour or so; and it is a very risky proceeding indeed to attempt direct introduction by any method when the queen has suffered a long confinement in a mailing cage.

Other things being equal, it is far easier to introduce young, vigorous queens of the current year than older ones. Very old queens are difficult to introduce unless they are unusually youthful for their age. This last fact is useful as a guide to the value of prospective breeding mothers. When I bring home one of these for introduction to a nucleus with the view to using her as a breeder next summer, I sometimes find the bees superseding her after only a few days or a week or two. When they do this, I make up my mind to accept their verdict that her usefulness is probably over. I have rescued such queens and given them to other nuclei; but they rarely survive the winter.

Condition of the Colony

The condition of a colony that is to be given a new queen is equally as important as the state of the queen to be introduced, and this matter must be brought out as far as possible while describing the various purposes which introduction is intended to serve, and the methods of introduction found most reliable.

First in importance is the replacing of old queens after the honey-flow, and of queens, not old, but otherwise unsatisfactory. Secondly we require, sometimes, to introduce queens in the work connected with swarm control. We have also to be able to give virgin queens to nuclei in the course of rearing queens.

General rules may, I think, be set down as follows. The stronger the stock, the more difficult the introduction. The larger the proportion of field bees in the colony, the more difficult it is to have a queen accepted. Stocks that have once rejected a queen, and have ceased to have unsealed brood, are next door to impossible, so far as getting them to accept a fertile queen goes, unless a considerable amount of unsealed brood is first given to them. Introduction during a heavy honey-flow is very easy, but is frequently followed by swarming. In early spring, stocks that happen to be found queenless, or with poor queens while still having brood, are very easily re-queened. At the close of the honey-flow, especially when this occurs suddenly, it is for some days virtually waste of time and queens to attempt introduction; but as the autumn draws on and bees become progressively more quiet with the cessation of nectar secretion, and as the older field bees die off, introduction becomes more and more likely to be a success; in fact, I hardly remember a case of rejection in October, unless, as does occasionally happen, a virgin has been present in the hive with the old queen. But we must use our queens as they are reared; we cannot hold them all until late in the year, and this brings us back to the methods that may be used with tolerable success at other times and seasons.

There are roughly three systems of introduction; direct, semi-direct, and by some form of caging. Taking the direct methods first, I may as well point out that it is always possible to transpose any two queen-right stocks and so have the whole of the flying population of the one enter the other, and vice versa, without consequent injury to either queen; at least, I have never known either queen to suffer in any way whatever through this proceeding. It would seem, therefore, that the field bees of a colony do not take any notice of the queen so long as she is surrounded by the bees that attend to her and to the brood. These are the young nurse bees, and it seems probable to me that direct introduction depends on the assumption that these young bees are not very discriminating, and do not take much notice of the queen that appeals to them for food. If this is so, and I think it is, we can readily see why a queen that runs right down into the brood-nest when in full laying condition should very commonly be accepted right off. The theory also accounts for the too frequent loss of such queens through their not going directly to the brood-nest where they would be accepted by the undiscerning nurses, but rather wandering off among the field bees which recognize them as alien.

Direct Introduction

Taking direct introduction first, we have the fasting plan of Simmins, the water method of Snelgrove, and the 'one-hour' idea of the same writer; also several plans based on the shaking of all the bees on to a board in front of the hive after removing their queen and dropping the new queen among the frightened bees as they run back into their hive; the smoke method and others.

The semi-direct plan is very useful in swarm control introduction. The queen is placed in a small, narrow cage that will fit between the top-bars of the frames, the egress hole being stopped with just enough candy to hold her imprisoned for an hour or two so that before the queen is free the stock shall have settled down after the disturbance of opening the hive. The cage methods must be treated in some detail, I am afraid, as they are really the only practicable plans for use on a bee farm of any extent.

The Simmins fasting plan is useful only for an apiary situated near the home of its owner. The queen is removed about midday; the new one is placed in a small box, alone and without food, for half an hour before introduction, which should be at, or after, dusk. At the end of the thirty minutes' fast, the queen is allowed to run down between the combs after a little smoke has driven back the bees.

I have long since abandoned this method after extensive tests, as being much too risky. All of 25 per cent of queens may be expected to be lost, so far as my experience goes: that is, of course, when the method is employed in the ordinary way for re-queening in August and September.

Of the water method of Snelgrove I have virtually no experience. I thought when I first read of it that here at long last we had the ideal plan for the man working a lot of out-apiaries. So I tried it three times—and I lost the queen three times. It may have been bad luck, I suppose, or bad management; but it was done as directed. It may have been pure coincidence; but another man who is an extensive bee farmer has had a similar experience on a larger scale, as he has told me. So I am afraid of this water plan, as being, like other direct methods, too uncertain.

The 'one-hour' plan I have never tried, so cannot say anything about it from my own experience. I will try it some day if I can, but as it is quite useless for out-apiaries far from home, and as all our bees are in out-apiaries, it is not easy to do so. The queen to be superseded is removed at dusk and killed or used elsewhere. At the same time a few of the bees of her colony are taken in a matchbox and kept without food for about ten minutes. As is well known, bees so treated will accept any queen that is given to them, so at the end of the ten minutes you put the new queen into that matchbox with those bees from the colony to which she is to be introduced. After one hour, lay the matchbox containing the bees and queen top down on the frames under the quilt (or over the feed-hole in the crown-board if your hives are of the more sensible sort that dispense with quilts), smoke a little and push the matchbox open to allow the queen and bees to run down into the hive. This plan is said to be very successful, and it certainly appears likely to be so, to judge from Mr. Snelgrove's description of it, for there can be no reasonable doubt that any direct introduction should be carried out after dark when all the bees are at home, and not while foragers are constantly streaming into the hive, for these incoming bees are not attuned to accept a new queen, having undergone no experience of queenlessness. Personally, I very much doubt if the preliminary introduction of the new queen to the isolated bees in the matchbox has any particular effect on the successfulness of this operation.

For a summary of all the plans put forward at different times the reader is referred to Mr. Snelgrove's exhaustive work: here I can only briefly describe those methods which I have found least discouraging in extensive trials over many years. And readers should remember that methods useful in a garden apiary are out of the question on a honey-farm where the bees are in apiaries that can be visited only at intervals of nine or ten days, a circumstance that does not appear to have occurred to Mr. Snelgrove.

The small cage for what I call semi-direct introduction, used as described in a later chapter dealing with swarm control, is a very simple one. I first had it, indirectly, from Brother Adam

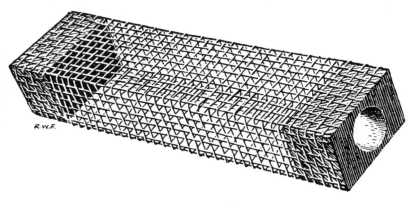

Figure 6

SEMI–DIRECT CAGE AS USED BY THE REV. BRO. ADAM

of Buckfast Abbey. I have since made many similar cages myself. It is just a compartment of wire cloth, narrow enough to fit between the top-bars of a hive, and with a wooden block at each end, through each of which a hole is bored. Brother Adam's cage has a hole only through one end; but it is much better to have both ends bored, so that one hole can be filled with candy and the other with a cork; otherwise, the candy must be inserted after the queen, and this is often very inconvenient. Such a cage can be readily made by anyone in a very few minutes.

Introduction by Caging

For general re-queening on a bee farm it is necessary to cage the queen. That much is certain: but what kind of cage is the best to use? All I can say is that on our place we have given up all other kinds in favour of a special one we make ourselves. I don't claim that it is perfect by any means; but it is the best we have been able to invent up to the present. We have also, during the seasons of 1942–4, experimented with it on a considerable scale with a view to finding the best method of using it. I shall not, therefore, occupy any space here in going into all the many designs of cages and methods of using them that have been put forward from time to time. Those who are interested in these matters can find them all described in the many books that deal with bee management generally and queen introduction particularly.

It may interest readers if I relate how, over the past fifteen or twenty years, I have gradually come to prefer caging on comb to any other form of introduction. As stated, I early found that the mailing cage could not be relied on; still less were many other cages found safe. I tried what is called the 'pipe-cover' cage. I need not describe it. The queen is caged on the comb and can be fed through the wire mesh by the bees. After a few days the hive is opened, any queen-cells that are present destroyed, and the queen released by taking away the cage. But results are far from satisfactory. At least that was so with me; and I don't believe the plan is ever very successful, for were this so, the method would have long ago become popular, whereas it is not much used anywhere so far as I know.

Some twenty years ago, or more, Jay Smith, a well-known queen-breeder of U.S.A., constructed a cage which embodied the queen-excluder system of Chantry. The fact having been discovered that a queen caged on a comb in an alien colony will not, as a rule, be injured by the bees so long as she remains in the cage, it followed that by the use of queen-excluder it is easy to have a queen confined in a push-in cage while allowing workers access to her through a slot of excluder zinc. If we so arrange matters that the bees do not have immediate access to the caged queen when she is inserted at the time of the removal of the old queen, it is really an extremely rare event for them to do her any injury; in fact when we do find a queen dead in the cage we strongly suspect the presence of a virgin in the hive: but a queen is killed on rare occasions.

Smith's cage was a somewhat clumsy arrangement, though the

principle of it was excellent. It was oblong and had a collar of the same shape with a lot of pointed teeth which could be pressed into the comb. These teeth were very liable to pierce the septum of the comb which caused the bees to bite holes through from the other side. This let out the queen before the desired time. Smith's idea was that the queen would be fed by her new workers and lay in the cells under the cage, and could then be released by means of candy. She would be accepted because, he says, she will lay in those few cells. She will, he asserts, lay again and again until the cells are almost full of eggs. I used this cage for some time as an experiment and found it a great improvement on those used before, though I have never known queens, either in it or in any other push-in-excluder cage, to lay quite so liberally as those of Mr. Smith.

There are some points about this cage that I dislike. I object to the rectangular shape of the collar of metal which must be pressed into the comb, often making it necessary to place one hand on the opposite side of the comb to prevent it from being pushed out by the pressure when placing the cage in position; I also very much dislike the point system of fixing the cage as I have mentioned above. So I got busy and made a number of cages that I thought were improvements on Smith's. The first that was really good was the square one illustrated here. It was a small square frame on which was mounted a round collar of perforated zinc which could be made to cut into the comb by a screwing motion. It had two holes, one of which was covered by a slot of excluder zinc. I was very successful with it, or at all events as successful as with Smith's cage; but it had faults, like the best of us. The method of use was to remove the old queen and at the same time cage the new one on a comb with the excluder-covered hole filled with candy, so that the bees could not enter the cage for some little time. The other hole was blocked with a plug of wood. After five days or so the hive was opened and any queen-cells destroyed, after which the wooden plug was replaced by a plug of candy and the hive closed. The results were fairly good—better than with any cage used before; but there were too many losses, and besides, the plan required two visits to do the introducing and a third to make sure that all was well. I was far from satisfied.

Some six or seven years ago my friend E. W. D. Madoc showed

me a cage which he had made which was a great improvement on mine, though in fact it was a development of the same idea. In this cage everything was identical with mine except that one of the four sides of the wooden frame was much wider than the other three, so that two entrance tunnels could be arranged side by side. The wide side being one and a quarter inches through, the tunnels were of that length. The idea was that by using this cage the introduction could be done in one operation instead of two. So it can. You half fill one tunnel with candy and fill the other right

Figure 7

ORIGINAL QUEEN-CAGE

up. In theory the bees enter the cage after eating out the half-filled tunnel, which is, of course, the one covered with excluder, and become familiar with the queen before the other tunnel is cleared. It *should* work, but in fact it doesn't in too high a percentage of cases.

We have now worked out a new system of introduction with the cage last described, with the best results of any I have tried. At the time of writing (the winter of 1944–5) I can only claim the experience of one season; but the improvement of the new method over the old would appear to be very great, for out of about four hundred queens given to stocks, only a very few were rejected. I cannot give the exact percentage; but leaving out a few losses caused by virgins which were present, unknown to us when the old queens were removed, I doubt if a dozen queens were lost that were given in straightforward introduction, when the old queen was removed and the new one given at the same operation. Of course, another season may show that this result cannot be relied upon always, but I am sanguine.[1]

When I first began to use the push-in cage with the excluder slot my method was first to cage the queen with a wooden plug blocking each of the two holes. Three days later I opened the hive and substituted candy for the plug that covered the hole guarded by excluder, thus allowing the bees to enter after eating out the candy. A few days later I again opened the hive and, after destroying all queen-cells, removed the other plug and filled that hole with candy. At my next visit I expected to find the new queen laying on the combs. She usually was; but not always.

I then tried caging the queen as before, but using only one wooden plug and filling the excluder hole with candy. Rather to my surprise, I found that the queens so caged were not injured by the bees. It probably took two or three hours to empty the hole of candy, so that before the workers reached the caged queen they had become sensible of queenlessness. That move saved one operation and a lot of time. But still some queens were killed when they left the cage, although they had usually laid quite well under it. What happened was this: the bees started queen-cells on the brood, either under the cage or on eggs laid by the new queen immediately after emergence from it. This is a disastrous business. The queen is often present, though not laying. She is not fed by the bees, and is usually being worried by them. I know of few more troublesome things in our business than dealing with this. Getting a new queen accepted is usually almost hopeless, and it is generally best to allow a virgin to emerge. You can rarely do anything else about it. If you can catch the queen, which is a very difficult matter, it is better to take her away, introduce her to a mating nucleus to be groomed up ready for use in some other colony. But you may not be able to catch her, or she may have been killed by the bees. In any case she will be destroyed as soon as a virgin emerges.

[1] Results in 1945 were even better.

Now the problem was, and is—why do the bees tend so often to reject a queen that is introduced to them in this way? I believe that it has a great deal to do with the actual point of time, after the removal of the old queen, at which the new one joins her new family. I have come to think that it is probably a mistake to have the new queen lay eggs under the cage. When a queen is held confined in a push-in cage long enough for the workers to join her and feed her to set her going as a layer, in five cases out of six the workers outside the cage will have started queen-cells, and once they have done this there has come into existence in the hive a reaction which sets free the instinct of supersedure. What my friend Wadey calls 'the hive mind' becomes, somehow, set in the direction of supersedure. The new queen is treated as if she were an old, worn-out mother that must be replaced for the good of the community.

This being so, how can it be got over? Once communal instinct takes any direction, it will obstinately continue to progress that way in spite of all we humans can do, in nine cases in ten. I thought about this for a long time. The curious fact that direct introduction is so often successful, and the undoubted fact of the invariably safe transposition of colonies, seemed to point out a theory that might be worked on. We tried putting much less candy into the excluder-covered hole of the cages, so that the bees could reach the queen almost immediately, thinking that maybe this would prevent the cell-building urge; but it made no difference at all. We tried all sorts of plans. We caged the queen for nine days, at the end of which time we destroyed all queen-cells, and allowed the bees to release the queen. This answered moderately well, but losses were still too large. Then we tried destroying the cells at the end of nine days and just lifting off the cage and letting the queen loose right away. This was no better, as the bees nearly always built queen-cells on the patch of brood laid under the cage: in fact losses by this plan were heavy. Then we tried scraping off the cells that had been covered by the cage and so destroying eggs and larvae: all to no purpose.

Another plan we tried was that of allowing a virgin to emerge under one of these cages. The cage was placed over a single cell nine days after the old queen had been removed, all other cells having been destroyed. This virgin was replaced by a fertile queen at our next visit. This plan was very successful, but has one or two snags. Firstly the virgin sometimes got out of the cage through its getting loose, which was a bad job, as a virgin in a big stock is difficult to find; and secondly the cell quite often failed to produce a living virgin at all, the grub having died for some reason, thus leaving us a hopelessly queenless stock which, as most beekeepers know, is almost impossible to re-queen without the addition of a good deal of young brood which cannot always be easily spared. Of course, readers of this will know very well that the easiest of all introductions is the substitution of a fertile queen for a virgin. That is why we tried the above.

I don't want to give the impression that all these plans were hopeless failures: they were not; but the percentage of rejections in all of them was too high. What we all want is 100 per cent success. That's what we want, though we shall never reach that ideal, I fear. However, there is no harm in trying, and we are still trying to improve our methods.

In 1944 Harry Wickens, who works with us here, suggested that it might be worth while to try putting only a very small amount of candy into the tunnel covered by excluder, and only slightly more into the other, the unguarded tunnel, so that the bees would gain access to the queen through the excluder within a very short time, perhaps a couple of hours, and that the other tunnel could be cleared within a slightly longer time, as nearly as we could guess, six or seven hours. The difficulty is, of course, to know just how long it will take to empty the holes of candy, for I have good reason to think that bees eat out candy at very different rates according to their condition at the time. However that may be, our first year with this method has given very greatly increased success in introducing queens, and we shall be trying it again in 1945. I think that the fact of the queen getting out of the cage before she has laid under it and joining the general community outside just at the time when they have missed their old queen, and before they have felt the instinctive urge to replace her by rearing another, is the reason for our much greater success with this method.

The Cage We Use

I will now briefly describe this cage, which is also illustrated here. Its frame is of African softwood to stand the use of many small nails, and is $\frac{1}{2}''$ x $\frac{1}{2}''$ as to three sides, and $\frac{1}{2}''$ x $1''$ or more as to the fourth. This last side has two holes bored through it to give two round tunnels of five-sixteenths of an inch bore. These holes must be burned by passing a red-hot iron through them in order to scorch off any fibres of wood that might prevent the passage of the queen. This is very important. I have had queens caught by such fibres

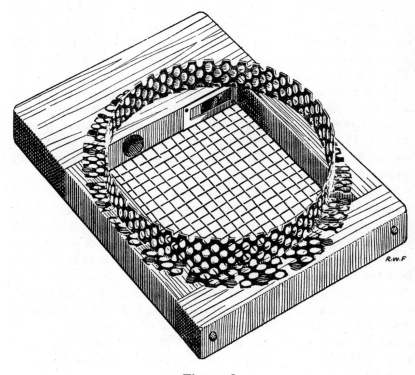

Figure 8

THE CAGE USED BY ME AS DESCRIBED

and die in the tunnel before I learned about scorching. One of these holes has a slot of excluder zinc nailed across its inside opening. The frame is covered with woven wire on one side, and on the other is fastened a collar of perforated zinc as shown. Perforated zinc is better than plain metal. It is more easily put on and holds to the comb better. For our latest method of use such a long hole as one inch is unnecessary, but it is as well to have long holes as these may be useful for introduction in other circumstances than the normal.

I suppose it will be appreciated that our latest plan has, quite apart from its greater efficiency in getting queens accepted, the enormous advantage of requiring only one visit to the stock when the queen is given. At our next routine visit we just remove the cage and make sure that the queen has been accepted. We have found that, so far as we have tried the method out, the queen is accepted in about 96 per cent of cases. When she has been rejected we allow the bees to do as they like, rearing a queen for themselves, and if we don't like the look of her we exchange her for another later on.

We use this cage as follows: the young queens are clipped as removed from the mating nuclei and carried to the apiaries in small cages made for that purpose. If not clipped they can only be transferred to the introducing cages inside a car or other enclosed place. The queen having been got into the cage, the open side is covered by a post card and can then be placed in position on the comb, the card slid from under the cage, and the latter pressed into the comb with a screwing movement, care being taken not to cut through the mid-rib.

We have found that the efficiency of this cage is increased if the comb it is on is spaced well away from its neighbour. As the cage will occasionally fall off when so spaced we now fix a crate staple, such as are used to fasten hives to their floors (American style hives, that is). These staples contact the face of the adjacent comb and prevent the cage from falling off. They give plenty of clustering space around the cage, and this seems to be of very considerable importance. I suppose that bees when able to cluster well over the cage while eating out the candy are enabled to make the acquaintance of their new queen more easily and so are less excited when finally she joins them on the combs.

If a swarm happens to be on hand during early summer, it is quite a good method of re-queening some inferior stock, of which there are always a few on the best managed of bee farms, to kill the queen of this stock and, having shaken most of the bees from its combs on to a sloping board in front of the hive, to throw the swarm, queen and all, down on top of the shaken bees and let the whole lot run into the hive together, hastening their going with a little smoke, with the result that a probably worthless stock will be turned into a good one.

It has often been said that it is very difficult to introduce virgin queens to mating nuclei immediately after removing a fertile queen; but this is one of the difficulties that the cage I have described does most certainly overcome. Any virgin, whether newly hatched or not, whether taken from another nucleus where she has been running free or from an incubator nursery, can be almost certainly introduced by first caging her for three days and allowing the workers no access whatever to the cage during that time, and then releasing her by filling the exit tunnel with candy.

Instinct

In managing bees we have to do with the very wonderful phenomenon of instinct. It is hard for us to understand that all, or very nearly all, the actions of these insects are governed by reflexes and not by conscious intelligence. One would think to read some bee books, that bees were creatures possessed, not merely of intelligence, but of reason. It is not so. We are often told of the marvellous intelligence of the bee; but, as a matter of fact, the hive-bee is among the least intelligent of insects. Anyone can see that this is so by watching, for instance, a bee bumbling about in a window which is partly open. A wasp will quickly nip round the corner and depart, but the bee is like a drunken man walking round and round a tree-guard in a park, trying to get out.

Then just what is the influence that pervades a colony of bees when the queen is removed? Conversely, what is the influence pervading a queen-right colony which holds that colony together as a perfectly organized going concern? I don't know. I have read how the removal of a queen termite belonging to an enormous colony extending under an entire house, completely upset the economy of that community within, I think, a matter of minutes. When bees lose their queen we cannot suppose that they 'know' that they have lost her; what happens is probably that, whereas the presence of a queen is an influence on the instinctive actions of the workers, keeping these normal, her sudden loss acts as a sort of trigger releasing reflex actions appropriate to queenlessness. A colony of bees, though made up of a large number of individuals working together as one organism, is a complete effective organism

22. What happens when very stale foundation is given to bees

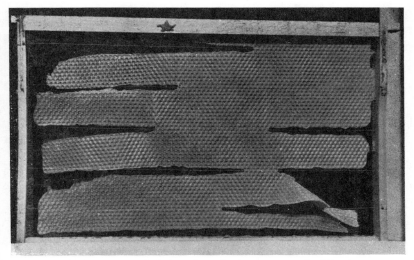

23. The result of giving foundation at unsuitable times

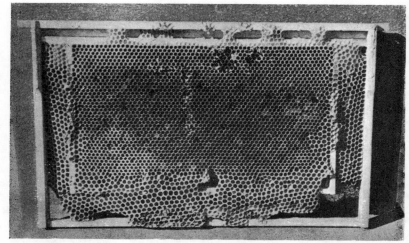

24. One way of transferring British standard to 'M.D.' frames

25. An apiary of British standard hives of the kind described in this book

only when all its component parts are present. I feel inclined to liken the influence of the queen's presence in a colony to that of hormones in the body of an intelligent being. We do not know the mechanism of the queen's influence, but we know that that influence is there. We also know that the safe introduction of alien queens to stocks depends in a large measure on our choosing the time correctly.

The introduction of queens to stocks having laying workers present in them cannot be accomplished by any direct or semi-direct method: the queen must be caged, but the only kind of cage I have found successful is that described above. Nobody knows exactly what happens when a queen is introduced direct to a colony with laying workers, except that the queen is usually killed. I believe she is killed by the normal workers, not by the layers, but who can be certain? At any rate, if a fertile queen is caged on a comb in one of my cages, so that the bees may have access to her by eating out the candy, and if she is allowed to remain in the cage, confined there by excluder for a week or thereabouts, she will be accepted more often than not, but will be killed in the cage in a considerable minority of cases.

We do not know how far a laying worker is accepted by the normal bees as their queen. We do not know how many laying workers may be present, but it is probable that in the majority of cases there are very many. They do not differ in appearance from normal workers; but their presence is easily determined by an examination of drone-cells at the edges of the combs, and of queen-cell stumps in the same position. No fertile or drone-breeding queen, no matter how small and dwarfed she may be, ever lays numbers of eggs in drone- or queen-cells on the borders of combs; but this is the favourite place for laying workers to plant their eggs, and they frequently lay them there by hundreds, many eggs being deposited in the same cell. In nuclei and stocks containing laying workers it is not infrequent to catch one in the act of laying in a queen-cell: this I have seen many times, and once or twice I have seen one laying in drone comb.

Probably the best way to replace laying workers by a fertile queen is to give (by caging) a virgin, or, easier still, a queen-cell. These are nearly always accepted, if properly introduced, and in due time a fertile queen arrives on the scene, whereupon the laying workers disappear. I don't know what happens to them; but they stop laying their eggs which are such a nuisance in a breeding apiary. I hate to have the miserable little runts of drones that arise from those eggs; but I am not at all sure that they are really a menace through mating young queens, for I think it very doubtful indeed if they can successfully mate virgins. I can't call to mind where, but somewhere I have seen an account of some research on this question, and this appeared to show that such drones are incapable of impregnating a queen.

Virgins

To introduce virgins to colonies that are strong, and have had their queens removed at the time, is generally considered very difficult, in fact it is really a waste of time from the standpoint of practical business; but when a colony has been long enough without a queen so that its brood has all emerged, it is much easier to introduce a virgin than a fertile queen. It may be done by caging with my cage in the normal way, but in such cases it is probably better to give a queen-cell if available, or, better still, give a whole comb of brood on which a queen-cell is already built, if there happens to be one to be had at the time.

Virgins can be introduced to mating nuclei immediately after the removal of their fertile queen in the following way with an exceedingly high percentage of success. The virgin is caged in one of my cages with *both* tunnels closed by wooden plugs and is left so for three days. The cage should cover both honey and pollen so that the young queen can feed as much as she likes. If the cage also covers a few cells of emerging brood, so much the better. After three days destroy any queen-cells that may have been started and substitute candy for the plug which stops the unguarded tunnel so that the queen can come out as soon as the candy has been eaten by the bees. She will almost always be all right, and will very soon be mated if weather is favourable. This is quicker than giving a queen-cell, and is especially useful in connection with an incubator. Of course, if one cares to take the extra trouble of first allowing the bees to enter the cage via the excluder-covered tunnel, success will be doubly assured; but I have rarely had a virgin turned down when released at once.

Other methods that may be mentioned as suitable for various

more or less unusual circumstances are as follows. A swarm brought away from an apiary and hived without its queen, she having been caught while hiving, or immediately after, will accept any queen whatever as soon as the bees become thoroughly distressed, and are seen to be running all over the hive in a state of great distress. She may be run in at the entrance, if clipped so that she cannot fly, or she may be run in through the feed-hole of the inner cover or under the quilts. The bees will almost immediately show that they have found her, and this will be seen to affect the whole swarm directly, the bees running into the hive and settling down at once. On rare occasions a queen so given may be injured, but nothing ever goes right with bees always. When giving a queen in this way it is necessary to give her just as soon as the bees show that they are ready for her; otherwise the whole swarm may leave the hive and enter, or try to enter another.

Finally, let me say that you cannot work by strict rule of thumb in introduction, or, for that matter, any branch of bee-management; you must develop a sort of sixth sense which enables you to judge with a good deal of accuracy how the bees will react to the treatment adopted at any particular juncture.

CHAPTER IX

MOVING BEES

I expect it would surprise most amateur beekeepers to know what a lot of moving bees there is to be done on a bee farm. We seem to be for ever carting our bees around for some reason or other. Apiaries must sometimes be moved to new sites, and stocks have to be transported from one apiary to another quite often in our work. Then most of us practise some sort of migratory beekeeping, as it is sometimes called; bees are taken to the moors for heather and to the fruit for pollination, and it is very necessary that good methods of confining, ventilating, and loading the bees shall be practised, for unless we take a great deal of care about these things, we stand a very good chance of suffering serious loss through the smothering of our colonies, one of the worst of all the forms of casualties. I know of very few more disheartening sights than that which a powerful stock, crammed with brood and bees, presents after being stifled.

In discussing this matter I propose to ignore the many kinds of fancy hives that are so generally used by amateurs in this country. Such contraptions as have legs, and consist of loose parts which are very troublesome to fasten together securely, particularly those with separate inner and outer bodies, like the very popular 'W.B.C.' hive, while they have points that appeal to the amateur, are quite useless where transportation is a matter of routine. The business honey farmer cannot use them if he would, so we need not notice them further here.

Having had a good deal of practice in the art of moving bees, and having worked out what I consider the best way of managing it, perhaps the simplest way of helping others will be for me to describe as clearly as I can, the way we set to work when we have to move a load of bees.

The hives used here are all either Modified Dadant, or are those previously described that are of the same size in every dimension except depth, so that they take British frames. Of these last we have only about 150; but the method of packing and loading is identical for both kinds, as are the fittings used. The floors are the same size as the hive-bodies and do not project. The hives are on rail stands as illustrated, and this makes packing up easier, as we shall see. The fittings required consist of a screen made of a wooden frame covered with woven wire, and exactly the size of the hive; a strip of stout perforated zinc, $2\frac{1}{2}$ inches wide and 18 inches long, having half an inch of its width folded over to a right angle, as shown in the photograph: four $1\frac{1}{2}$-inch screws; some 2-inch crate staples, and some kind of strapping or wiring implement, such as merchants use for securing crates and boxes. We use a 'Signode' bander with $\frac{1}{2}$-inch strapping.

The job is done as follows. If the stocks are to travel supered, the screens are first of all fastened on to the supers by means of the four screws. (The frames of the screens, of course, are already bored and the holes countersunk to receive the screws.) This can be done at home, and the screened supers taken to the apiary ready to put on to the hives. This saves time. If the hives are to travel without supers, the screens, of course, must be fastened on to the hives in the apiary. When bees are to be moved in winter or in cold weather, no screens are needed. Bees never smother in cold weather. If we are moving bees during the active season, as is nearly always the case, the job must be done at two operations. On the first day we take the supers and all the paraphernalia with us and having set the supers in place over queen-excluders, drive four staples into the sides of the super and hive-body, and fasten the hive to its floor in the same way, as shown in the illustration. We then pass the steel strap around the hive and super and pull it up tight, just as crates are banded for the rail. The steel band holds floor, hive-body, excluder, super, and screen firmly together, reinforcing the crate staples in keeping the whole thing as rigid as possible. We have found that for long journeys, and especially in cases where we expect to have the bees handled by strangers, neither banding nor stapling is by itself entirely to be trusted, but that used together they are efficient. When hives stand on rails it is easier to do the strapping up because the bands can be passed around the hives freely and without lifting them.

There is one rather important point that I must mention regarding the use of these banding tools. Hives swell when damped by wet weather and shrink when they dry, especially when not painted; it is therefore better to do the banding while hives are dry, for if done when wet they will shrink on drying and leave the band loose. In taking bees to the heather in wet weather it may be necessary to cut the straps and refasten them when bees have to be brought home, and in all cases it is well to allow a few inches overlap of the strapping when packing up, so that it may be cut and pulled up tight again when bringing home the hives. If this overlap of, say, six inches be left, there is no difficulty in catching the two ends of the band with the strainer and refastening them.

As soon as the hive has been strapped, the inner cover is set in its place over the screen, and the roof is placed over all, and the whole thing left until the next evening, or until we are ready to load the bees for transport.

When we are ready to load the bees, we come to the apiary either in the chill of early morning or towards dusk when flying is over for the day, and immediately close all entrances by means of the perforated zinc guards already described. This is done by pinning them on to the floors with four or five large drawing-pins. I may here point out that by the use of the short floor and bent zinc guard we entirely do away with the rather serious difficulty met with when closing the entrances of hives with projecting floors, with which this plan cannot be used. With the short floor and the bent zinc guard, even if the hive-body moves quite a bit in relation to the floor, the guard will remain unaffected, since it is fastened to the floor alone. Entrance guards for hives with projecting floors are almost of necessity fastened to the hive-body, and in that case the least movement between body and floor will be apt to buckle the guard and release bees. At all events, such closure must always be troublesome and clumsy as compared with the other, and will always be somewhat unsafe, in my opinion, anyhow.

Having shut in the bees, we take off the roof and set it bottom up on the ground, and put the inner cover into it with its propolized side up, so that it will not stick to the inside of the roof, and then, lifting the hive by its hand-holds, we set it right into its roof, and this done to all the hives to be moved, we are ready to load. The darkening of the entrance by setting the hive bodily in its roof is really a very useful thing, as it keeps the bees from continually struggling to get out. The top screens give all the ventilation needed at any time, so long as the hive is large enough for the bees it contains. If the bees are too tightly packed they will become overheated and must be given more room by adding a super. I believe that almost all cases of bees being smothered when a full-sized screen of woven wire is provided, are to be attributed to overheating through too much crowding, rather than to lack of air.

There are one or two points I ought to mention with regard to the method of shutting in the bees with a strip of perforated zinc. When making these guards it is important that the fold shall not coincide with the straight rows of perforations, but should run the other way, for thus we get a much stronger entrance guard, and one that will be unlikely to break at the fold. Also, I should point out that each floor must have a very shallow recess or notch cut at the upper edges of its front cleats as shown in the illustration. Unless this is done it is very difficult to get the guard in when closing the hive, and this is important, as these guards should be easily inserted so that the job can be done in an instant without disturbing the bees.

Another point is this. If the screened supers that we are to put on are wet with honey after extraction, they must be put on *just before dark only* and left for at least twenty-four hours before the bees are moved. They cause great excitement; but if put on late in the evening, all will be quiet by the next morning. It is better, however, to leave the apiary alone until thirty-six hours after putting on these wet supers.

Our method of loading hives has been devised with a view to economy of space on the lorry, and the safety of the bees. A row of three or four hives, according to the size of the lorry, is placed at the forward end of the vehicle, next to the cab. Across these hives, one in front and one behind, are laid two pieces of $3'' \times 1\frac{1}{2}''$ deal, long enough to project at each side of the lorry a little beyond the hives. On these are then placed a second tier of hives, and after that, a third layer over two more bars of wood. All these hives, of course, are standing in their roofs, and the crosspieces of timber are to ensure a free passage of air over the wire screens. They also greatly conduce to making the whole load of hives travel securely, for they combine with the ropes to bind the whole firmly together.

A second row of hives is loaded in a similar way, and then a third and so on until the lorry is full, when the whole load is carefully and strongly roped in order that nothing shall move on the journey. We have found that if the ropes are pulled tightly in direct contact with the screens on the top hives, those screens are liable to be moved out of position or even broken, so we now put some wide boards set edgeways as shown in the photograph. By doing this we avoid any contact between ropes and screens, since the ropes go into the spaces between the rows of hives and rest upon the edges of these boards. This was the idea of Harry Wickens who helps us run our bees.

We have found it quite easy to transport ninety-six supered M.D. hives on a six-ton lorry, that is to say, eight rows of four hives abreast, tiered three high. A smaller truck, such as a two tonner, will take sixty-three hives in rows of three abreast and three high. Without supers, hives of M.D. size can be tiered four high. I think that standard hives without supers might be stacked five high, but I have never tried it. The photographs will show the details of loading and how a load of bees looks.

It will be readily seen how greatly the short floors facilitate the moving of bees, since the roofs take up virtually no room at all, whereas if they must be carried separately from the hives, as when long floors are used, their accommodation is something of a problem.

Before closing this section it may be well to mention a few facts that bear on the cause of the stifling of bees in confinement. Bees may be confined to their hives in cold weather without risk, and in cool, wet weather it is usually possible to move them for considerable distances without any other ventilation than what is given by an entrance guard of perforated zinc. Bees don't try to get out of the hive much when it is cool. On the other hand bees will very quickly smother, even when the whole top of the hive is covered by a woven wire screen, if the weather is very hot and the hive is not roomy enough to allow the necessary expansion of the cluster. For safety the heat must radiate away sufficiently rapidly to keep the temperature of the interior low enough for the bees to exist in comfort. The moment the temperature rises high enough to make the bees uncomfortable, they panic, and crowd all over the wire screen in a frantic attempt to get out to the open air. This action is very soon fatal for them, because by crowding over the wire they prevent the heated air from escaping, whereupon the inside temperature quickly rises higher than the melting point of beeswax, the combs melt, the bees immediately discharge the honey which they have gorged, and in a matter of seconds 95 per cent of them are dead, leaving only a sticky mass of half-animate bedraggled survivors.

The almost instantaneous end of a colony of bees when allowed thus to become overheated is not usually realized by beekeepers until experience has taught them a lesson. The experience comes to most of us some time or other, and we learn in that way; but it's hard on the bees. I remember once having a very fine stock of bees stifled in this way at the heather. We had unloaded the bees (about 130 colonies) and had lifted the hives out of their roofs. The day was hot, and it is essential that in hot weather bees shall be allowed to fly before putting on the roofs of the hives, so we were releasing the bees as fast as we could. As always happens, as soon as the bees were released they began to crowd over the screens of the hives indiscriminately, which is a nuisance, as it makes it difficult to put on the inner covers over the screens without crushing the bees that are crawling all over them, trying to get into the hives they cover; and it is quite troublesome, too, to brush the bees off, for they keep pushing themselves into the way all the time. Well, just at the last, when only two hives remained to be dealt with, thinking it could not matter if a cover were laid on a hive just for a moment while the entrance was still closed, one of us covered the screen. (I believe it was I that did it.) In one second, before one could say 'Jack Robinson', that stock was destroyed. So it is best to take no risks of that kind.

Combless colonies, such as swarms and driven bees, travel well in confinement even in very hot weather, if allowed plenty of room and ventilation, provided they suffer no sudden jar that throws the mass of the bees down in a heap; but a violent shake of the container may, and often does, result in the almost instantaneous death of the entire swarm. I have known a large swarm to be destroyed in very hot weather by simply bumping the skep containing it, preparatory to throwing the bees into or in front of its new home when hiving. So we can't be too careful.

It may be worth while to point out to the inexperienced in the art of moving bees, that it is always heat and not cold that injures bees while confined to their hives for travelling. We are all a little inclined to fear the effect of chilling on the brood of packed colonies; but in fact very little harm ever results from exposure in this way. For instance, suppose a colony is confined to its hive by means of a woven wire screen right over it and by the closure of its entrance, and after being loaded on to a vehicle for transport, a cold rain comes on and lasts for hours, while the temperature falls from summer heat to little above freezing. Theoretically, one would think harm would be done, but in practice this does not seem to be so. On the other hand, transporting strong colonies, except by night, in very hot weather is liable to result in very serious damage both to brood and adult population, and will sometimes cause the death of the entire stock. In any case, there is no doubt at all that overheating, even if its results are in no way fatal, is always serious; much more damage seems to be done than appears at first. The rule, then, in moving bees, is to provide ample ventilation and plenty of clustering space, and to keep them cool. It is a good plan to move by night, if possible, when the moving is to be done in summer.

CHAPTER X

HEATHER

Heather honey is a very valuable product. Its flavour does not suit everyone's palate, but it is greatly preferred by those who do like it, so much so, that there is always a demand for it that far exceeds the supply, and consequently its price is higher than that of ordinary honey. Some people think it more nutritious than the honey from the clovers and other summer flowers, and will choose it every time if they have the chance. I remember when I was in a nursing home for a serious operation, offering my nurse the choice of heather or ordinary honey; she took the heather at once, and when I asked her why, she said: 'It's so much more *nourishing*!' I am not a honey eater myself; but I must say that if I had to eat it, I think I would choose heather honey. In fact the only honey I have ever tasted that I really liked, was some almost pure hawthorn honey stored in 1911. The flavour of that is rather strong, though quite different from heather. But it should never be forgotten that the common bell-heather and cross-leaved heath, though they give plenty of honey, do not give heather honey, and it is not to get bell-heather honey that beekeepers take their bees to the moors.

The plant I am dealing with here is the familiar ling heath (*Calluna vulgaris*). It comes into bloom after the summer flowers are over, and this makes it far more valuable to the bee farmer than it would be if it yielded its honey at the same time; for he is able to move bees to the moors, if not too distant, and at least to stand a good chance of adding to his main crop a supplementary harvest of heather honey. It gives him, in fact, a second string to his bow; and I think it is a fact that it is only very rarely that there is a failure of both early honey and heather honey.

The honey from ling is a distinctive product, being a jelly and not a flowing liquid, except when agitated. When, however, it is stirred up it becomes much like any other honey, but only for a short time: it soon re-jellifies again. This peculiar property is called 'thixotropy', and those who like to call things by long names can use that term instead of saying that heather honey jellies. If you cut a comb of ling honey it will not run, and after it has been in jars for a short time, you can turn the bottles upside down and the honey will no more run out of them than ordinary honey will, after it has granulated solid.

It is stated by some people that pure ling honey will not granulate; but whether this is really so, I don't know. It seems to me probable that ling honey stored in a perfectly pure state is a very rare thing, for there are probably few places where no other plants are available to the bees while ling is in bloom. Willow herb, wood sage, bramble, bell and cross-leaved heaths are all contemporary with ling heather. Whether it is ever stored quite pure or not, certainly the bulk of it is to some extent mixed with other honeys.

A great deal of what seems to me to be poetical nonsense has been talked and written about the wonderful superiority of the ling honey from Scotland over all other ling honeys. I need not say that this claim is usually made by Scotsmen! English heather honey, they say, is poor stuff compared with the wonderful product of the glorious moors and mountainsides of 'Old Scotland'. Personally I doubt if Scotch ling honey is any more superior to other ling honey than Scotland is older than any other country. At any rate, if you can produce heather honey in England, you will find it quite easy to sell at just as high a price as our Scottish friends can get for theirs; and in spite of the immense area of heather in Scotland, I have my doubts whether honey is produced from the Scottish moors in any quantity at all commensurate with their extent. One would expect that if Scottish beekeepers could produce heather honey in paying quantities, we ought to see a great deal more of it on the London markets. I strongly suspect that up on the mountains of Scotland the climate renders honey gathering a rather precarious and uncertain business. It must, I imagine, be either that, or else want of enterprise or lack of method that hinders production. One might expect that the beekeepers of Scotland would produce hundreds of tons of heather honey each year, but there is no evidence of its being done.

When this war is over, I am, if I have health and strength, going to have a look round those famous Scottish moorlands; for if the ling yields as well as it does in England I think it would pay to take bees to those moors, even from the south of England. Why not?

The extra distance would not of itself make so much difference. If bees pay one a good profit when taken eighty or a hundred miles, to carry them three times that distance to get the advantage of wider areas of heather would not matter—if the moors yield better and more honey. But are the Scottish moors better? I don't know, but some day I may. I can't help thinking that if there were really such good prospects in the North, some of the beekeepers of Scotland would before now have built up large and paying bee farms; systematically working on the best clover districts in June and July, and organizing regular treks to the moors after the clover time. Of course it could hardly pay a real dividend to try to produce heather honey in Scotland or anywhere else while using the pitiful equipment and methods of management that appear to be so generally in favour. I had no idea how absolutely futile and footling those methods were until I got a copy of Herrod-Hempsall's *Beekeeping, New and Old*. There you have the whole thing, photographs and all, and it is obvious that it is carried on with the most complete lack of business organization possible to be conceived. There is one picture of, I think, twelve men taking about eight or ten hives to a moor! This is not honey production, but playing at it.

The distinctive characteristic of jellying makes it impossible to remove heather honey from the combs by means of the centrifugal honey extractors. It must be pressed out as a general rule, but there are implements called 'honey-looseners' that are supposed to make extracting possible. They consist of a number of blunt metal needles that are arranged so that they can be jiggled up and down in the cells, thus causing the jellied honey to liquefy, after which the combs are put through an extractor quickly before the honey can rejellify. I don't think it pays to bother with these things, myself.

The gelatinous nature of this honey has the effect of making it retain all air bubbles that are introduced in pressing it from the combs, and these bubbles remain suspended in it, even if the honey is heated enough to make it run through a fine strainer. The bubbles give the product a very distinctive and pleasing appearance, which is, however, completely lost when granulation takes place.

The colour of heather honey varies a good deal according to the district it comes from: probably the soil has something to do with this. Its flavour also varies, being stronger in honey from the granite districts of Scotland than from many other localities. The particular distinction of heather honey flavour is that it is a sort of bitter-sweet, and is without the cloying effect that most honey has on some people. Those who like clover honey, don't, as a rule, like heather. Although some consumers in England prefer the strong-flavoured almost pure ling honey, I think the majority prefer a milder honey which, though chiefly heather, has an admixture of honey from other flowers; heather blend, in fact.

It is only during the last few years that I have had any personal experience of heather honey work, and what knowledge I have has been got in the course of eight seasons, during which I have produced for the market not more than about eight tons; but I have found the methods pursued fairly successful, and expect to extend these operations as circumstances permit. I began the business in a very tentative and limited way, increasing the extent of my operations each season. I began by taking thirty-three colonies to the heather, and so far have extended the business to the extent of taking 330. But it is an uncertain affair, taking bees to heather. One year you get a big yield; another you may get nothing. That was what happened in 1944. There was not so much as the smell of the stuff in the hives; but on two occasions the crop was quite a large one. There must have been quite seventy pounds in the supers of many of the hives.

Taking bees to heather is quite a simple job. In the last chapter I have described our way of packing and transporting bees, and all I need do here is to try to give some idea of how stocks should be prepared for this work. In the first place, Italian strains will beat brown bees all to pieces at the heather, at all events in the south of England, because they keep breeding so much later. This, while rather a nuisance after the main flow, is a distinct advantage when bees are to go to the moors, and makes it possible for a stock that has done good work in the summer to go on storing well at the heather.

Stocks that are taken to the heather should be as strong as possible at the close of the main flow, and should, if it can possibly be managed, have young queens; I mean queens of the current season, for these will not be likely to reduce the rate of their egg laying. Still, there is no doubt that good stocks with year-old queens will generally do quite well, though more honey may be stored in the brood combs than would be the case were a young queen in the hive.

Heather-going stocks should be supered just before being taken to the moors, and should have excluders on them to keep pollen out of the super combs as much as possible, for pollen is a great nuisance in the heather honey press. Choose newly built combs with bases of thick foundation. The importance of this will be apparent when we come to press the honey. The hives are then packed up and loaded as described earlier in this book. We try to get an early start in order to arrive at the moor and have the bees unloaded and released before the day becomes warm. For long journeys it is undoubtedly best to travel by night, arriving at the moors in the early morning. Bees always travel better by night than by day. On arrival at their destination the hives are unloaded and placed on the ground in sets of two to eight, and are faced in different directions. Never set heather stocks in rows or they will drift badly. They should be released as soon as possible after reaching their destination, and you may then expect a good deal of stinging if you give the bees a chance to get at you, for they always seem vicious at these times.

The heather plant, ling, is a rather erratic yielder of nectar. Sometimes bees are able to begin to store from it directly the first flowers open; at other times the bees may stand in the midst of huge quantities of heather bloom and get nothing from it. It is usually a bad sign, I think, when you see bees working bell-heath and other flowers, such as belated wood sage or willow herb, while ling is in flower, for if ling is yielding bees are inclined to ignore all other plants, I think. I have seen bees working ling eagerly within a quarter of an hour after being released on arrival at the heath, and I have known them fail to do anything with it for weeks. Some four or five years ago I went down to see what the bees were doing about a fortnight after they had been set out on the heather moors, and was very disappointed to find that, while the heather was almost past its best, in appearance at all events, the bees had done nothing at all with it. Supers were hardly occupied and there was no smell of heather honey at all. After about ten days I again went to have a look, thinking the bees might perhaps as well be brought home. The weather was not, in my judgment, any better during this second period than during the early part of the time; but on arriving on a motor-cycle within about three hundred yards, the wind being a gentle breeze blowing towards me from the bees, I could plainly smell the honey. On getting close up to the bees, the odour was so strong as to be almost sickening (to me), and on looking into the hives I found whole supers filled right up and the need for more storage room obvious. So instead of bringing the bees home, we took more supers to them, and a good many of these were partly filled within a few days.

Heather honey-flows begin suddenly and leave off in the same abrupt manner, in my experience. They may begin right at the first flowering, or be delayed until almost the end. A heather honey-flow may last a fortnight or it may only continue for a day or two—or it may not occur at all. But a really heavy heather honey-flow is an inspiring thing. Bees gather the stuff so rapidly and store it so fast in the combs that everything seems to become blocked up with honey in a very short time. When one of these flows is going on, a remarkable circumstance is the profuse secretion of wax. Every corner seems to be used to deposit wax, and a great deal of brace comb may be built. There must, I think, be some special property of heather honey that conduces to the secretion of beeswax, for I have found that when, as we sometimes do, we give the wet supers after the honey has been scraped from the combs, to colonies that we want to feed, the bees deposit masses of wax all around the feed-holes in the inner covers through which they are allowed access to the supers.

When there is a heavy flow from ling a curious circumstance is that although you may walk through the heather and hear a continual hum all around you, you can hardly see a single bee. The reason is that heather blooms in compact masses, the flowers almost in contact, so that when the bees reach the flowers they scramble from one to another without flight, but keep up a gentle humming all the time. Much the same thing is seen when a thick plant of white clover is yielding heavily. I cannot hear these sounds, being deaf; but I could once. Lack of adequate hearing is a serious misfortune for a beekeeper, or indeed, for anyone.

Another curious fact about heather honey is that while bees are working the ling plant they are almost always unusually spiteful.

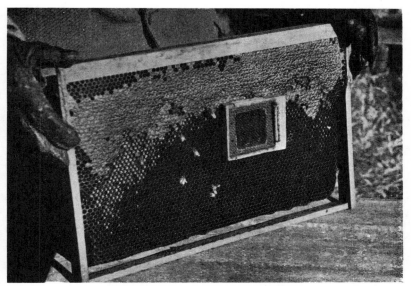

26. One of the introducing cages described, as used.
Queen can be seen inside

27. Home-made travelling box, after the design of
Messrs. Burtt and Son

28. Loading bees for return from heather

29. How we load bees. There are 96 supered 'M.D.' hives
on this load

It is hardly ever possible, in my experience, to go among hives of bees that are engaged with a flow of heather nectar, without a veil. In a good flow from clover or similar plants it is generally possible, not only to pass among the stocks, but even to open and handle them without a veil; but in the case of heather honey-flows the case is very different.

It is usually considered, chiefly by those who have no experience of them, that Modified Dadant hives are too large for heather work. Well, perhaps they may be: I don't know; but we do pretty well with them, often having supers filled, and occasionally having a few stocks get well on with a second super. M.D. supers hold about fifty pounds when full, and of course the brood-chambers generally come away well stocked for winter.

It is well to feed ten pounds of sugar on the return of the bees, because heather honey does not winter bees very well in long cold winters, though in mild winters one could wish for nothing better. However, a ten-pound feed of good syrup will work wonders, as the bees will as a rule use that first, or at any rate they will use some of it, and will not subsist entirely on the heather honey. For rapid building up in spring, heather honey is not to be surpassed. This may, I think, be partly because when bees store a nice lot of heather honey, they also store a large amount of pollen with it, for ling, like white clover, is a very free yielder of pollen, and partly through the nature of the honey itself: I do not know.

Heather honey, however, appears to have the curious quality of being very quickly used up in spring when bees are breeding rapidly; it hardly seems to last much more than half as long at that time as ordinary honey does. I don't know why this is; I only know the fact by experience. Several times I have been quite taken aback in spring to find stocks that a month before were so heavy as to be difficult to lift, quite light and in need of feeding, though extremely strong in bees.

Standard hives with twelve combs, as used by us, have been found very good for heather work; but I cannot say that they give more super honey than the Dadants do. Theoretically it would seem that they ought to do so, as the smaller combs late in the season as heather-time is, should tend to push honey upstairs, but it does not seem to me to be so. We have taken both sizes to heather in considerable numbers, but there is no difference that we have been able to see so far as average super yields are concerned.

A very good way of producing heather honey is available to those who can do with increase. Early in June make up nuclei in the following manner. Strong nuclei are required, such as standard six-comb or Dadant four-comb. Make them up by taking a comb of brood and bees from each of a number of stocks and putting them into new hives. As each of these combs is taken from its hive it should be hung in the new hive in such a way that it hangs well apart from the others, that is to say that the six standard combs will at first about fill a ten-frame hive-body, with wide spaces between them. This is done in order to keep the bees on the different combs from contacting one another more than necessary, for they, being strangers, might fight if put close together. It takes some little time to get the six combs, as the queen of each stock from which a comb is taken *must be seen* in order to make perfectly certain that she is not removed with the comb taken.

As soon as all six combs (four, if M.D.) are in the new hive, (which is, of course, closed by an entrance-guard), the combs and bees are pushed over to one side of the hive, a dummy is pushed up next to them and secured by means of a couple of wooden blocks tacked to the hive walls; or the hive may be filled up with frames of foundation or comb at the time the nucleus is made up. The hive cover is then put on and the hive given a thump or two to frighten the bees and make them unite peaceably. Plenty of bees should be shaken from other combs if there do not appear to be enough adhering to the combs taken, so that brood may be well covered. The hive with the nucleus is now removed to another apiary, preferably the home apiary, and a young queen is introduced. If this colony is well cared for, and fed if necessary, it will become an ideal stock to go to the heather in August, for by that time it will be just at its best and well into its super.

There is never any great hurry about bringing home the bees so long as this is done early enough to allow for the removal of the supers and the feeding of the stocks. About the second week in September seems a good time for doing this, and it is well to choose cool weather unless someone is prepared to go to the bees very early in the morning in order to confine them, a job that takes longer than you might think when there are a lot of hives to be secured. If the weather is cold and misty, as it often is in September, the matter is easy; but if the chosen day should turn out to be one of those glorious days that make up the 'Indian summer', why the earlier one can reach the hives the better.

When they reach home the bees are set out in their permanent sites, and a day or two later, after they have had time to become accustomed to the change of residence, hives are unfastened and bee-escape boards are placed under the supers, and a couple of days later all the supers are brought home and someone proceeds to press out the honey.

This is a rather slow job unless more than one press is available, or some spectacular arrangement like that which Buckfast Abbey has installed. This machinery must have cost a great deal, and those of us who have no money to burn will manage quite well to press a large quantity of heather honey without anything at all extravagant in the form of presses. Here we use a press of the Rymer type, as made by the late William Meadows. I give an illustration of this press in use. It is quite simple, and very easy to use, but like all hand-operated presses, it must be small to be efficient. If you are in a hurry, have two of them. The combs are taken one at a time and the honey and wax is scraped off the mid-rib, i.e. the foundation. This is why the combs should be new and the foundation heavy. The mush of honey and wax is allowed to fall into a pail, and the spoon or other tool used (we can find nothing better than a prosaic kitchen spoon of large size and strong make) is scraped out on a wooden projection provided for the purpose (see illustration).

As soon as about a gallon of the mixture of honey and wax is ready it is emptied into the press which is lined with strong unbleached linen cheese-cloth. This cloth is carefully lapped over, and the pressing plate is lowered and pressure applied by means of the lathe-cut screw. Pressing requires time: never hurry it; that is why two presses are better than one if it is required to push on fast with the job. This press, used in this way, will extract practically all the honey, leaving only a thin cake of nearly dry wax which is thrown into a receptacle to wait until we are ready to boil it up to render the wax. One man can press about three hundredweights in a day.

We used to bottle heather honey direct from the press, but have lately found it better to run off into 28-lb. tins and heat it in water for a short time. This requires care, for the honey must not be heated too much or its flavour and aroma will be seriously injured, but if it is heated to about 150 degrees F. with the lids of the tins securely in place, very little harm will be done. We find it best to pour the honey into a settling tank through a fine strainer while still hot, and to bottle it up the next morning when its temperature will be just right to allow rapid bottling. Treated in this way heather honey will keep its nice distinctive appearance, will not granulate for a long time and, above all, will not ferment.

Fermentation is probably the worst of the heather honey producer's troubles. Almost always a good deal of this honey is still unsealed when supers are taken off and if treated as above, all the honey, sealed or unsealed, can be blended together, the whole product having a good selling quality. I may here mention what seems to me a very curious fact about this honey which has come to my notice every year since I have had to do with it. When we are pressing it we always find a few combs here and there that are obviously fermenting, and these combs are just as often fully sealed ones as not. Moreover, hardly a year passes that we do not find in the spring a comb or two of unsealed heather honey that has been overlooked when pressing, and has been stored in an outdoor building, quite unheated, which shows no sign of fermentation whatever. I don't understand this, but it is a fact.

It is generally impressed upon beekeepers that heather honey should be produced in the form of sections of comb honey. There is, apparently, a vague notion that in the case of heather honey this is more economical; in fact, during the war the Government actually took the trouble to prohibit the sale of sections for use in the production of any honey other than heather honey. This absurdity, incredible as it may seem, was actually implemented, but with what real effect I don't know. For my part, after some years of experience, I emphatically disagree. Sections are very liable to be left unfinished in all classes of comb honey work; a large percentage always are, I think. This is somewhat wasteful in ordinary honey which can be extracted; but in the case of heather honey it is much more so. When we consider that by scraping the honey off the septum of the combs for pressing, we leave a frame fitted with foundation which is very soon rebuilt next summer; and furthermore, when we remember that many combs will not be filled with honey, but will have only a central patch of it which can be scraped off without interfering with the empty part of the combs, it will be fairly apparent that the section way is much more wasteful.

It will, of course, be contended that the partly filled sections can be sold as such by weight, but even then it means that two or three sections will be required to go with a pound of honey. To produce a number of first-class sections of heather honey is both interesting and profitable, for some comb honey should always be produced if possible in normal times, for it forms one of our best advertisements. There is something peculiarly attractive about honey in the comb, and I know of nothing that sells better than fine sections; but I am quite sure that the bee farmer, as such, should never attempt to make comb honey, whether heather or not, a main, or even a considerable element in his total production.

CHAPTER XI

HARVEST

The end of the honey-flow comes at rather different times in different seasons and in various localities. It may stop quite suddenly, as if a tap had been turned off, without any easily recognizable reason; or the cause may be very evident in an abrupt change in the weather. On the other hand, there may be a gradual decrease in the income of honey as plants slowly lessen their secretion of nectar. But however the honey-flow closes, the fact is immediately apparent to any beekeeper with experience, for he seems to feel the difference at once, and no matter how the end may come, bees should not be meddled with more than is absolutely necessary for several days. This is especially important when the stoppage is sudden, for it is at this crisis that serious robbing is very apt to start; but after a week or ten days it is safe enough to begin the work of harvesting the honey.

Unless it is necessary to obtain some early honey for some particular purpose, I think it is best to take the whole of the honey off at one operation at the end of the season. This has the advantage of reducing labour and saving time, neither of which is too plentiful on bee farms at harvest time. This plan also makes it easy to have a general blending of the honeys collected in the different apiaries during the whole summer, so that the entire production of the farm is approximately uniform as delivered to the consumers. This is an asset when large stores or similar retail distributors are to be supplied with honey throughout the year under the producer's label. It also saves journeys with motor vehicles, and expense as well.

Removing the Crop

When the crop is ready for removal, this is the way we go to work on our bee farm. First a load of bee-escape boards are put into a light van, and taken to the apiary that is to be dealt with. We generally do about three apiaries in a day, and keep enough boards with escape traps fitted in them for the purpose. To put the boards on the hives quickly requires three people, two of whom must be fairly strong men, while the third may be a boy or any reasonably active person. On reaching the bees we first of all contract the entrances of all the hives by inserting the entrance blocks which, of course, have been absent all the summer. Next, we lean a bee-escape board against each hive ready for use. We are now ready to put the escape boards under the supers, and for this purpose the men take their positions, one in front and one behind a hive, the hives being in pairs on stands as shown in the illustration. The entrance having been slightly smoked, the two men with steel hive-tools lever up the supers together with the excluder, and lifting the whole about eight or ten inches, hold it in that position for a moment. Meanwhile the other helper, holding the board in one hand and the smoker in the other, blows a little smoke into the gap that is made as the supers are levered up, and then quickly places the board in position on the brood-chamber, whereupon the supers are gently replaced. The third man will usually drop the smoker after using it in order to have both hands free to hold the board so that it can be set quickly and accurately in position. The whole job is done in a few seconds, and a whole apiary can be 'escaped off' in a very short time.

I think that the escape should always be placed under the excluder in case there should be any drones in the super through the hive not having had an excluder put on it when first supered, or through some queen having passed the excluder as does sometimes happen. With an excluder over the bee escape, drones cannot reach the trap and block it by getting stuck while trying to pass through.

When there is a moderately good crop of honey, this way of taking off all the supers at one operation entails a lot of heavy lifting. We use Modified Dadant shallow supers on all our hives, whether the brood-chambers are M.D. or standard British, and in seasons when the average surplus comes out at about fifty to sixty pounds, there will always be at least some stocks in some apiaries with three or four full supers on them, and to lift three full supers of this size (or, of course, a similar weight in smaller supers) requires some effort even for two able-bodied men, while to lift four is quite a strain, and as much as most people can comfortably manage. I occasionally have five of these large supers filled, and on rare occasions, six, and when this happens it is probably best, I think, to make two bites of the cherry. This does not make a second visit to the apiary necessary, though, for all that is needed is to set the top super, or the two top ones, as the case may be, over another colony. All that is required is to put the escape boards on a stock that has only one super on it, or if you are lucky enough to have none like that, one with two supers will do. Then smoke the top super of the heavy stock a little and just set one or two supers from it on to the smaller lot. There won't be any fighting to speak of, and all the bees left in the supers from the big stock will pass down through the escape in a perfectly normal manner.

Three of our supers, really full, weigh more than 200 lbs., honey, combs, frames and the super itself. Unfortunately, only a small minority of our stocks fill three of these supers in ordinary seasons, but there are nearly always some that do it, and in really good years, such as 1928, for instance, more than half of them may give 150 lbs. of honey. This would mean an average all round of about 90 lbs., quite a rare thing in England, in my experience.

When an apiary has been treated as described we leave it alone for forty-eight hours and then go again with a vehicle that has a sufficient carrying capacity to take away the whole crop at one shot. The lorry is loaded as quickly as possible, each stack of supers being covered with an escape board, as soon as piled high enough, in order to keep out bees, for it is important not to start robbing, If, however, the job is done quickly there will be very little danger of that, for since the whole of the stocks will have been disturbed and frightened, all will be on the defensive rather than on pillage bent.

A few extra bee-escape boards or inner covers should be taken when going to fetch honey so that each pile of supers as it is stacked on the lorry can be covered to exclude bees.

When we start to take off the supers we expect to find them practically clear of bees; but occasionally we find a super that they have not left, and then it will be necessary to shake the bees off each comb separately, which is a nuisance. Sometimes the failure to leave the super is caused by a blocked trap; but usually it is through a queen having got into the super through some flaw in the excluder, or because the queen herself is a very small one. (Such queens should be 'liquidated' as soon as possible.) If there is brood in the supers it should be left to emerge, after putting the queen below another excluder, if it is the excluder that is at fault. In the case of a very small queen, kill her and re-queen at next visit.

In taking off honey we lift the supers with the excluder, leaving the brood-chamber covered by the escape board; but before lifting, we remove the inner cover and lean it against the hive. We can either leave all the boards in place until we have loaded all supers, or we can lift them and, after jarring off the bees that cling to them in front of the hive, use them for covering supers as loaded. To take off the escapes and replace by the inner covers is the work of a moment only.

There will always be some bees in the supers if the weather is warm when doing this work, for they are very quick to find their way to honey, and in order to get rid of them it is a good plan, when all the honey has been loaded, and everything is ready for departure, to run the truck a few hundred yards away and remove all the escape boards or the sheet, or whatever the supers have been covered with, and let the bees fly. Nearly all will fly off to their hives directly. The supers can remain uncovered all the way home unless rain falls. Any bees on the combs will generally soon fly off and go back home; but if a few hang on too long, I'm afraid there is nothing we can do about it. As soon as the honey arrives at the extracting house it must be unloaded as fast as possible and the supers stacked in the extracting room. It is a good thing to cover the load with a tarpaulin sheet as soon as it arrives in order to keep bees out of the supers for the few minutes it takes to unload.

Extracting

Honey should be extracted as soon as possible after being taken off the hives. This is particularly necessary in those districts where there is a lot of charlock, mustard, or other honey with a strong tendency to rapid granulation, for if such honey stands for a few days, it is liable to granulate in the combs. When this occurs, the combs have to be cut out and melted down, which is a waste of time and material. Here on the Chiltern Hills and Berkshire Downs, we often have to cut our combs, through the honey in them having set before being taken off the hives at all, and this is especially so in seasons when large areas of turnip, swede, kale, etc., have been allowed to run to seed. We therefore keep the extractor going every day throughout the honey harvest, so far as we possibly can, one man being left at home to do that work.

The extracting is carried out on our premises in a very simple manner, and without any of the pumping and straining arrangements used by some producers. Some day, maybe, we shall decide to set up a large and up-to-date plant; but whether it will pay, only trial can show. The extractor we have is not a very large one, but has sufficient capacity to enable one man to deal with about seventeen to twenty hundredweights a day. No doubt this could be stepped up a good deal by installing a larger machine; but at present we still use an old eight-comb Lewis-Markle extractor, a very fine tangential machine, but on the small side. Our business has grown, but the extractor is the same size as ever. It is driven by an electric motor, and has never given the slightest trouble. I must say that in many ways I think this is one of the best machines made. It is certainly much the easiest of all extractors to keep clean, for there is no top-hamper at all. However, it has not now been produced for many years, as the cheaply constructed radial machines have superseded it. I only hope it will hang together until this war is over and we can either import good machines or have them made in this country.

I have said that one man does the extracting, but not the same man every day, of course. We find that if we try to get on faster than one man can uncap, feed the extractor, and take the honey from it, we lose honey through incomplete extraction. It seems much better to take more time and let the machine run longer. If we only get a pound more out of each super it pays well to do it, and I think in some cases when the honey is dense, we get as much as two or three pounds by allowing a long run in the extractor.

We use a cappings melter of the channel pattern as distinct from the corrugated. It is very easy to clean, and is washed off with boiling water after each day's extracting. This melter is heated by electric boiling rings which give heat without fumes, and the steam-heated uncapping-knife is fed from a pressure boiler also heated over an electric ring. In uncapping, the knife is held in contact with the top and bottom bars of the frames I have already described, and the cappings, together with all the honey above the level of the top and bottom bars, falls on to the sloping bed of the melter and runs away quickly into the channels and finally into a bucket set under the out-fall. Several of these buckets are used, so that, as they fill up, they can be set aside until the wax has solidified. The round, flat cake of wax is then lifted off the warm honey and put into a draining tank so that any honey on it can run off, and the honey is emptied into the large settling tank where it mixes with the honey coming from the extractor.

I may here remark that it has often been asserted that the honey from a cappings melter is spoiled honey. Well, it isn't so with ours. And I think that the reason for this is that most people, when uncapping, try their utmost to pass the knife just under the cappings in order to take only very little honey while doing this work. This probably derives from two ideas: the standard orthodox teaching that the knife should pass through the air-space under the cappings so as to leave practically all the honey behind when the cappings have been removed; and the notion that honey that has been made hot enough so that the wax with it is melted, must necessarily be spoiled. Now, although those who only keep a few stocks of bees as a hobby will do best to follow the orthodox advice, we who have to deal with large amounts of honey can't possibly mess around with that sort of thing, and some sort of cappings melter is virtually a necessity. You will find, if you will keep the melter really hot and cut the combs down to the level of the wood of the frames, that you will not injure your honey to any extent; in fact I have never been able to see that there is any injury at all, not even darkening. You see, when a lot of honey falls on to the melter with a little wax, the great bulk of that honey runs off the hot bed of the melter long before its temperature rises high enough to do it any harm, and what little does reach the melting point of wax (which is only about 145 degrees F.) is not sufficient to have any noticeable effect on the mass of the honey from the extractor.

It is also recommended in orthodox circles that all combs having unsealed honey in them should be put through the extractor before being uncapped, so that this unsealed honey, which is, I gather, supposed to be unripe and liable to ferment, can be used for feeding back to the bees or for making vinegar or that other delightful beverage, mead. I am afraid that if you want to make your living out of honey production in this country, you will find it necessary to be a heretic; but all the same, there is good sense in this advice, because most small amateur beekeepers find themselves quite unable to leave the honey on the hives long enough for it to ripen properly, and when it is taken off too soon that part not sealed will ferment. But what a messy business! Take your honey off in the middle of the flow, extract the unsealed and feed that back; then put the combs back on the hives again, and all because the beekeeper can't wait a week or two!

In America of late years a new style of cappings melter has been tried and found a success. This is the 'Brand' melter, and the principle of it is that the heat that melts the cappings is carried by tubes above the honey and wax. Steam circulates through the tubes. This melter separates the honey from the cappings and allows the honey to flow directly to the settling tank. It melts the cappings, separates the slumgum, and runs the pure wax into the casting vessels. Gale has one; so has Pearson. I wish I had.

The 'cappings dryer' has of late come into fashion in the U.S.A. The idea is to extract the great bulk of the honey from cappings by centrifugal force, by whirling them around either in a specially made machine or in the rotor of an ordinary extractor by means of some sort of suitable fitting. I confess that this idea seems to me a rather feeble one, and I would prefer to melt the whole lot up at one operation and be done with it. When this is done you get all the honey and all the wax, and no amount of centrifugal swinging will do that: there will always be some honey remaining, and in any case, when there is any tendency to granulation in the honey, melting is an absolute necessity. But in the U.S.A., colour is considered such a very important quality that they dread the slightest darkening of their honey, and heat does tend to bring this about.

My opinion is that if you leave your honey on the hives for some days after the close of the flow and remove it all before the weather begins to get cool, no extracting of unsealed honey is needed. I have never yet met a bee farmer who had to live on his honey production or who made any considerable part of his living from it, who does not put all his super combs through the extractor just as they come to hand, unless some of them are known to be in a state which indicates that they should be kept separate from the main bulk. In that case it is best to extract them as they are and then bring them to a temperature of about 120 degrees F. by standing the storage tins in hot water directly after extracting.

The honey from the extractor is run off into a bucket as required to keep the level of it in the extractor below the rotor, and is emptied into a large tank, one of three or four that are placed on a low bench close by. These tanks hold from five to eight hundred-weights, and are filled to the brim.

The honey in these tanks is, of course, warm, and will not become quite cold for two or three days. We allow it to stand for about eighteen or twenty-four hours before running it off into 28-lb. lacquered tins for storage. Before emptying the tanks we skim the surface of the honey, thus removing the froth, wax particles, and any floating debris that lies on the surface. This froth is put into honey tins and dealt with after extracting is over for the year. The tins containing it are then set in hot water for a considerable time and the whole is passed through a fine strainer into a settling tank of small size, say two hundredweights, and allowed to remain for a few hours when the tap can be opened and the clear honey at the bottom allowed to run off into tins. There will be several pounds of froth left which we used to throw away, but now send to a friend who says she likes it better than the honey itself!

We find that the skimming of the honey as it stands in the settling tanks is a useful procedure, for it keeps the tank sides clean. When not skimmed, the honey, as its level falls as the tank is emptied, leaves a film of waxy foam all down the inside walls of the tank, and as a new layer is deposited every time the vessel is emptied, there is very soon a thick coat all over the inside of the tank which it is quite troublesome to remove, for this mixture of froth and particles of wax forms a glutinous mass which adheres very tightly to the metal.

As the tins are filled, they are removed to the honey store where they are stacked in rows and tiered up six or seven high. I don't know how high they may safely be piled up, never having exceeded seven, but Gale told me once that he had found it safe to tier up to eight or nine high, the tins showing no sign of collapsing.

In order to facilitate automatic blending of the honey from the different apiaries, the tins should be ranged in long rows, backing to a wall, and the tiering done as the honey comes from the extracting room. The stack should be planned according to the estimated amount of the total crop, and arranged in such a way that when we bottle the honey we can, by working from the end of the rows, take the honey in layers of tins that form a cross section, as it were, of the whole.

When the honey has all been extracted and stored away, it must be left alone while autumn work is done; but just as soon as feeding is finished and all the bees are settled in their winter quarters, the preparation of the crop for marketing should be begun without delay.

If the honey is to be sold in bulk to packers, nothing more is required than to deliver it in the tins, as they are. Small quantities can be put on rail in tea-chests, four to the chest. The top should be left open, but a piece of plywood may be laid over the tins and some cord passed across it and through holes in the sides of the chest, just to keep anyone from opening the tins. Honey travels well in this way; but should be so sent only in the solid form. Tins of liquid honey should have their lids fastened on with three or four dabs of solder and the lids themselves must be tight fitting. When large quantities of honey in tins are to be sent out it is better to deliver by one's own vehicle or to hire one for the purpose.

But if you want to build up a stable trade for your honey, the only way is to bottle every pound of it in retail glass jars, and sell it under your own label. You want the consuming public to grow accustomed to your particular brand, and to ask for it in the shops. To bring this about it is necessary to supply the consumer with what he wants, and you will find that the better the honey is, the better your consumers will like it, and the more they will buy of it. This, again, will suit your retailers, for they like a good selling line about which they have no complaints from their customers.

Now the honey-eating public in different parts of the land often likes rather different flavours in honey, but speaking generally, the people of London and Southern England prefer a rather mild-flavoured honey, and, apart from heather honey, which a few prefer, light honeys of the clover type sell best. I shall be told, I expect, by beekeepers whose product is dark and strong-flavoured tree honey, that their consumers like that kind best, and that they can make more money of it than of the lighter, milder honeys. That is all right, of course, and perfectly true; but it is a fact, all the same, that it is not in normal times at all easy to place any large quantity of dark, strong honey on the London market.

Tastes differ, and the bulk of English honey eaters like it light in colour and mild in flavour. I remember being given a taste of some very special honey in Sussex once. I think it was stated to be from holly, and I was told that it was greatly liked locally and fetched twopence per pound more than ordinary honey. I am very far from being a judge, and don't like honey and never did, but I would have thought that stuff would have been enough to make a hippopotamus vomit; so there is truth in the adage: one man's meat is another's poison.

Packing the Honey

Well, having decided to pack in glass for sale to retailers, we must set about the job systematically, according to the amount to be dealt with. To get and hold a firm trade in this product it is quite necessary that great care be taken in the packing and general get up of the retail packages. We should take some care in choosing a really nice jar, preferably one with a closure like that of the old Ministry jar that can be adjusted by about a quarter turn of the cap. The new Ministry jar is of excellent shape in the one-pound size, but has the very bad feature of a screw thread. The half-pound size is very bad indeed in my opinion, nothing would induce me to use it. All honey jars should be low enough so that the bottoms are easily reached with an ordinary jam spoon, and should be round, and not square, on any account. The metal caps should be of good tin-plate and lacquered inside and out. The label is of great importance, and should be chosen to suit the jars that are used and its colour should not clash with the colouring of the lacquer on the cap. Everyone to his humour, of course, and we all may probably prefer something that we individually like; but I feel sure that too much elaboration and too much colour is a mistake on a honey label. Nice clean labels and bright, clear glass bottles will help to sell honey; but never forget that these are only the trimmings. Unless your product is good stuff, no label will help you much.

This is the way we pack our honey. I will first describe the process when the honey is to be put up for sale in the granulated form. It is probably a fact that about 99 per cent of those who eat granulated honey regularly very much prefer it to be soft, so that it can be taken out of the jars easily without bending the spoon, and can also be easily spread on bread and butter. Now it is a common practice to bottle straight from the settling tanks and to allow it to set in the jars. It is said that the flavour is better; but I think it is less to preserve flavour than to save trouble that this course of action is adopted. When so bottled, honey sets as hard as a stone, and frequently shows that rather ugly appearance called 'frosting'. This seems to be caused by a certain shrinking of the mass of the honey and consequent parting of it from the glass which leaves a slight space. Honey so bottled is also more liable to ferment if kept until the hot weather of the following summer; for hardly any honey is absolutely safe from fermentation unless heated sufficiently to kill any ferments that may be present; and one can never be certain that this trouble will not show itself in warm weather, no matter how ripe the honey when extracted, or how carefully packed. The commanding necessity of supplying honey in the soft state is that nearly all consumers like it better so.

In America very little honey is sold in the granulated state; the public there always want it clear. It is sold almost entirely on its colour and appearance, flavour counting as nothing against a shade or two of colour. I once showed Mr. Tollafield of Roots' a jar of honey from sainfoin and white clover chiefly. It was what we should call a light golden colour. He said at once that, though it was very good honey, its colour would put it right out of the best grades in the U.S.A. In America honey is put on the table in jugs and very tall, narrow glass jars, the latter to make it look as light as possible. I used to wonder why honey is not sold in America in the granulated form; but I know now. In the hot summers they have there, granulated honey melts and gets into an awful-looking mess. But why they put so much stress on having 'water white' honey, I can't imagine. However, the moral for us is, sell on real merit, not looks, otherwise we may find ourselves selling our product at less than the price of refined sugar, just like our Yankee friends.

To bottle honey so that the granulation will be even and will remain soft in the jars, we proceed as follows. All honey is allowed to stand in the 28-lb. storage tins until thoroughly set, when it is ready for bottling. We use electric heaters that hold two to four hundredweights each. The honey is put into these in the evening and the heat turned on. This is so arranged that in the morning when we are ready to start work, the honey will be quite soft throughout. We use a boiler that holds four 28-lb. tins at a time, standing on a wooden rack fitted to the pan, and the water in this boiler is heated until it is so hot that a tin of this warm, soft honey stood in it for a minute or so will have the outer layer of the honey liquefied. As soon as the water is hot enough we set the tins of honey in it, four at a time, for a few moments and then take it out and empty into the bottling tank. We do this to facilitate emptying the honey quickly and cleanly, for when this extra heating is not done, granulated honey, however soft, sticks to the bottom and sides of the tin; but when the whole has been set in the almost boiling water for a few seconds, the tin is left with hardly a trace of honey in it after being allowed to stay tipped mouth downwards over the bottling tank for a few minutes. A good plan for holding the tins in this position is to have some straight pieces of wood about one inch by one inch by about two feet long, according to the diameter of the tank. When the bulk of the honey has been emptied into the tank, the end of one of these wooden bars is shoved up into the tin which is then allowed to slip down into the tank as far as the rod will allow, so that it hangs tipped downwards to allow the honey to run out of it for a few minutes. The rod is notched in the right place so that the notch will engage the edge of the tank and prevent the tin from slipping.

As soon as the tins of honey are taken out of the hot water, and before the honey is emptied from them into the bottling tank, they are opened and the surface of the honey in them is skimmed off. There is generally a little froth, and sometimes a few small specks of debris, and sometimes the body of a wasp that has committed suicide just before the tin was closed. Besides this, I am of the opinion that this skimming has a good effect in another direction: it removes just that film in which most of the ferments are, I think, generally lodged.

When enough honey has been emptied into the bottling tank, it is thoroughly stirred up and mixed, so that the whole is reduced to a uniform mass of semi-fluid mush which runs from the bottling valve quickly, and it is then ready for immediate filling into the jars which should be ready washed and labelled. The whole process is readily and quickly carried out in practice, though it takes some time to describe. Two people who know how to do it and have enough heaters, can easily bottle sixteen to twenty hundred-weights a day in 1-lb. and ½-lb. jars, provided that these are all in readiness. To find the time needed to soften the honey thoroughly without making it too hot and melting it, requires experience. It varies with the time of year, the hardness of the stored honey, and the temperature of the atmosphere. When bottled, the honey should be allowed to stand for about a week or ten days in a not-too-cold place, so that it may have time to set in the jars before being delivered to customers.

It is probably best for honey to be sold granulated or 'set', as we call it; but some consumers like it better clear, and as the customer is always right until we can persuade him differently, it is necessary to cater for this demand. Besides, clear honey has uses that set honey cannot serve: it is used a good deal for eating with breakfast cereal foods, and we ought to encourage such customs as much as possible. Now if honey is to be sold in the liquid or clear state, it is important that it should remain clear, at least for several weeks. But nearly all honey, after being melted down to render it clear, will regranulate after a short time, and this second granulation is uneven, and gives the honey a very unattractive appearance. It is neither one thing nor the other when this happens, and this means that it requires rather more labour and fuel to bottle honey in this form if it is to be satisfactory and keep its bright clear look. The work is done in this way.

The honey is warmed in the electric heaters in the same way as with the granulated, but more heat is allowed so that in the morning it is liquefied right through. It is then emptied into the bottling tanks through a fine strainer cloth which, being hot, it will pass rapidly. The tank, when filled, is left standing until the next morning. If a small one, it may need to be wrapped up in some warm material to prevent the honey from cooling too quickly, which would make the bottling a very slow job. In the morning the honey can be bottled off quickly, the caps of the jars being at once tightly affixed.

But honey so treated, if not further dealt with, will very soon begin to show unsightly granules, and to avoid this the jars are set in a shallow tray of rain water, having a wooden rack in its bottom to prevent direct contact of the bottles with the tank bottom. This flat tank or tray is set on gas, oil, or electric boiling rings and the water, which should reach to the shoulders of the jars, is heated until the jars are just so hot that it is only possible to hold them in the hand for a moment. They are then removed and allowed to cool as quickly as possible, and the honey will remain clear for long enough for most purposes. Throughout this operation the metal lids of the jars should be kept tightly screwed on. It has often been asserted that the jars must be opened while being heated or else they will burst; but this is a fairy-tale which may be disregarded.

There are one or two points, however, that I ought to mention. It is risky to put cold jars directly into hot water. Generally they will stand it, but occasionally one will crack. In the case of jars of poor quality, this risk is greatly increased, and in any case it will be safer to add some cold water before putting a fresh batch of jars into the heating tray. A good large heating tank of this kind may be made to hold about ten or twelve dozen of the common semi-squat kind: the very low jars of the Ministry type take a lot more room. Another point is that it is wise to use rain water for this job, for if there is lime in your drinking water a deposit is apt to form on the jars of honey while in the water. Of course honey treated in this way must be labelled after treatment, and this is best done while the jars are still warm as the paste dries immediately in that case.

The washing of bottles is a rather unpleasant job, and it is best to get as forward as possible with it while the weather is warm. I have no experience of a bottle-washing machine, and to work for hours with very cold water is not nice. In any case a vessel of water should be kept hot to take the chill off each new filling of washing water. It is for jobs like this that an independent boiler is so good. We wash our jars in a large sink and stand them first to drain on a large board like those used in sculleries, and then place them in large cartons which are tipped up a little so that the drop which always forms on the convex bottoms of the jars can run off down the sides and leave the bottle dry.

Labels should always be ungummed unless only a few are needed. To buy a large quantity of gummed labels is asking for trouble. As sure as fate they will become damp at some time and stick together so that the bundles get like a lot of bricks, when they are quite useless. Do not use lithographed labels on foil paper, they are very poor things to wear. If you decide to use gold or silver foil, get a recessed die made and print in black or other colour on the foil so as to leave the lettering in raised gold or silver. There is much to be said for having a die made, however you decide to print; I mean, that even when you intend to print on ordinary paper it pays to do it. The die printing breaks the texture of the paper to some extent, and that seems to prevent the rolling up of the labels; one of the greatest hindrances with ordinary printed paper.

When putting on labels, the whole surface of each label should be wetted with the paste so as to allow stretching before application to the jars. This prevents subsequent wrinkling.

Beeswax

Dealing with wax is a messy job, but if we go about it in a sensible manner, it need not be so very bad, and will not take up much time. My way of dealing with old combs is to put aside all those discarded throughout the spring and summer, cutting them out of the frames and storing them in tea-chests until wanted. When all are collected, which is usually the case before any honey has to be extracted, I melt the combs in the same 20-gallon boiler as we use for making syrup. Plenty of rainwater is used and the comb is boiled in this, the mush being dipped out into a press from time to time with a hand bowl. My press is a very old one which I bought from the Root Co. more than thirty years ago, and it still does its work quite well. This press is of the steam variety, having a false bottom to take water; the theory being to steam the combs and then press out the wax; but that part of it is useless, and I have always used it as a press, pure and simple. I think the deep outer case which holds in the heat is an advantage over the usual presses. There is a perforated metal basket inside, which rests on a very strong grating, and into this we put a strong bag of coarse sacking material. The boiling mush is dipped into this from the boiler. About half a dozen bowlfuls are enough for one pressing. When ready to press, the bag is loosely tied or even just folded over and a round flat disk, made for the purpose, is put on it and the pressure applied by running down the heavy lathe-cut screw with its spider. Great pressure can be applied, and when we have squeezed out as much as possible, we take out screw and disc and with a pair of pincers, pull the bag of slumgum up and move it about, and then again apply pressure; after which there is very little wax left and the bag is emptied on to the floor on a large sheet of paper or cardboard, and the process repeated with another lot until all is done. If properly carried out one can in this way make sure that hardly any wax is left, even in very old combs.

The wax, as it flows from the press, is allowed to fall into a large tank of rainwater in which it quickly solidifies in all sorts of queer shapes. When cold, it can be put into a bag and stored away until after extracting and heather honey pressing are over, when it is melted up again with the cappings wax and the wax from the heather honeycombs.

The cappings wax comes from the melter in almost pure, clean discs which have set on the cooling honey in the pails. This is treated as described below; but the wax coming from the heather press must be dealt with separately. It is much more easily treated than old comb, but is more trouble than cappings. It comes from the press in thin flat cakes, and no matter how well pressed, will always contain a little honey. This honey is not reclaimable by any method I know of, so we just boil up the whole of this heather wax in our boiler as with old comb, and pass it through the wax press; but it requires very little pressing and the job is very quickly done, for there are no cocoons included in the wax—or pollen either—if we are careful how we remove the honey from the frames.

When this heather wax has been rendered, we take one good day to reboil and cast the whole of the year's wax crop. We get up a good hot fire of *wood* under the boiler, provide plenty of clean rainwater, and into the hot water we put the wax, lump by lump, as fast as we can melt it. Adjoining the boiler we have a large round tank, about $1\frac{1}{2}$ feet deep, and over this we arrange a strainer of cheese-cloth (be sure to buy the unbleached kind as the other soon falls to bits). It is a good plan to fasten this strainer to a ring of wood like a child's hoop, made just large enough to drop over the tank; the whole thing can then be lifted off without having to untie the string.

The melted wax is ladled from the boiler on to the strainer, and is helped to pass through by scraping the cloth with the dipping bowl. When the tank is full up to the cloth, we take off the strainer and dip most of the wax out into casting vessels. Of course we keep on putting fresh wax into the boiler, and also more water as required, until all the wax has been dealt with. When dipping out of the boiler, both wax and water will be taken, and it is quite necessary to take some water in order that there shall be at least three inches of it at the bottom of the tank into which the wax is put, so that dirt can settle down into it; but after the start the less water taken the better. You are bound to take some water when dipping out the wax as the boiling of the mixture brings the water up as you are dipping it. When treated in this way the wax comes out quite clean and fit to be cast right away, and foundation makers will take it without wanting to make allowance for dross.

We used to cast in wash-hand basins, bread-pans and other similar vessels, but have lately found that it is better to take a number of square tins, such as the 4-gallon petrol tins that are thrown away by the army when on manœuvres. From these we cut the tops with a can opener of the wheel type, and then take four strips of wood about 1-inch square by 8-inches long, and tie them, one on each side. The strings are made tight enough to press in the sides of the tin. A pint of boiling rainwater is poured into a tin and it is then filled with wax to within about two inches of the top, by dipping from the settling tank with the bowl, taking care not to dip deeply. When cold, the pieces of wood are removed, the sides of the tin spring out, and the block of wax slips from the tin quite easily. This plan came out of one of the American papers; *Gleanings*, I think. Two men can boil up and cast about ten hundredweights in a day.

Rainwater only should be allowed to come into contact with melted wax under any circumstances; but the use of water with a high lime content is the worst of any, in its effect on beeswax.

A wood fire is preferred for boiling wax, as it can be quickly increased or decreased as required. A coal or coke fire is very liable to get excessively hot and is difficult to reduce or increase quickly, and it is important to be able always to control a fire that is boiling wax. Make it an *invariable rule* to have a large can of cold rainwater close by the boiler so that boiling can be arrested instantly at any moment. *On no account must boiling wax be left even for a minute,* for that would be very dangerous. If the wax were suddenly to boil over the whole building might very soon be on fire. *Never on any pretext place a lid or cover of any kind on any vessel or boiler while dealing with beeswax.*

CHAPTER XII

DISEASES AND PESTS

Honey-bees suffer at times from various ailments, and are assailed by enemies just like all other living things, and it seems likely that in the case of the diseases there has been increase during the past fifty years or so. Beekeeping with poor management, and movable combs in the hands of the incompetent on the one hand, and on the other the preservation of the unfit by the coddling of strains that lack stamina, may, I think, have tended to weaken the natural resistance of some of our bees to the attacks of diseases. It is also thought by some, with good reason I believe, that over-reliance on feeding with sugar as a substitute for honey may also have had its effect.

One point, missed by some beekeepers in relation to bee disease, is that so far as practical considerations are concerned, all bee diseases are incurable; that is to say, the individual bee cannot be cured, and, so far as I know, never recovers from any of the maladies we know as bee diseases. When we speak of curing disease we mean that we rid colonies of infected or infested bees while avoiding the spread of the trouble to hitherto healthy bees in that colony.

It has long been known that the brood of bees suffers from disease, but the specification of the different ailments is quite recent. It is now well established that there are two principal diseases of brood known, respectively, as American foul brood and European foul brood, which are shortly called 'A.f.b.' and 'E.f.b.'

American Foul Brood

American foul brood is a dangerous, insidious trouble, caused by a spore-bearing organism, *B. larvae*, which kills the sealed larvae and even pupae, but not larvae that are still feeding and growing. The grubs all die at about the same age, and their remains take on a distinctive uniform appearance. No photograph is of much use in helping the uninitiated beekeeper to recognize this complaint, but I am reproducing the best illustration I know of, a drawing by Mr. Snodgrass. Every beekeeper must, somehow or other, manage to see the disease for himself; there is no other way. Once diagnosed, there is only one thing to be done, destroy all the combs and honey; everything, in fact, except the hive, with the possible exception, in certain circumstances, of the bees. Weak stocks should in every case and at all times be ruthlessly and utterly destroyed, bees, brood, frames, combs, honey, and quilts, and the hive must be thoroughly scorched out.

During a few weeks of summer, from about 1st May to about 14th July, very strong stocks may be treated by the shaking method, that is to say, by shaking all the bees from the diseased combs into a clean hive fitted with foundation only. This operation may also be carried out by the use of the fumes of saltpetre, the idea being that the fumes quickly make the bees insensible and cause them to drop from their combs, which are then removed and a fresh hive fitted with foundation given to them. I have no experience of this plan, as I find the shaking plan quick and satisfactory as carried out by me in the occasional instances when I have to get rid of foul brood.

The way I do the trick is this. If cells of A.f.b. are found in a strong stock in the early part of the summer, I usually bring the whole thing home for treatment, though the job can be done at the apiary if preferred. Either during a good honey-flow in the day-time, or at some time when no bees are flying, I dig a hole near the hive about three feet across and a foot deep. The hive containing the diseased colony is then gently lifted to a position behind its original site, but close to it, the hole being also quite near. The hole is filled with dry straw or some other inflammable material, and will burn all the more quickly if sprinkled with petroleum or creosote. The hive into which the bees are to be shaken is placed in the exact position formerly occupied by the diseased stock; it is fitted with new frames of foundation, a few of which are taken out and leaned conveniently against the hive.

Now we are ready to shake. Take the frames, one by one, and, holding them well down into the clean hive, give them a sharp jar or two to throw off the bees clear down into the hive, so that should any newly stored and watery nectar be thrown out of the combs, it will all fall right into the hive and not be scattered outside. Any bees that hold on to the combs after this should be rapidly brushed off with a feather. There is nothing like a feather, as it does not disintegrate like a bunch of grass, and, unlike a bee-brush, it can be burned without regrets. This job is a matter of only about a minute, when two or three people are working together, and as each comb is placed on the straw in the hole, the straw having been fired at the moment of commencing the shaking, it will be seen that all comb and honey, in fact all the especially dangerous material, is enveloped in smoke and flame almost instantly. When all this material has been thoroughly burned, and all quilts, floor-scrapings, etc., put on the fire and consumed, the whole is buried out of sight. The big swarm, for that is what it amounts to, is now in a new hive, on new frames and foundation, and should be fed fairly heavily, whether there is a honey-flow or not. The infected hive must be thoroughly scorched out by means of a blow torch before being again used.

I have never known this plan to fail to produce a perfect and permanent cure in my hands; but it must be carried out with the most scrupulous care; otherwise it is more likely to spread the trouble to healthy colonies than to have the desired effect. The shaking system has been very largely rejected of late years. Dr. E. F. Phillips in the U.S.A. advocated it for years, and it was extensively tried in that country, but was a failure on the whole, and the government has reverted to total destruction by fire. When one considers the way the shaking was often done, as described and illustrated in American bee literature, one can hardly wonder at this, for those who did the work do not appear to have grasped the necessity for taking the most scrupulous care in carrying it out. We even read of boiling up the combs in the open air to salvage the wax! Such methods could hardly be expected to succeed, but if properly done, I think the shaking method an almost certain way of ridding an apiary of A.f.b.

The total destruction of all stocks at all times has been widely recommended of late years, and there is no doubt at all that this way is always the best when those who are to do the cleaning up are not fully competent. It does seem a pity to destroy what is a very fine swarm of bees in May or June if it can be avoided without undue risk. In skilled hands this can be done; but inexperienced or careless people had much better destroy every diseased stock at once, no matter what the season or how strong the colony. Now the total destruction of the stock, bees, combs, and all, needs just as much care and skill as the shaking of the bees in treating the disease, with the additional bother of killing the bees. To do this job, dig a hole and fill with straw as before. Shut the unfortunate bees into their hive after dark and kill them by pouring a pint of petrol through the feed-hole of the crown-board or through the quilts. As soon as they are dead, which will be in a minute or two, carry the hive with its contents to the side of the hole, to windward; light the fire, open the hive and put all the frames and combs, quilts, etc., on the fire, scraping off the floor and throwing all scrapings, dead bees, and other rubbish on to the flames. Close the hive and take it to headquarters for thorough scorching out. Meanwhile see that the fire consumes everything burnable and then bury the ashes.

There have been attempts, from time to time, to sterilize combs containing the remains of larvae that have died of A.f.b., but this proceeding is a very risky one, for the spores massed by millions in the remains of the dead grubs, and which take the form of hard, tightly adherent scales, are extremely tenacious of life, and there is no known method of sterilization that can really be relied on. A solution of formaldehyde and alcohol was tried at one time, but even in those cases wherein it seemed to be effectual, it is more than doubtful if it was worth the trouble. After all, it seems hardly worth while to take such a risk when frames and foundation can be had at quite a reasonable cost. My advice is to have nothing to do with any such thing, but to burn all infected material, except extracting combs that have never been bred in at all. These can be readily made safe by soaking in formalin-alcohol solution or by treatment with formalin gas. I carried out this process extensively and with complete success when I had to deal with a bad outbreak of A.f.b. many years ago. It is *necessary*, after this treatment of combs, that they shall be thoroughly washed out in two or three changes of water before being given to bees, otherwise the stocks they are given to will be poisoned. This happened to my bees when I tried it, and that is how I found it out. Gassing requires a gas-chamber, a gas-tight container. Messrs. Burtt & Son made the one I used, which was sold to another bee farmer after I had done with it. It was entirely satisfactory in my hands and, I believe, in his.

But was it the gassing and soaking that sterilized those combs? Were those combs, in fact, infectious at all? I don't know. It may have been that the washing removed the honey, and with the honey the infection. It may have been that the formalin killed the germs in these extracting combs much more easily than in the brood-combs. In the latter, the spores are massed together in enormous numbers in the scales; in the former, they are probably few in number and unattached, and thus more easily acted on by the germicide and quite readily swept away by the water in washing.

One very eminent personage in the beekeeping world who has been especially identified with bee disease research, once told me that he considered that any combs that had never been bred in could always be made safe by simply washing them out thoroughly in running water; but, 'If you try it, Manley, be sure that the water from the washing goes right into the drain or into the Thames, and *don't say I told you.*'

That B. larvae is carried almost exclusively in honey, I believe to be a fact, for otherwise I do not see how we can account for some things that we know occur. The theory explains why shaken bees do not carry the disease with them; why natural swarms that have to build their own combs do not carry it. Also why extracting combs that have never been bred in will probably not propagate the disease if thoroughly washed out in water. It also, I fancy, may explain why there are any bees left alive at all.

American foul brood, then, is a disease carried in honey, and infected honey is a deadly thing if bees can get access to it; but I very much doubt if the trouble is otherwise infectious. I don't think it is spread from stock to stock in an apiary except by the robbing of honey from diseased colonies by healthy ones, or through the bees gaining access to exposed honey, and in about nineteen cases out of twenty, it is spread by the beekeeper himself. One of the most effective means by which A.f.b. is spread far and wide is the abominable habit of a great many small beekeepers of setting out their cappings and extracting combs to be cleaned up by the bees in the open. This should be a criminal offence, and I hope it will be, when we get some measure of bee-disease control and registration of beekeepers.

I had an apiary some years ago where one or two stocks always became infected with A.f.b., in a very virulent form, every August, as regularly as the month came round. This was undoubtedly caused by the setting out of the cappings, etc., from diseased stocks at some considerable distance. It could not have been done nearby, for in that case all my stocks would have been sure to have found it out, and to have brought home the infected honey. Probably someone about a mile away was the culprit; anyway, I moved from that place altogether on account of the trouble. One interesting thing about it was this. I divided a stock at that apiary into two, moving one part away to another place. Soon after this I found foul brood in the part left. The case was a very bad one indeed. In a week or two the brood was mostly dead and putrid, showing that infection had been wholesale; in fact the evidence pointed to the sudden influx of a large amount of heavily infected honey which had been immediately fed to the larvae. Well, this lot was, of course, destroyed and I rushed off to deal with the other half, the part that had been taken to another apiary; but when I came to examine that stock I found it to be perfectly normal; no disease of any kind, and it has been healthy ever since then—eight years ago. So it is perfectly evident, to me at all events, that just after the division was made, my neighbour, whoever he was, had extracted his honey and set his combs out; my bees had cleaned them, or helped to do it, and had become infected immediately, while the divided half colony that had been removed was saved.

Regarding other possible ways of conveying infection, I should, I suppose, mention that it is usually considered that tools, clothes, hands, etc., should be disinfected. I think this is just nonsense. That everything that has contacted honey in a diseased stock should be well washed is quite certain; but what is the use of disinfecting when the spores of foul brood are known and proved to be entirely unaffected by all disinfectants and germicides that could by any possibility be used on one's hands or clothes: I think such teaching simply creates a false sense of security. Wash your hands and hive-tools after attending to foul colonies and burn everything else that touches the honey and never wear gloves when dealing with a foul stock; you may then feel safe.

European Foul Brood

The disease known as European foul brood or E.f.b. is much less prevalent than the other; but in some cases, at any rate, is more difficult to get rid of. Its cause is, even now, not decided with certainty, but is believed to be an organism called B. pluton or Streptococcus pluton, a rather elusive germ which may turn out to be a form of what Cheshire and Cheyne called *B. alvei*. Those who wish to find out all that is known about the causal agent of this trouble should look the matter up in current writings, such as Miss Betts's *Diseases of Bees*.

E.f.b. is now believed to be spread by drifting nurse bees, as from hive to hive, and by individual nurse bees, as from larva to larva within the colony, by the fact that emerging bees get their mouth parts infected in the act of biting their way through the cappings of their cells, so that when they feed larvae the food given is infected.

E.f.b. is a malady that kills brood in the growing stages, and even sealed brood may be attacked, but, so far as I know, pupae are immune. The accompanying illustration may help to assist in diagnosis, but as in the case of A.f.b., the beekeeper must manage to see the disease for himself. The trouble is said to pass away, sometimes, without any other treatment than the removal of the queen, and her replacement by another after a suitable interval to allow all brood to emerge; at least that is what happened to me in 1928 when I had a number of stocks badly infected. Of course, I can't swear that it was E.f.b., but it had all the known signs down to the minutest detail; visible signs, that is. I have never had any trouble with it since, but I have seen it in the apiaries of Mr. Teal of Wiltshire, who has had great difficulty in getting rid of it. In his case it was necessary, I believe, to destroy combs and bees and make a new start.

Other Brood Diseases

Those are the two most serious maladies of the brood, but there are a few minor troubles that will probably be met with from time to time by the bee farmer. Chalk brood is common, but not very serious. It often disappears without any action by the bee man, but persistent cases should be re-queened with queens of Italian strain or, if weak, may as well be destroyed.

Sac brood I have never seen; but it is said to occur in this country. It is really of little account, and the bee farmer will be unlikely to have any serious trouble with it.

I now come to a trouble that I do not understand, which is apt to occur early in the year, round about May as a rule. Grubs of all ages die, and there is none of the uniform appearance of A.f.b. The dead larvae lie in all sorts of positions and dry into irregularly shaped scales that do not adhere to the cells. The whole thing passes away without any treatment so far as my experience goes. Miss Betts's description of what is called para-foul brood exactly fits it, except that I have never noticed any reddish colour. Para-foul brood is spread by robbing, so it is said; but I know nothing about it.

Diagnosis of brood disease is very important. B. larvae, or A.f.b., is easily identified, once seen a few times; but other maladies are more difficult. The matter has been further complicated by a brood ailment called 'Addled brood' which is not thought to be a disease brought about by pathogenic germs, but to be caused by some degenerative change in the queen. I do not know what the cause may be, but have had some trouble with it on occasion. The brood dies in the pupal stage. A change of queen brings complete relief. This trouble may be confounded with foul brood (A.f.b.), while para-foul brood may quite easily be mistaken for E.f.b.

Another complication has been the propagation, long after the belief was proved to be a mistaken one, of the idea that the two primary brood diseases are simply different stages of the same. You may see illustrations of European foul brood and of para-foul brood labelled 'incipient foul brood'. This nonsense should be discounted at once, for there is no such thing as incipient foul brood. There is A.f.b. (B. larvae) and E.f.b. (B. or S. pluton) and each a distinct disease; there is no visible incipient stage of either. The term incipient has also sometimes been used to describe the early stages of these diseases. Apart altogether from the silly idea that because grubs die at an earlier period of their lives when attacked by E.f.b. than when A.f.b. is the cause of their deaths, therefore E.f.b. is just incipient A.f.b., there has arisen the idea that these troubles are incipient when only a few larvae in a colony have died from their action. Don't fall for this nonsense either, if you want to be a successful beekeeper, but make up your mind that once a single grub has succumbed to B. larvae, American foul brood is established in the colony.

Another point I would like to make is this. A lot has been said and written suggesting that it is comparatively easy to get rid of foul brood if caught in its early stage, meaning that if it is discovered before it has spread much over the combs and while there are consequently only a few dead larvae, it can be got rid of without the destruction of combs. It has been asserted that if such stocks are treated with drugs of various kinds, izal, naphthol beta, formaldehyde, etc., the colony will rid itself of the disease. Such notions are dangerous, for they are founded upon a complete misapprehension, and it is necessary to state explicitly that once B. larvae is present in a colony, and has brought about the death of a single larva, no drug treatment of any kind is of any value whatever.[1] The differences in the rapidity of progress made by the disease when once it has gained a foothold, are probably caused by the extent of the initial inoculations. If only a drop or two of infected honey have been brought into the hive, only a few larvae can be infected, and the disease will not spread through the larval population until the remains of the first larvae to die have had time to infect honey placed in the cells which contain them and to be dispersed by nurse bees to feeding grubs. If, on the other hand, a large amount of infected honey is suddenly brought into a colony by robbing bees, this honey is immediately fed to a large percentage of the grubs, with the result of wholesale infection, and an advanced case of the disease in a few days, as in the case I have recounted.

Of course, when we find a colony of bees that is strong and otherwise prosperous in April, May, or June, having a few of its larvae dead of A.f.b., we naturally treat it rather differently from an advanced case. The infection, though undoubtedly present, is not extensive and, although we may be sure that if left alone the end would be death, such a case may always be profitably treated by shaking. My method in cases like this is to remove the queen; using her elsewhere if she is any good (queens isolated from their workers never carry A.f.b.) and at the end of three weeks shake the colony on to foundation in the usual manner. By this time a young queen will generally be laying or on the point of starting to lay, and the swarm will usually do well. But do not forget that,

[1] Quite promising experiments are now being made with one of the Sulphonamides, I understand; but I think that the statement made here must stand until these experiments have been carried much further.

no matter how few larvae are seen to be dead of the disease, exactly the same attention to detail and the same scrupulous care must be devoted to the work as if the very worst case ever seen were being treated. And it will certainly be discovered at the end of the three weeks, when the brood is all hatched out, that there are many more dead grubs and scales in the combs than the bee-keeper had any idea of at the beginning. To sum up: the motto of the bee farmer should be, 'You can't be too careful.' The price of success is constant vigilance.

Acarine Disease

When I first began to keep bees 'foul brood' was about the only malady that anyone seemed to consider of any serious account. We used to hear about dysentery, May pest, etc., but nobody seemed to bother much about any trouble of mature bees. It was not until the first few years of this present century that we were all roughly wakened up by the epidemic of 'Isle of Wight disease'. This ailment is now called Acarine disease, and it is pretty thoroughly understood to-day. For years investigators spent their energies in exploring the digestive system of bees, where they found plenty of germs of various kinds, but it was not until fifteen years had been spent in hunting for the causal agent in the bees' alimentary tract that the brilliant idea occurred to someone, Dr. Rennie, I think, to look somewhere else. So the breathing system was examined and the mite that causes the trouble was, of course, found without difficulty.

It has always been a mystery to me why this little creature was not found ten years earlier, for it is so very easy to see, that one would have expected that some amateur with a microscope or lens would surely have stumbled on it when examining the anatomy of bees. Well, it *was* found; first by Miss E. Harvey, in December 1919, I believe. The research was conducted by the late Dr. Rennie and financed by the late Mr. Wood, after whom the species was named *Acarapis woodi*. The whole report was published in 1921 by the Royal Society of Edinburgh in a large, beautifully illustrated and printed pamphlet, at nine shillings a copy, one of which, autographed by Rennie, I possess.

Acarapis woodi is a very small mite which lives within the breathing tubes of the bee, called the tracheae. Only the pair of tubes

DISEASES AND PESTS

that open into the thoracic spiracles are affected. The mites live by sucking the juices from the tracheal walls, which they puncture with their piercing mouth parts. Let us suppose that a pregnant female mite has gained access to the trachea of a bee. She feeds on the bee and lays her eggs. These eggs hatch within a very short time, producing a larval form of the mite which has only six legs, against the eight of the adult. The larva in due course is converted into a mature specimen, either male or female. These mate, of course, but I don't know whether they do so before leaving their first home or not. Miss Betts thinks they do, though this, if general, would seem to imply very intensive inbreeding. When the food supply provided by the unfortunate host bee is becoming exhausted, or when the fast-increasing family of mites is getting crowded, females leave their home and go out in search of new pastures. Probably they are already mated when they do this, though I suppose mating is possible outside the bee. Anyway the migrating female looks out for a tender young bee that has just emerged from her cell, and as this bee comes into contact with the one whose spiracle she has just left, the mite clings to the hair of that bee and pushes through the spiracle into the trachea, where she presumably first takes some refreshment and then proceeds to lay an egg.

Now the following fact is very important to us beekeepers. It is only into very young bees that these mites penetrate. This discovery was made by Dr. Morgenthaler in Switzerland, to whom we owe much. I don't know why the mites never enter older bees, but I have thought that the reason may be that the fringe of setae that guard the spiracles may be soft and pliable at first, but become stiff after a few days; anyway, it is an ascertained fact that bees after five days from emergence are immune to attack by *A. woodi*. Therefore, although the mites can increase within a bee's tracheae, they cannot pass from bee to bee unless there are newly emerged bees in the colony. It thus follows that if we can find a means by which the mites can be prevented from migrating while breeding is going on among the bees until all mite-carrying bees have died out, we have got rid of the trouble.

During winter, when no breeding of bees is going on, the mites can only stay at home and breed there, but they cause great discomfort to their hosts, and stocks so infested never winter well, and often don't winter at all. The winter symptoms of the presence of acarine disease are unseasonable activity of bees, warmth over the cluster, and entrances smudged with excreta. These signs may indicate other troubles, but in four cases out of five the cause of them is mite infestation. In the active seasons its signs are the well-known 'crawling' or inability to fly. As almost all diseases of adult bees have this symptom in common, microscopic examination is necessary before one can be certain whether the trouble is acarine disease or not. A small dissecting instrument with an aplanatic lens having a magnifying power of fifteen diameters is very suitable for this purpose. With its aid, together with a couple of mounted needles and a razor blade, anyone can make quick and certain examinations, after having been shown how to do it by someone who knows. I would advise all those who intend to become bee farmers to see this operation carried out: it is a perfectly simple one.

To an experienced person it is fairly easy to judge by the appearance of the bees whether the trouble is probably acarine disease or not; there is something about the look of the crawlers that indicates what the trouble is, though, of course, no one can be *certain* without using a microscope or magnifying glass. There is, however, one sign that is very nearly conclusive, and which any beginner may note: it is almost certainly acarine disease if bees are seen flying before their hive with one of their small wings immovable and sticking out as if dislocated. Such a bee will now and then give a kind of sideslip or stagger in the air, and when this is seen, acarine disease may be diagnosed with a very high degree of probability.

I know of only two ways of dealing successfully with this trouble on a bee farm: stocks can be treated with what is known as the 'Frow' mixture, discovered by R. W. Frow, or with methyl salycilate, a synthetic preparation similar to oil of wintergreen, the remedy suggested by the late Dr. Rennie. Both treatments are successful up to a point. The safrol-nitrobenzene-petrol mixture of Frow is applied with the purpose of killing the mites within the bees' tracheae, and it is a very wonderful fact that it actually does do this in the majority of cases when suitably administered under the right conditions. It is not, as one might expect, by any means always to be relied upon to destroy all the mites. I believe, myself, that in a large minority of cases not all the mites in all the bees in the colony are destroyed, and I have given a full treatment many times and found the mites as lively as ever a month later. The Frow treatment has the extremely serious fault that it is very apt to cause wholesale robbing. No matter whether all the stocks in an apiary are treated simultaneously or not, if the weather is warm enough for bees to fly at all freely, robbing will start; and if the weather is not fairly mild the treatment is likely to fail because the drugs do not evaporate as they should.

The Frow treatment was a perfect godsend when it was given to beekeepers by its discoverer, and we can hardly be grateful enough to Mr. Frow for what he did; but in working a large number of colonies in many apiaries I have found it such a nuisance through its setting up wholesale robbing that for several years I have not used it. It is troublesome to administer when your bees are away in far apiaries, and its effectiveness is rather uncertain. After all, it is a really marvellous thing that this combination of drugs can and generally will kill these mites without doing the bees any harm.

Frow treatment is usually administered by giving small doses of about 20 or 30 minims on a felt pad daily for six or seven days, and withdrawing the pad on the tenth day; but this plan is, of course, out of the question on a bee farm where apiaries may be many miles from headquarters. There was, however, at no time any reason to suppose that this system had any special virtue, in fact I think that the result of these daily doses is frequently bad. If the weather is cold the drugs evaporate only very slowly, and the adding of a small daily dose merely provides for the accumulation of a heavy one, which, on a change to mild weather, will occasionally provide, by rapid evaporation, far too rich an atmosphere. I have found it better to give a single dose of about 70 to 90 minims and to let it go at that, removing the pad at the end of ten days or so. This I have found to be equally as effective as six or seven daily doses, and it is possible to practise it on a bee farm.

Since it is not practicable to make microscopical examinations of samples of bees from hundreds of stocks each year, the bee farmer is obliged to have recourse to preventive general treatment, and to dose all his colonies once a year. In using the Frow mixture I found it absolutely necessary that this should be done with the bees confined to their hives. This seems to do them no harm, though they often struggle to get out of the hives if the weather turns sunny and warm during the treatment. At first this worried me, but I found that the bees were none the worse for it in the spring. On one occasion an apiary was left confined for almost eight weeks through a mistake or confusion of some sort; but that apiary turned out one of our best in the spring. My friend E. W. D. Madoc has had a similar experience with confinement. In any case, with a warm spell during treatment when bees are not confined, a furious robbing bout is, in my experience, inevitable, and the damage to the bees is generally very serious when this occurs. I think that February is the best time for this treatment. If done early in winter bees may not get a flight for months after it; but done in February they are pretty certain to fly well within a month.

For some years, now, I have been using methyl salycilate as a preventive treatment instead of the Frow stuff. Since I have systematically applied this drug we have had no serious loss through acarine disease; less, in fact, than when the Frow mixture was used in the same way. We certainly do have a few cases every year, but these are insignificant in proportion to the total number, and they are probably to a large extent accounted for by the fact that we have been experimenting to find out the best method of administering the treatment.

I think there can be no doubt at all that in methyl salycilate we have a substance that will enable us to control acarine disease once we have discovered the proper method of application, and I know of no other way of finding that out except by trial and error. Methyl salycilate has the very great advantage over the Frow treatment of not tending to induce robbing in the slightest degree, in fact it has rather the opposite effect. It does not appear to have any undesirable effect on the brood either; or on the bees, when used in moderate quantities. I keep a small bottle of it with a wick, or a small flat tin with a perforated lid, in each of my 4-comb mating nuclei all the year round without causing any inconvenience to the bees, that I can see. It requires no repeated applications, no confinement of the bees under treatment, and it can be left in the hive indefinitely.

Probably the most effective way of giving the methyl salycilate treatment as a general preventive course, or for definite purpose of getting rid of the disease in stocks known to be infested by mites, is to use a small bottle holding about one ounce. This bottle must be fitted with a wick of soft cotton such as may be purchased in balls, like string. You will need to take about four or six strands of this cut in lengths of about four inches. Tie a loose knot near one end of it to prevent the wick from slipping into the bottle: fill the bottle nearly full of methyl salycilate, introduce the wick and stand the whole thing behind a dummy on the floor of the hive at the rear. If the hive will have to be moved about while the bottle is in it, the overturning of the bottle can be prevented by cutting a piece out of the rear corner of a dummy so that the bottle will be held in the recess so provided. A comb is taken from the hive, the bottle stood in the rear corner of it, and the dummy is then lowered into its place instead of the comb so that the recess in it will correspond to the bottle. The bottle, then, cannot be upset.

Another method of giving this treatment is by means of flat tins, such as shoe polish is sold in. These may have a number of large holes about three-eighths of an inch in diameter punched out of their lids and be filled with cotton-wool which is then saturated with the drug; or they may have a wide slit cut in their lids which is fitted with a piece of lamp wick. I have used this plan extensively; but have now abandoned it. It was found that at least three or four of these tins of methyl salycilate were required to make sure of ridding an infested colony of mites. That made the treatment too expensive in both time and material, for we have virtually proved that one bottle with a wick is equal to four tins as a mite controlling agent.

Methyl salycilate is not of much use between September and April, although its presence in a hive even in winter does sometimes have a beneficial effect. I have more than once known an infested colony treated with methyl salycilate in October, to come out perfectly free of mites the following spring; but generally speaking, methyl salycilate is only to be depended upon when the weather is warm and the bees active. That at this time a one-ounce bottle with a spreading wick will rid a stock of mites, I know, for I have seen it happen many times. Even quite late in the autumn I have got rid of mites that way; but the flat tins are quite useless except in warm weather, for evaporation seems to take place much more slowly from them.

In our apiaries we tried a rather extensive experiment in 1944.

I would have liked to have got the drug into the hives a little earlier, but shortage of labour prevented our getting everything ready until a little later than I consider ideal. We divided our bees into three sections and to one-third we gave one flat tin of methyl salycilate, to one-third we gave two tins, and to the remaining third we gave a one-ounce bottle with a spreading cotton wick. About eight apiaries were treated each way, and the whole of the colonies treated amounted to many hundreds. In the early spring following, only in one apiary where the bottles were given was any sign of acarine disease noticed, and in that several stocks were known to be infested heavily when the treatment was applied. In this apiary the treatment was applied rather too late in the fall, I think, and it is probable that the infested bees found in the spring were old bees that had survived. In the apiaries treated with two flat tins, only a few cases of infestation were found, but in those that had only a single tin of methyl salycilate given to them, quite a number showed the disease in the spring, and several died out from it.

Such experiments have value and are possible only for the extensive bee farmer. They are, of course, not scientifically exact, but they give pretty clear indications of the best way to control this serious trouble, and until some better method shall have been discovered, I propose to use bottles with wicks, placing them in the hives in spring and early autumn.

We now have to find out the best way of applying the methyl salycilate treatment, and with this in view we should bear in mind that all parasites of this character have stages in their life cycles during which the continuity of their species is exposed to greater risks than ordinary, and it is at such times that we should try to destroy them. Now it has been shown, as pointed out earlier in this chapter, that only young bees are vulnerable to the attack of mites, and it is pretty certain that the presence of methyl salycilate in the hive prevents migration. Bees cease to breed in October, as a rule, and begin again in January or February; there is, therefore, a period every year, of two or three months, during which no young bees are present in the hives. During this interval mites cannot extend their footing by leaving their present hosts for others, so that while infested bees may suffer an increase in the number of the parasites they carry, the latter are in a rather precarious position; for should the host die, all the mites infesting it must die too; and furthermore, the more these mites breed and the more they injure the bee's tissues on which they feed, the more probable becomes the bee's death. It is a fact that on a mild winter day, when the sun shines warmly after a cold spell, diseased colonies may be seen to have hundreds of heavily infested bees crawling about in front of them, and unless the beekeeper has been silly enough to provide one of those long sloping boards to help flightless bees back into their hives, all those crawlers will die, and all their parasites with them.

Infested stocks that survive until breeding again begins will have all their mites concentrated in the old bees that were infested at the close of the breeding season, and such bees will not live long; therefore it behoves the pregnant female mites to get a move on quickly if they are to escape disaster and carry forward their kind at all; and so directly the first young bees emerge, these old mites must transfer to them without a moment's loss of time. And they do it, unless hindered by the action of the beekeeper. This is where the introduction of methyl salycilate into the hive comes in.

Dr. Rennie considered that there might be some specific scent or some attractive emanation connected with the thoracic spiracles through which the mites enter their chosen homes, and he suggested that the smell of some drug might, by counteracting or smothering this hypothetical odour, so confuse the migrating parasites as to prevent them from finding the spiracles of which they are in search, and he suggested oil of wintergreen or methyl salicilate for this purpose. Certainly this is effective; but I am myself inclined to think that its odour may act by preventing the mites from finding out that there are young bees present in the colony. I think it unlikely that pregnant female mites leave their hosts indiscriminately at any time; but rather believe that the presence of bees of a suitable age for new infestation may make itself felt by the mites that are awaiting an opportunity to transfer themselves to such bees, by some influence, perhaps scent; perhaps something else; but at all events some sort of influence that the fumes of methyl salycilate counteract. Whatever the truth may be, it seems clear to me that the break in the continuity of breeding of the bees is the period of danger for mites to which we should direct our attention.

Most of the bees that will carry a stock through the winter months will be those that emerge during the period between the end of the honey-flow and the cessation of breeding; so that if we can save those from becoming infested we may say that we have in all probability rid the colony of mites. Hence the reason for inserting the methyl salycilate at the close of the honey season. Again, if the treatment is repeated early in the spring, should any mites remain, the first emerging young bees will in like manner be saved from their attacks, and unless we are entirely mistaken in supposing that this treatment is of use, it would seem almost certain that the incidence of acarine disease can be, for all practical purposes, eliminated by careful work along these lines. There is plenty of room for practical experiment, of course, but I cannot help hoping that we have now in our hands a real solution of a very difficult problem.

It will be seen by those who have considered the matter with care, that if the fumes of methyl salycilate can be maintained in the hive continually, no acarine disease can get a hold on a colony. If, moreover, those fumes can be kept present from any given point of time until all the bees then present in the hive have died out in the ordinary course of nature, then, since no young ones will become infested while the drug is present, the colony must be free of mites by that time. Now the difficulty is to arrange matters so that the fumes do remain present for a long enough time, while being maintained in sufficient strength to be effective. I have found the bottles, as described, more satisfactory than anything else tried so far, but I have been rather puzzled to understand why the whole ounce of the methyl salycilate will often evaporate in a couple of weeks in some cases, while in others the process may take eight or even ten weeks. But I found, quite by accident, that the protruding end of the wick should be rather short, so that when it becomes wet with the rising of the drug it shall not fall over and touch the side of the bottle neck, for when this happens the liquid is conducted down the bottle sides after the manner of a syphon. This causes rapid evaporation, and should be guarded against.

There is another aspect of this question that it is very necessary that I should touch upon. It is considered by some people that it is wrong in principle for us to attempt to control disease by curative treatment, that even preventive treatment should be avoided, and that we should rely on breeding bees for constitutional resistance to disease. I feel very far from scoffing at this theory, but frankly I do not quite understand how one can carry out this breeding for disease resistance as a speciality. There are so many other desirable characters that we require in our bees that it is my opinion that the best way to manage the breeding of bees is to try to produce strains that get a good lot of honey and are not vicious. If you will keep on systematically breeding for those two traits, I think that you will probably produce a fairly sound strain of bees in every other direction. Bees prone to disease, as undoubtedly some strains are, will not produce very good yields of honey; of that you can be certain.

The idea is, of course, that what Darwin called 'natural selection' will weed out the unfit; but it seems to me that a good many of those who write to the bee-press advocating this course of action, do not realize as clearly as they should, that natural selection can only operate under natural conditions. There is no doubt whatever that there are strains of bees that will not survive long in this country, but which become infested with acari very quickly. These strains, at least those that have come my way, are all imported from the United States. Acarine disease is unknown in the New World, so far as I know, and this probably accounts for the bees from there being very susceptible to acarine infestation. This does not apply to European bees which are all survivors of acarine attacks at some time or other, I expect, and French and Italian bees are just as liable to carry the mites as are British. I think it probable that were mites to get into the apiaries of North America, there would be a holocaust that would put our past experience into the shade entirely.

I have been keeping bees for a long time now, and remember the days before the Isle of Wight epidemic. I have also read a good deal of matter dealing with bees as they were understood long before my time. I may, of course, be quite mistaken; but I do not believe that the Acarine mite we are familiar with is a new species as a bee parasite. A new species it certainly cannot be, of course; but it has been suggested that its parasitism on the honey-bee may have been a new development early in this century. I don't for a moment believe this myself, though I cannot prove that I am right any more than those who think the reverse can prove the correctness of their views. My idea is that this mite has been parasitic on honey-bees for ages past.

If you read up old books on bees and beekeeping, you will find that, while there is hardly any mention of any other trouble of the adult bees, dysentery is very frequently described, and seems to have given a good deal of trouble in the old days. Now we have most of us had colonies of bees die out in winter from acarine infestation, and a common symptom of this is dysentery. When you go round your bees in the early spring to see how things are, you sometimes find a colony with a number of spots and smudges of excreta around the entrance of the hive, and on opening the hive and turning back the quilts or lifting the inner cover, you see splashes of excreta on the frames and combs. When this is seen, you know that in all probability that stock, whether alive or dead, is a bad case of acarine disease. I think that the dysentery we so often find references to in the books of old-time beekeepers is nothing less nor more than the dysentery that is such a common sign of acarine disease.

Why did the mites suddenly spread far and wide with such devastating consequences? I don't know; but my guess is that this trouble is liable to produce sudden epidemics of the kind, for there are references to such in ancient records, I believe. The outbreak of thirty-five years ago *may* have been much assisted by the importation of some strain of bees that was susceptible, or it *may* have been brought about by deterioration in the British native stock, for we all noticed how quickly the native black bees disappeared at that time.

My opinion, after a good many years of experiment, is that we should try to prevent the mites from getting hold of our bees by the use of prophylactic treatment of a not too drastic nature, and that any stocks that do not readily prove amenable to such preventive measures are best dead and done with; if they don't die out themselves they should be destroyed or at least re-queened before any further attempt is made to rid them of mites. It is here that I think methyl salycilate may be better for us and our bees than the more drastic Frow treatment. The latter's purpose is to kill the mites within the bees, of course; but its weak point is simply that it fails to kill *all* the mites in *all* the bees in *all* the hives treated. I am almost certain that I have here stated a fact, though others may dispute this. I am open to be convinced that I am wrong, for we ought always to be ready to change our views on any matter in face of proof that we are mistaken, but at present I think I am correct. Now it follows that unless we destroy *all* the mites in a colony, those not killed will be the ones that can resist the poison best—the most effective mites, in fact. I think readers will find that when Frow treatment is used, the colony that is still infested some weeks or months after treatment, will always die out. I have treated many times when it has appeared, by examination of samples of bees, that all mites were dead, but a few months later the disease has been found quite extensively distributed through the stock. I have not yet noticed this when methyl salycilate has been used. We are all rather in a fog here and should keep an open mind while conducting as many experiments as possible.

The idea of simply letting the disease rip, has been advanced by some enthusiasts who believe that by this means natural selection would give us a resistant strain, as it doubtless would. What these gentlemen don't tell us is what we are to live on while this process is in course of action. If any domesticated stock is let go wild like that, we certainly get a hardy strain; but the trouble is that hardy wild strains are of no use to us for domestic purposes. Probably, the fundamental fact is that it is impossible to produce a strain of any domesticated animal having those characteristics especially developed which make that strain particularly useful to civilized man, without at the same time sacrificing to a large extent the qualities that have enabled that species to exist in a state of nature. Natural selection will promote those variations which are useful to a species under wholly natural conditions, while selection, as practised by man, chooses out those qualities that are most useful to him. Let us not too hastily decide to rely upon natural selection to produce the type of bee we want.

Nosema Apis

Nosema apis is another disease of adult bees. It is caused by a minute animal parasite which has the power of producing spores that are readily stained, and are not very difficult to see unstained if a suitable microscope be used. I have no experience of this disease so far as I am aware, though there is very little doubt that some spring dwindling and some winter casualties may be caused by it. I have sent a great many samples to various experts for examination, but on no occasion has Nosema apis been confirmed as the cause of whatever the bees were suffering from. It is considered by some, e.g. Miss Betts in England, and Dr. Farrar and others in the U.S.A., to be a very serious trouble. Dr. Phillips, on the other hand, does not appear to attach any very grave consequences to the presence of this parasite in bees. Dr. Caird, in this country, assured me some years ago, that it was with him quite unusual to *fail* to find Nosema apis in any sample of bees examined by him. Phillips rather tends to confirm this (*Gleanings*, p. 316, July 1944) in an exceedingly interesting article. I gather that this disease is like many of the troubles that prey upon humanity; it lurks in the bodies of a large proportion of its host species, generally without perceptible ill-effect, but at such times as its environment becomes favourable, it breaks out as a destructive pestilence causing death far and wide. I don't know what is the right attitude in the matter, but I should say that the best way to guard against loss from the attacks of such generally prevalent organisms is to see to it that our bees are kept dry and well fed and cared for, and that only sound strains of good stamina are bred from. I myself do not propose to lie awake at night worrying about Nosema apis until I find myself suffering definitely from its assaults.

The disease is infectious, and the infection is supposed to be carried in the water bees take from pools, gutters and other places where stagnant water may be fouled by the excrement of diseased bees. In so far as I gather from Miss Betts's book, 'treatment' seems to consist of total destruction by fire, followed by sterilization of the hive (for details see *Diseases of Bees*).

Paralysis

There may be several diseases included under this head, but the only one I have had experience with is a really serious malady at times. The symptoms are a number of shiny bees scattered over the combs among the healthy ones. Outside the hive, on the ground below the entrance, are seen numerous dead bees lying in a heap where they have fallen when thrown out by their friends within. A few, still living, but obviously moribund, may usually be seen feebly crawling about or faintly moving their legs. This mass of dead may vary from a small handful to pretty well a peck, and in the latter case the smell is horrible. Within the hive, and at the entrance, unaffected bees may be seen endeavouring to drag diseased ones out. The entrance, at all times when bees are active, has an appearance of idleness; bees stand about doing nothing. I suppose they are feeling pretty rotten, and are just waiting for death.

If taken in time, re-queening will generally clear up the whole trouble, in fact I have so far never had a failure, unless the colony has become too weak to recover. Unless there is sufficient strength to care for enough of the new queen's brood to start a new family of bees, nothing is of any avail. I feel almost certain that this particular form of paralysis is hereditary; but of course I don't really *know* anything about that, as any scientist would say at once; but I know that certain strains seem to carry this disease, and that by substituting for the queens of stocks that suffer from it, other queens of different strains, it is virtually always got rid of. In this disease the queen herself is quite frequently a victim, and I have known a virgin in a mating nucleus, which became infected with the malady, to die of it before she could get time to mate. This virgin died in four days from first showing the typical signs. I need not say that the whole nucleus was immediately destroyed.

Some time ago we tried a form of colloidal sulphur as an attempted remedy. We succeeded completely, so far as we could tell; but after that first bottle we had to experiment with the makers went out of business and no other solution tried has been of the slightest use. What we succeeded with was sold as colloidal sulphur; but it was not a pure solution, for it had a very powerful and sickening odour of hydrogen sulphide which later purchases were quite free from. With the stuff we had first, we completely cured several stocks that were suffering badly, by feeding about one-third of a pint in a gallon of thick syrup; but whether we shall ever rediscover this stuff I cannot tell. Meanwhile we re-queen all cases as soon as possible after seeing infected bees.

Since writing the above notes on paralysis, I have had a little further experience of this trouble, and have come to the conclusion that the kind of paralysis described can in virtually every case be cleaned up by the re-queening of the affected stock, providing that the bees have not become too much weakened to care for the new queen's brood. Care must, of course, be taken that the new queen is not of a similar strain to the one she replaces.

It seems rather difficult to account for this, and research would seem to be required if the matter is to be satisfactorily explained; but there is one point that we have noticed here in this connection: in almost every case of paralysis of this kind, the queen has been an extra prolific one, the combs being a mass of brood. This results in a colony, usually with no spare stores, but with almost more brood than such bees as remain apparently healthy can care for, from which bees are constantly falling to the ground or being ejected by their fellows.

For other less important and more or less obscure diseases of bees the reader is referred to other works on the subject.

Enemies of Hive-bees

It is usual to add a few notes about the various larger creatures that are, or are supposed to be, injurious to bees. The acarine mite is usually listed with the diseases as an internal parasite, though a very large and highly developed one: it has already been described, and we therefore come first to insect assailants. There are two species of moth whose larvae live upon the combs of bees, devouring the wax of which they are made. These are a great nuisance to stored combs, and to weak colonies. The large moth's caterpillars will very quickly destroy combs stored away if once introduced to them. The moths may be found by hundreds, sometimes, in neglected hives of combs, and in such cases the whole will be a mass of webbing and excreta, with cocoons and larvae. Fire is the best remedy when this is the case. It is hard on the caterpillars and moths, but one can't be sentimental at such times. In this country these caterpillars are almost confined to British standard hives where the split top-bars and the textile quilts form a real preserve for them; American style hives with spaced inner covers are rarely bothered with them here.

The lesser wax moth is also a nuisance in stored combs, but it gets into sections of comb honey, too, where it does a good deal of mischief at times. Neither of these insects is a really serious menace in the British Isles if the beekeeper knows his job and stores his combs away suitably. Both dislike cold weather and do no damage in winter unless in warm storerooms or in a house; but if the moth has laid eggs in such combs these ought to be treated in some way to kill the resulting grubs and moths. I have never had occasion to do this, but Mr. Wedmore gives several methods of fumigating combs in storage. Personally, I should try a sulphur candle if I had to use anything.

Wasps are in some seasons very serious enemies of our bees. I have only suffered considerable loss from these insects on two or three occasions. Usually very little trouble is required to counter-act them, but in 1942 and 1944, for the first times in my experience, wasps completely wiped out a number of quite good queen-right colonies. All those destroyed were summer nuclei just becoming strong, and with a queen of the current year. I suppose that there were not enough old fighting bees in them to enable them to keep out the wasps. Wasps, therefore, do sometimes rob out colonies of bees, especially if the entrances of the hives are large. On these occasions, on opening the robbed hive after the battle, it will be found crowded with thousands of bloated wasps which might well be mistaken for queens at a first glance. Wasps, however, are in most years no more than a very minor nuisance, and about all one can do is to contract all entrances to assist the bees to keep them out. Wasps, however, are far stronger and more determined than bees; they are, apparently, more intelligent, and almost seem to employ reason in their manœuvres. This comes from their being less specialized than bees, I suppose. You can destroy their nests, no doubt—if you can find them; but I have destroyed a great many in some seasons without producing the smallest noticeable reduction in the number of wasps seen about the hives.

There is one very bad thing about having a lot of wasps prowling about in the autumn. Some are sure to find their way into hives and to establish a regular system of quiet robbery which persists long after the bees have formed their winter cluster. At this time such wasps as still remain active will often carry on right up to January in seasons when the early part of the winter is very mild. A sort of vicious circle is established. The wasps would die out were there no hives to rob, but manage to live on upon the honey or syrup that they fetch daily from the bees' stores. I have often seen wasps working in and out of hives long after frost, and the amount of food stolen in this way is probably much greater than is commonly supposed. In the year 1944 some of our apiaries were quite seriously lightened by wasps before Christmas, and another bee farmer told me that he estimated the loss in his apiaries at two tons of sugar or honey.

In seasons when wasps are very bad we can assist the bees greatly by placing suitable traps for them in all apiaries where they seem very numerous. In fact it would be a good plan to keep such traps in all apiaries every year; placing them in position in July. The traps I use are simply 28-lb. honey tins with porter bee escape traps fixed under a hole in the lids. These are baited with a pint of syrup and are stood in a sloping position, so that any rain that falls on the recessed lever lid will run off at the side before it accumulates sufficiently to run down the hole through the trap. This is important, as if the tins are placed level, the rain may soon drown the syrup and cause it to ferment. It is wise to use syrup with thymol added to it.

The very large parasite known as Braula coeca (or caeca), or as the bee louse, is not a louse, but a wingless fly, and a very remarkable little creature. It is chiefly troublesome in spoiling the appearance of comb honey by the tunnels its larvae make through the cappings. The queen is the bee that suffers most from its adult form, and queens at the end of autumn will sometimes be found to be covered almost all over with these little brutes. Over one hundred may sometimes be found on a single queen in August. They soon disappear, however, leaving the queen none the worse, and no doubt die off after mating and laying their eggs. They are white when first they attain the perfect form, but turn to a bright reddish-brown as they mature. It was Herrod-Hempsall who first discovered the connection between the tunnels in the cappings and Braula coeca, I believe. As we don't work for comb honey we do nothing about these parasites, and I can't see that we are any the worse for them; but it is easy enough to rid a queen of her load by placing her in a matchbox and blowing in a little strong tobacco smoke. They all fall off in a few moments, as can be seen if the box is closed with a piece of glass instead of its own cover.

No birds are a menace that any bee farmer need worry about, with the exception of the woodpeckers. These are a serious nuisance in cold winters when ant-heaps are frozen too hard to allow the birds to dig into them; but we have found that if at the beginning of hard weather scares are fixed up at the apiaries, the woodpeckers will be kept off; they are very shy birds, and a wire or two stretched across an apiary from tree to tree or otherwise, with a few strings supporting feathers, light tin cans, or some unusual-looking objects hanging from them so that they move in the breeze, will quite unnerve them for long enough to carry the apiary over the severe spell, and until the birds are able to resume their usual diet.

The damage woodpeckers will do to hives in a few hours is often very serious. They tear out entrance-blocks, and peck holes clear through the hive sides, even getting through into the hive itself and destroying the frames, combs, and bees. But their delight is in single-walled hives with roofs too shallow to cover the hand-holds cut in them, for at those spots one of these birds will make a hole in half a dozen strokes of its beak. Besides all the material damage done to hives, it is a serious thing to have the clusters disturbed by the hammering of the beaks in making the holes, for a bird will often visit twenty hives in a few hours, thereby disturbing the bees in very cold weather. We ought not to kill these beautiful birds, I suppose, but I confess it makes me feel rather bloodthirsty when they are an unusually bad plague. However, it seldom lasts, and scares seem effectual.

Mice are the only animals that bother bees to any extent, unless it be rats. I have had rats pull out entrance blocks in severe weather when these animals have been numerous and more hungry than ordinary, but they have never done me much damage. Mice, especially fieldmice, can make themselves a great nuisance, unless they are kept right out of hives. But it is a simple matter to keep them out, and this should always be done. If they do enter, either fieldmice or house-mice will do a great deal of damage, frequently destroying the stock altogether; so keep them out.

Lists of various living creatures have been compiled by enthusiastic writers on beekeeping as being injurious to bees; but few of them do much injury, and these catalogues of horrors are probably compiled with a subconscious idea of making our flesh creep. No one's honey crop is going to be much reduced, you may be sure, by the depredations of badgers, snakes, toads, frogs, sparrows, swallows, shrikes, flycatchers, hornets, earwigs, deaths-head moths, tom-tits, and other ferocious fauna, so I will not bother with them here.

CHAPTER XIII

FOR BEGINNERS

Before bringing this book to an end, I think I ought to give a little advice and a few hints to those young people who may read what I have written, and who are minded to try to earn a living by honey production in this country.

Honey-bees are very interesting insects. There is a fascination about them which is liable to lead to unprofitable enthusiasm and the spending of money and energy uselessly. No other insect is nearly so useful to mankind, and the hive-bee is the only one whose domestic affairs can be laid bare and made amenable to human control; but in bee farming for a living our interest in all this must be restrained.

If we are to make the most of life and do the greatest service to ourselves and others, we must choose for our life's work some congenial pursuit which gives us real pleasure, so that our efforts shall not be directed wholly to making money, but rather to producing something of value that would not exist but for our exertions. I think there is something stimulating in the idea that you are really doing this. But if you are thinking of beekeeping as a congenial occupation, you had better make sure that you clearly understand what this implies. I know how it looks to the enthusiastic beginner, for I was one myself once; and I suspect that some of those who look seriously towards honey production as a possible life's work *don't* know quite what is involved. Gray wrote:

> *Alas, regardless of their doom,*
> *The little victims play!*
> *No sense have they of ills to come,*
> *Nor cares beyond to-day:*
> *Yet see how all around 'em wait*
> *The ministers of human fate,*
> *And black misfortune's baleful train! . . .*

And I often think of them when some young enthusiast tells me all about his plans for the future. It seems so hard and unsympathetic to throw cold water on all this excitement; but I am sure it is better for the serious beginner to understand the realities of the case right from the start.

In most of the cases that have been known to me, those concerned had only the vaguest idea of what was before them. All of us who have been enthusiastic beekeepers know very well what a powerful attraction bees have for those who become interested. The spell that bees put upon us is proverbial, and has even earned the name of 'bee-fever'. It amounts, for a time at least, to a veritable craze; and we all pass through this phase, or rather pass into it, for some never recover their complete sanity. Now, although I doubt if anyone will ever do much good at serious beekeeping from the business point of view who has not at some time suffered from this form of temporary insanity, I am sure that no one who remains so afflicted will make a success of it. A hobby may be carried on while the brain is fevered, but the reason must not be clouded by undue enthusiasm when a question of business has to be decided.

I have had a good many young men come to me about beekeeping as a means of livelihood at one time and another; but in the majority of cases nothing has come of it; in fact I only remember two that can be said to have really succeeded in what they set out to do, and one of these two found himself unable to live by honey production alone and switched off to other branches of the business. The general impression seems to be that bee farming requires hardly any capital, whereas the fact is that this branch of production from the soil needs a good deal of money invested in it if the honey producer is to have much chance of getting on and making a good business of it. That is the point that seems to be the most misunderstood of all. Some of the things printed in books about beekeeping are almost wicked in the way they tend to mislead. Why is this so?

It is a fact that virtually all those who become interested in beekeeping in this country are initiated into the mysteries of the craft of bee management via the teachings of amateurs, who are, in fact, nothing more than enthusiasts who keep bees purely as a hobby. There is, of course, nothing to be said against such people. There can hardly be a more pleasant and interesting diversion than to keep a few stocks of bees; but try to run a honey farm on the system usually taught in Britain, and into the bankruptcy court you go. I am not decrying the British system in any carping spirit; I am only stating the cold fact as I see it. It would be less than honest on my part, in such a book as this, were I not to make this plain statement of a truth of which I am convinced.

I must say plainly, that the greatest handicap the young prospective honey farmer has to surmount is the result of making a false start, and spending time, labour, and money on it; sometimes spoiling what would otherwise have been a good chance by expending too much of what is usually a strictly limited capital upon equipment which is of little use to him for the purpose of bee farming. At the time of writing, as it happens, I have in my mind a typical case of this kind. A young man had, after a hard struggle for several years against difficulties caused by lack of capital, got togéther about one hundred hives of bees, all hand-made by himself. But the hives are quite hopeless for the purpose of honey farming and will have to be replaced. It would be a nightmare to have to manage two or three hundred stocks in such hives: but they are made pretty much after the orthodox plan for what used to be called the 'cottager hive'. It makes me feel really savage to think of fellows being misled so, for it means not only loss of money and labour, but of time—years. Had this man started off in a sensible way with some sort of British standard hive suitable for the job, such as I have described earlier in this book, or with Langstroth or Dadant equipment, he might now be running 250 stocks and making a decent living. As it is, it will take him some years, I expect, to get that far, even if helped a good deal.

So don't try to start off bee farming with the usual equipment that is orthodox here, or to work on orthodox lines, either. It is no use at all: you cannot run a large honey farm with British-type equipment, or on the lines advocated by the majority of writers and lecturers on beekeeping in this country. No one has, so far as I know, ever done it, and I do not believe it to be possible. You can work a considerable number of colonies that will pay a fair profit if you do not reckon labour; but that is sideline beekeeping, and these part-time apiaries are numerous, but they never grow into large enterprises unless a complete changeover is made. You have only to read contemporary literature to recognize this. *The British Beekeepers' Guide Book* has for many years been looked upon as the beekeeper's almost inspired counsellor; but Cowan had no conception of what bee farming implies. He was an amateur, pure and simple, and is usually depicted as manipulating his bees in an extremely impressive and dignified manner, while wearing a frock coat. But if you go in for bee farming, you will find that you won't want any frock coat; but a boiler-suit, a pair of gloves, and a veil.

And while I think of it, I will say that I consider one of the silliest customs that have gained a sort of traditional importance in teaching beginners, is that of telling them that veils and gloves are to be used only until you become accustomed to handling bees. The big guns are always shown manipulating bees without veils, and beginners don't understand that the handled bees are generally well subdued, specially for the purpose of being manipulated by dignified experts, who would pretty soon leg it and disappear into the horizon if they had to handle without veils such stocks as you and I will have to manage every summer day. Gloves are especially held up to scorn. Well, I use gloves all the summer, and so do all of us here; but except when we have to deal with some particularly vicious stock, or when we have to work the bees in weather that makes bees bad tempered, we use the gloves more to keep propolis off our hands than to avoid being stung. We soon get used to stings and pay very little attention to them, but it is bad to get the hands ingrained with propolis.

Most of the advice given to beginners in this country is all right for what is intended, that is, to tell the hobbyist how to ride his hobby; but these teachings have nothing to do with the business of working large numbers of bees in a series of apiaries, and depending upon the production of honey for a living. To the young and hopeful I would say: Keep always in mind that it is *honey* you are after; honey by the ton. No one can live by honey production unless he or she can produce an average of at least five or six tons annually. That is the absolute minimum, and is the bed-rock of the whole thing. What you require, to make a success of it, is a business consisting of from 400 colonies upwards. You want a comfortable living, not an uneasy existence. And you can't live at all on the sentimental attributes of bees; to live you must produce honey—real honey that can be sold, not imaginary honey that you can brag about.

Honey production is a branch of agriculture, which is one of the basic industries, and the most important of them all, and the oldest; it is in no sense trade or commerce. It is production in a rather different sense from the production of manufactured goods; it depends on the seasons and the weather, and there is only one way of increasing the output of honey, except, of course, in so far as good management will assist in this, and that is by increasing the number of apiaries operated. There is no possibility of getting more than one crop of honey each year. Once the last flow is over, nothing more can be got until the following summer. The manufacturer can go on making and selling his product all through the year, but the farmer cannot.

I remember something a very good friend of mine, who is gone, once said to me. He had been employed in the Post Office all his life, and when he retired with a pension, he took up market gardening and bees, in which two things he had always been interested. He told me that it seemed so very strange, after having worked for a salary all his life, to find that nothing came in unless he first paid out. This struck me very forcibly at the time, for I had not thought of that side of the matter, having always worked for myself and never having received a penny of wages or salary in my life. Perhaps some of those situated like my friend, Elsdon, may find the matter worth thinking about. For all these businesses that rely on production from the land require a good deal of outlay before they can be made productive, so don't be deceived by wishful thinking. *If you have no money, don't go in for bee farming.*

You will frequently see accounts in our bee papers of large 'takes' of honey; averages of 100 pounds, and so on. These statements are sometimes true, no doubt; but they are usually produced by cooking. I have myself taken as much as 380 pounds of honey from a single stock and a nucleus made from it, but such a crop is no more representative of the average weight I have produced in my apiaries than Daniel Lambert's 52 stones represented the weight of the average Englishman of his time. If you can average 40 to 50 pounds of genuine surplus honey, calculated on the number of colonies of bees you have packed up for winter in the previous autumn, and if you can really do this over a series of years, you will be able to make a very good living. And it is quite possible to better this, though not anything like so easy as you might think, to judge from contributions to the bee-press. I have on three occasions averaged over 100 pounds on over 100 stocks of bees, autumn count: I may do it again; but that is not annual average surplus, you know.

Winter losses on a bee farm will average, taking one year with another, about 6 or 8 per cent at least. Oh! I know, I know, that's bad beekeeping; but you will find that *your* beekeeping will be at least that bad. People who have no winter losses are more lucky, or much better beekeepers, or more imaginative than you are likely to be. So build on probabilities, not possibilities.

Just to open the eyes of any very optimistic and enthusiastic beginner who may chance to read this, I think I will just mention the various causes of losses of stocks of bees that I have personally experienced at one time or another. All the diseases do at times cause colony deaths. Acarine disease is by far the worst offender, for the mites make the bees uneasy which leads to undue activity and extra store consumption, and sometimes to death during a cold spell. You may think that you will be too good a beekeeper to allow your bees to become infested; but my guess is that you won't. Foul brood does very occasionally cause winter loss; but this should never be the case on a bee farm that is at all well looked after. Paralysis sometimes causes the loss of stocks; but if all colonies that show the least sign of this trouble in summer are re-queened, very little winter loss should be experienced from it; but some there will be occasionally. I have lost colonies in winter and early spring from amoeba disease, too. Nosema apis is, I think, sometimes a serious trouble, and may cause heavy winter casualties. I may have lost stocks from it; but am not certain.

Starvation will cause you loss at times, do what you will. The insidious robbing by late wasps, and even by bees, may cause this. After a wasp season I generally lose a few stocks in the early spring, for the wasps will sometimes take away the food from the outside combs before their own colonies die out, especially if the winter is mild before Christmas. I have had a mouse get into a hive occasionally when the guard has been torn off by rats or woodpeckers, and this generally means a dead stock. Woodpeckers will sometimes get right into a hive and cause the death of the bees by constant disturbance in cold weather. Of course fences should always be kept well looked to, but I have had horses break them down in winter and turn hives over, with fatal consequences. I have had tree branches break off and smash down on hives, thus destroying the bees in very cold weather. I have many times had hives turned over by the human species for mere mischief, and have had the roofs taken off and left off on purpose to injure bees, for the same reason. I have also had the bees destroyed for the sake of the honey, which was stolen.

The largest winter loss, however, is caused by queenlessness in spring. Sometimes a late-introduced queen will be superseded; but usually the cause is an old queen which ought to have been replaced in the previous autumn. Bees, too, will sometimes attempt supersedure on their own account when it is too late for it to be successful. So the man who can avoid all these troubles will be a very good beekeeper indeed. Much more so than I ever shall be, or any other bee farmer that I have so far come across.

Another pitfall that prospective bee farmers are liable to stumble into is the craze for numbers. Never become obsessed by the craving for more and more stocks of bees until you are really in a position to run them. It is a very serious mistake to begin by trying to pile up a large number of hives of bees while not at the same time accumulating the necessary accessories. A stock of bees as a unit of production on a honey farm, means a hive fitted with frames, combs, bees, and three supers (British standard), a queen excluder, and some sort of stand. When you have 100 stocks you must have 300 supers and 100 excluders. You must also have feeders, smokers, and the necessary extracting machinery. It is useless to go on to 150 stocks before you are ready to care for them.

In lectures and books on British beekeeping, you will find minute descriptions of how to carry out the most trivial and often entirely unnecessary operations. We are told how to paint a hive, using knotting, putty, glass-paper, and all that kind of thing; all wholly unnecessary, for you will get just as much honey if you give your hives a coat or two of 'Cuprinol', or even creosote. Supers need not be treated in any way, as they are stored away in the dry during eight months of the year, and those the months when hives get wet and stay so. They will last you fifty years, and another fifty beyond it, whether treated or not. Just imagine the cost in time and labour on a large bee farm if all the hives were painted every year or two, as they would have to be, if the painting were to be of much service.

Then there are all the elaborate hives, I had almost said freak hives, that are so strongly commended by experts and lecturers from time to time. Imagine a 1,000-colony honey farm with all the bees hived in 'Glen', 'W.B.C.' or similar hives, and painted every year or two! These things are all right for the hobbyist, or even, perhaps, for the sideliner, if he has a great fancy for them; but if you wish to live by producing honey, avoid them as a plague. No honey farm of sufficient extent to bring its owner a good living could by any conceivable possibility be successfully carried on with these appliances. They are fads. Bees in them do not give an ounce more honey than in hives of the business type. Do not be deceived by photographs of large apiaries of spick-and-span, white-painted W.B.C. or similar hives. They look very pretty, and are often advertisements; or perhaps some well-off enthusiast is riding his hobby in a more than usually glorious manner. Don't go by the look of the hives if the owner of such a display should show it to you as an example of what beekeeping ought to be, but ask to see the audited accounts for three years.

If you are to run a honey farm, you must remember that every hive must be so made as to be readily packed up and loaded on a lorry, and must be so shaped that it will take up the least possible room on the load. This one matter puts all hives with legs, gabled or sloping roofs, or other excrescences, completely out of court. If prospective bee farmers will notice the articles contributed to our bee-press by men who are usually regarded as rather important members of the beekeeping fraternity, they will at once be struck by the total failure, in most cases, of any realization whatever of this necessity for easily transportable hives, showing that the writers are not really bee farmers at all, but only keepers of bees that are allowed to stand always in one place. The honey farmer must keep his bees in out-apiaries: there is no possible way out of it; and out-apiaries mean transport, which in turn implies hives suitable for being moved. Besides, there is always the possibility of taking bees to heather after the main flow is done.

In this connection it will be wise, for the beginner who intends to go in for honey production seriously, to note that there is in existence only one class of hive that meets the requirements of a

bee farm, usually called the American type. This means a hive
without any loose or overlapping parts, such as the fillets or plinths
of the common British-style hives, and certainly it means that no
double cases such as form the leading feature of the W.B.C. hives,
can be tolerated. It means, also, that the roof must be flat. It
certainly does not imply that the hives should be of foreign manufacture, or the use of any particular frame. Do not be misled by
silly talk of how these plain hives are easily disintegrated by a push
or by the wind, or by any similar nonsense. I have been told that
a stock turn of one lecturer, fanatically opposed to the single-
walled American style of hives, was to set an empty Langstroth
hive on his platform, and then to push off the super in order, presumably, to persuade a gullible audience that such hives are
useless!

It is a very good rule, when you are trying to pick up knowledge
of beekeeping, or any other matter, to be careful whose ideas you
accept. If you have no ideas of your own, you are in a position to
take in the views of others; but you know what happens when the
blind lead the blind, and many a beekeeper has found the ditch
through lack of judgment in choosing his guide.

This leads me to another warning. You will find that the beekeepers of this country are divided into camps—factions. It is
something like religious fanaticism. There are the orthodox and
the rest. That is to say, each party considers itself right and all the
rest wrong, for all religions are orthodox from the view-point of
their votaries. Each 'sect' has its own hierarchy, and clings to the
tenets of its particular creed without much regard to reason, but
with great persistence and faithfulness. Now it won't do for you to
become entangled in these controversies, unless perhaps as a sort
of recreation, for no one will ever make a living that way; unless
it may be the leaders, or, as one may say, the prophets; and I have
never heard of one of these who got his living by carrying out his
own precepts for managing bees. All the same, if you don't take
these things too seriously, a good deal of amusement can be got
out of them.

The beekeepers' associations are almost entirely in the hands of
amateurs, and are concerned with those aspects of beekeeping
which interest the amateur; but you should join one or two associations, for there are many good men in them who will be willing

to give you a hand. You will meet other beekeepers, and will form friendships, in all probability. While the associations may not prove of much practical service to you in your actual work, they are the best media for arranging insurance against risk to third parties through stinging by bees. Every bee farmer should keep himself fully insured against the danger of damage to men and animals by his bees. No one is safe unless this is done. The costs are insignificant, and some of the beekeeping magazines give free insurance to all paid-up subscribers.

When I began to write this chapter, I tried to put myself in the position of a young man who, having made up his mind to go in for honey production for his livelihood, is anxious to set about it in the most sensible and economical manner. I certainly did not start that way myself; but I am not sure that this fact does not make it easier for me to advise others. I began in the wrong way altogether. I learned all the orthodox stuff out of Cowan's little book, and wasted many years before I found out what nonsense all that sort of thing is, considered from the point of view of serious honey production. I had to unlearn all that, first of all, and then to start all over again on the more sound lines that bitter experience had taught me were alone of any use to me. I had to adapt my enterprise in accordance with the lessons learned, and having been moderately successful since, I do feel that I may really know something about the subject that can be passed on to those who have not yet wandered away beyond recall into that maze of uneconomic procedure which is British orthodox amateur beekeeping practice.

I set to work to think of the probable road that I should follow now, if I could have my time all over again, and be a boy of twenty once more. That can't be; but I may help some boy to-day, perhaps. I should, no doubt, have some bees in hand, probably a few stocks in the usual variety of British hives. I should know a little about how to handle bees, and should also have read everything about them that I could get hold of. I know, of course, that some people hate reading, and seem incapable of taking in ideas from the written word, but as none such will read this, I need not bother with that type of humanity.

The first problem of the prospective bee farmer is how to live while the business is being got on to its legs. If he has capital enough, he can, of course, live on some of it while he is building up his bee farm; but if he has only just enough money to finance the business itself, he must work for someone else at some sort of job for a few years. Some boys, of course, are able to live on their parents while they get things going, and these are the lucky ones. Anyway, the first job is to get together about one hundred stocks of bees with all the necessary equipment. This is easy enough if you know a little about it, and have the necessary capital; but if you have no money, or very little, it is a very hard row you have to hoe before you finally establish yourself in a paying honey farm.

I must, I think, warn any young fellow who is almost without capital that he must be *very* careful to avoid the mistake I have already indicated—that of trying to accumulate more colonies of bees than he can properly establish. I have known years to be spent in accumulating a whole lot of miscellaneous and impracticable hives at a cost in time, labour, and cash, that would have set up an efficient apiary of half the number, and which would have been a real nucleus from which a bee farm could have been built up. Time is a rather important item in this matter. We are only young once. Time jumps on us. When we are twenty we feel as if all eternity were before us; but as the years pass they seem to go more and more quickly. We are thirty before we realize it, and then forty, and fifty; so a young bee-man must take time by the forelock, and make few mistakes if he cannot afford the money to make up for them.

One who lives with parents and earns a good salary himself, and devotes all his spare time to his bees, will not be so many years before he will have eighty or one hundred stocks well found; but then comes the second hurdle. How to pass from the spare-time apiary to the whole-time honey farm is one of the most difficult of all beekeeping questions. With plenty of capital it is easy; but without it, very difficult indeed. It may be possible for such a man to take a job where he could work for three days of the week; but such employment is not at all easy to find. Of course it *might* be possible to work part-time for another bee farmer; but that would be a rather unlikely thing. I confess that I don't see how this transition can be effected by the man without capital. That is why I always warn people to leave large-scale beekeeping alone unless they have the necessary capital to finance it. We have all heard of men who have built up businesses from nothing, by their own efforts, but we may be very sure that in these cases, unless the man is a veritable genius for business, he has, in actual fact, had more assistance than is supposed; I mean, of course, when the business is one that requires considerable capital outlay. The idea that a man without money can build up a farming business from nothing, and without outside help in the matter of capital, is quite foolish: it can't be done. Even in those businesses that do not require much capital, it is very difficult to build up anything much within a working life unless some unusual stroke of good fortune should happen to come along; and honey farming is certainly not one of those. A hard-working, painstaking young fellow with brains and a notion how to use them, might, of course, start by working for some large bee farmer and in time obtain an interest in the business; but the thing is exceedingly difficult without capital.

Now comes the next problem. Once a bee farm is well on its legs, and, let us say, 200 stocks are well established, we have to consider the next step, for no one with any go in him will rest content with a small one-man bee farm, which is the least profitable type of bee business there is. With capital this stage is easy; all you have to do is to buy the necessary equipment, employ assistance, and go ahead making increase every year from your own bees. Never buy bees for this purpose if you can help it. I have bought bees many times, and sometimes I have thought that I had got a bargain; but I have nearly always regretted doing it.

There comes a time in the growth of every bee farm when the work is too much for one, but not enough to employ two people all the time. This can easily be tided over if one has capital, for 200 stocks can be turned into 300 in one season, and into 450 in the next. Without capital to do this, the only thing that I can see for the bee-man to do is to halt at about 200 stocks, live cheaply, and save profits for four or five years, or as long as necessary, and then launch out. It is always a hard struggle for the moneyless man, let there be no mistake about that.

Now I suppose I must try and say something as to the amount of capital required. I can start by pointing out that a rather aggravating circumstance is that the more capital you have, the less you need. Money makes money, you know, and if you are in a position to buy in large quantities for cash on the nail, you can buy very much more cheaply than would be the case were it necessary for you to buy by driblets and pay as slowly as possible. I have often known a man with very little money, to work like a coolie for weeks in order to save money on hives, and have myself been able to buy much better hives all ready to nail together for less money than the other fellow had to pay for the timber used.

I am afraid it is necessary to buy a little land. You can't very well build on land belonging to others, and build you must, if you are to run a honey farm. Of course it is easy to buy land without actually having to put all the cash down, for you can mortgage it for two-thirds of its value, by paying interest. Then buildings will cost a good deal, and it is better to strain things a bit rather than put up something so small that it will be almost useless before long. Of course at the time of writing building is impossible, but after the war is over it will be possible again. I think that about £350 for land and necessary buildings, water and electricity wiring ought to cover early needs, and then the buildings can be added to as necessary. I am basing this estimate on pre-war costs, for anything else would be just a guess. I believe, as I have said before, that my estimate given in the book *Honey Production*, in 1936, was very fairly accurate. I put it at about £6 per stock for a farm of 200 units. The next 200 should require much less in capital per unit, and 1,000 stocks would be capitalized for very much less. At the date of writing this, early in 1945, money buys about half as much of most things as it did in 1936, and timber stands at a fantastic figure, if obtainable. But there will be plenty of short lengths to be had from War Department dumps as soon as peace comes, so there may be a fair chance for bee-men after that.

As for profits, we should have been in a bad way during the war but for the fact of honey not being rationed; but this fact handed the retail trade over to the producer, so that the otherwise quite uneconomic price of 2s. 9d. per pound jar was made profitable. The enormous rise in every cost connected with the production of honey could not have been met had the producer been obliged to rely on sales to retailers for practically all his honey as in pre-war days. I am not intending to go into details of costs and profits here; the present times are not settled enough even to justify a rough forecast; but this I can say: once a large bee farm has been well established, it is, if well managed, a rather paying concern;

a very profitable business in a smallish way: and not so very small a way either. But notice that I say a *large* and *well-managed* honey farm.

Yes, honey farming is a grand job for those who love bees and are interested in producing something from the land; who are hard workers and able to enjoy country life in all weathers. I have been at it for a long while, and my one regret is that I did not start with bee farming when I was twenty instead of going in for general agriculture and stock raising until I was forty; but every friend and relative I had was dead against it. It was regarded as mere idiocy to think of getting a living from beekeeping; so I wasted twenty years with bees as a sideline to which I could not devote my entire energies. I know now that if I had defied everyone and taken the bull by the horns, I should be much better off to-day than I am. However, I am not complaining: I have not done too badly as it is. I have thoroughly enjoyed the last twenty years during which I have depended entirely for my livelihood on one business only—Honey Farming.

INDEX

289

INDEX

MAGAZINES

AUTHORS AND BOOKS